GREENBOOK ®

Guide To

The Enesco

PRECIOUS MOMENTS®

Collection

Seventh Edition

Old Coach at Main, Box 515
East Setauket, New York 11733
(516) 689-8466
FAX (516) 689-8177

ISBN 0-923628-12-6

Photography by Anthony Lopez, East End Studio, Miller Place, NY

Printed and bound by Searles Graphics, East Patchogue, NY

Published in East Setauket, NY

GREENBOOK Secondary Market Prices published in *The GREENBOOK Guide To The Enesco PRECIOUS MOMENTS Collection, The GREENBOOK Guide To The MEMORIES OF YESTERDAY Collection by Enesco, The GREENBOOK Guide To Ornaments Including The Hallmark Keepsake, Enesco Treasury Of Christmas, & Carlton/Summit Heirloom Collections,* and *The GREENBOOK Guide To Department 56* are obtained from retailers and collectors. Enesco Corporation, Hallmark Cards, Inc., Carlton Cards, and Department 56 verify factual information only and are not consulted or involved in any way in determining GREENBOOK Secondary Market Prices.

All line drawings in this book are copyrighted by Samuel J. Butcher, 1975-1992. PRECIOUS MOMENTS, PRECIOUS MOMENTS COLLECTORS' CLUB, PRECIOUS MOMENTS BIRTHDAY CLUB, and SUGAR TOWN are trademarks and service marks of Mr. Butcher. ENESCO CORP. is the licensee under Mr. Butcher's rights and is also the registered owner of the ENESCO trademark.

ACKNOWLEDGEMENTS

The GREENBOOK would like to thank -

Sam Butcher, for the use of his copyrighted
line drawings.

Enesco, for assisting in the compilation of the
factual information contained in this Guide.

The dealers and collectors across the country
who supply us with information including
secondary market status and prices.

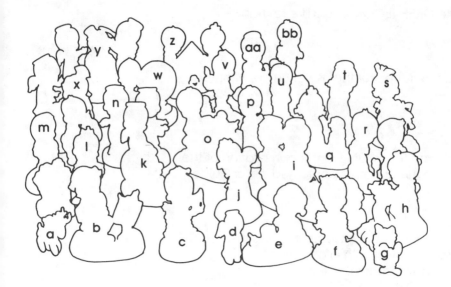

On the Cover...

...we asked Secondary Market Retailers to list the HTF (Hardest To Find) pieces in the Collection. Our informal survey came up with these pieces pictured on the cover:

a.	102466	Reindeer
b.	E-7162	Love Is Sharing
c.	PM-822	Put On A Happy Face
d.	E-5629	Let The Heavens Rejoice
e.	E-2805	Wishing You A Season Filled With Joy
f.	E-3107	Blessed Are The Peacemakers
g.	E-2381	Mouse With Cheese
h.	E-0530	His Eye Is On The Sparrow
i	E-2801	Jesus Is Born
j.	E-3118	Eggs Over Easy
k.	E-2804	Peace On Earth
l.	E-1378	God Loveth A Cheerful Giver
m.	E-9263	How Can Two Walk Together Except They Agree
n.	E-2351	Holy Smokes
o.	E-5202	Thank You For Coming To My Ade
p.	PM-811	Hello Lord, It's Me Again
q.	E-4722	Love Cannot Break A True Friendship
r.	E-1375B	Prayer Changes Things
s.	E-3111	Be Not Weary In Well Doing
t.	E-9288	Sending You A Rainbow
u.	E-3119	It's What's Inside That Counts
v.	E-0525	You Can't Run Away From God
w.	E-1381	Jesus Is The Answer
x.	E-5642	Silent Knight
y.	12351	Halo, And Merry Christmas
z.	E-7164	Bless This House
aa.	520640	I'm So Glad You Fluttered Into My Life
bb.	E-5203	Let Not The Sun Go Down Upon Your Wrath

NOTE FROM THE PUBLISHER

My just turned four-year-old daughter has yesterday and tomorrow mixed up. Our printer thinks it's hereditary - I bring the Guide in on computer disk today and want books delivered to the warehouse yesterday...

"Go Fish..."

Call the GREENBOOK offices trying to locate a piece on the secondary market and chances are pretty good we can give you the names of several retailers who have the piece in stock. Although GREENBOOK does not buy and sell on the secondary market, we are in close contact with those that do - the logic being if you participate in buying and selling you are not the publisher of a price **guide** but rather **your own price list**. Knowing the ropes, so to speak, as we do, it's highly unusual for us to tell someone, "Go Fish..." Such was the case this year with the Angel with the Butterfly Net, "I'm So Glad You Fluttered Into My Life." And it got me to thinking about what should be obvious but we all tend to forget - supply and demand. "I'm So Glad You Fluttered Into My Life" was one of two pieces out of the six retired in August 1991 that was a "drop-dead retirement," i.e. retailers received no allocations after retirement. In addition, it was one of sixty pieces temporarily removed from production the second half of 1991. What's it all mean? Quite simply, secondary market prices ranging from $250 to $375, depending on the annual symbol. I know there are many who will disagree, but I think it's great to get back to where part of the fun of collecting Precious Moment is in the hunt and the find!

"FIRST MARKS"

We've said this for the past couple years but I believe the data in this Edition takes it from opinion to fact - if you are a serious collector, interested in investment potential, it's worth the time and effort to acquire "first marks" (the first annual symbol existing on a piece). Again, back to supply and demand, with the supply of new pieces so plentiful, owning the "first marks" gives you something truly limited. This is absolutely the case for Spring Introductions that are crafted in the previous year's annual symbol.

They say for every letter you get there are many others who feel the same way who don't take the time to write. So, to all who are angry when information in the Guide changes to document an earlier annual symbol, please understand: 1. the Guide is always changing based on new information received and verified. Would you prefer we not update it to reflect new information?, and 2. we list what we consider to be the first production annual symbol. Sample pieces don't count.

THE STATUS OF E-7156

Like everyone else, we were confused this year about the status of E-7156. Did the announced retirement of E-7156R mean we were to consider E-7156 retired as well? The answer is yes. Over the years, Enesco has said different things, particularly in regard to suspended pieces. We asked for clarification and got it. You'll find Enesco's definitions of retired, suspended, and re-

NOTE FROM THE PUBLISHER CONTINUED

introduced in the QUICK REFERENCE SECTION in boxes that start out "...From The Enesco Dictionary." Essentially they have said a piece can be suspended for an indefinite period of time, a piece will not move from the suspended list to the retired list without first being re-introduced, and all re-introduced pieces will be re-sculpted. (To get you back to confused, doesn't this kind-of-sort-of mean we can consider all suspended pieces as good as retired since they will never again be produced in identical form?!)

THE NOBODY'S PERFECT! MONSTER

We've created a monster. It's name is "Nobody's Perfect!" After answering a zillion letters from collectors who are counting dots on dresses etc. we ask you to remember Precious Moments collectibles are hand crafted. Differences occur naturally as a result of firing and painting. In general, errors must be highly visible or be an announced production change before secondary market prices are affected appreciably. The format for presenting this information has changed with this Edition. And we've deemed some, "Classic Variations."

SUGAR TOWN

If you're a computer head or maybe just know enough to be dangerous, you can probably guess GREENBOOK works with Macintosh. One of the neat things about it is as you move from application to application, even though they are from different software companies, the commands are the same. Keeping that in mind, we've appropriated the house format from another of our popular guides, and made SUGAR TOWN a guide within a guide. Let us know what you think.

A FAVOR?

I have a favor to ask. We enjoy exhibiting at the collectible shows sponsored by the Collectibles & Platemakers Guild, Inc. and the National Association Of Limited Edition Dealers and are a member of both organizations. There's talk in the industry and show management has expressed the opinion that publications do not belong in the collectible shows. If you feel differently, would you let them know? Correspondence should be addressed to: McRand International, Ltd. Expositions, One Westminster Place, Lake Forest, IL 60045, (708) 295-4444.

We're still having fun. Thanks for the support.

Louise L. Patterson Langenfeld
Publisher

TABLE OF CONTENTS

INTRODUCTION

The GREENBOOK provides information about The Enesco PRECIOUS MOMENTS Collection in the form of GREENBOOK Market Prices plus factual information describing each piece. The factual information includes:

- Inspirational Title
- Descriptive Title
- Type of Product
- Enesco Item Number
- Year of Issue
- Edition Size
- Issue Price when first issued as well as each year the annual symbol is/was changed
- Size
- Certification
- Is it individually numbered?
- Is it part of a set or series?
- Annual Symbol

The factual information is compiled by the GREENBOOK with assistance from Enesco. It appears in the Guide in many different forms making it possible for a new collector as well as the experienced collector to identify the pieces in their collection or the pieces they wish to buy or sell. The inclusion of GREEN-BOOK Market Prices, as reported by retailers and collectors, make it possible to determine the value of each piece.

Market prices are important for insurance purposes as well as buying and selling.

The GREENBOOK also affords collectors an opportunity to become familiar with the *entire* PRECIOUS MOMENTS Collection - not just the pieces that are currently available at Suggested Retail and displayed in stores. Current, Retired, Suspended, Discontinued, Annuals, Two-Year Collectibles, Limited Editions, and earlier issue figurines, plates, bells, musicals, ornaments, etc. are included.

The GREENBOOK's exclusive ART CHART contains authorized reproductions of 613 line drawings. In addition, it lists the Enesco Item Number for the figurine, plate, bell, musical, ornament, doll, thimble, frame, candle climber, box, night light, egg, plaque, wreath, medallion, stocking hanger, and tree topper derived from each drawing. Also, it is noted if each piece is a Dated Annual, an Annual, a Two-Year Collectible, a Limited Edition, Retired, Suspended, has a special Inspirational Title or is derived from only a portion of the line drawing.

The ART CHART is designed to provide a graphic illustration of how individual pieces relate to each other and to the entire Collection as well as add to the fun of collecting PRECIOUS MOMENTS.

The GREENBOOK's exclusive ALPHA-LOG lists PRECIOUS MOMENTS Inspirational Titles alphabetically cross-referencing the Descriptive Title, GREENBOOK ART CHART Number, and Enesco Item Number for each figurine, plate, bell, musical, ornament, doll, thimble, frame, candle climber, box, night light, egg, plaque, wreath, medallion, stocking hanger, and tree topper with that Inspirational Title. In addition, it is noted if each piece is a Dated Annual, an Annual, a Two-Year Collectible, a Limited Edition, Retired, or Suspended.

Many times certain pieces become important as part of a group. PRECIOUS MOMENTS groups that have become important are included in the QUICK REFERENCE SECTION. Groups included are The "Original 21," Limited Editions, Retired pieces, Suspended pieces, Re-introduced pieces, pieces that have moved from the Suspended list to the Retired list, Dated Annuals, Annuals - Not Dated, Two-Year Collectibles, The Enesco PRECIOUS MOMENTS Birthday Club pieces, and The Enesco PRECIOUS MOMENTS Collectors' Club pieces.

In addition, the OUTLINE OF ANNUALS Section groups annual collectibles by series and product type. The OUTLINE OF THE SERIES Section itemizes the individual pieces that comprise each series. There's a QUICK REFERENCE CALENDAR as well. It's a summary, by year, of Retired, Suspended, and Annual pieces.

The GREENBOOK LISTINGS are where specific factual information as well as GREENBOOK Market Prices for each collectible can be found. GREENBOOK Listings are in Enesco Item Number order. The Enesco PRECIOUS MOMENTS Collectors' Club and The Enesco PRECIOUS MOMENTS Birthday Club pieces are in separate sections at the end of the Listings. Enesco Item Numbers can be found on the understamp of most pieces produced from 1982 to the present. If you don't know the Enesco Item Number, but you do know the Inspirational Title, use the ALPHA-LOG to obtain the Enesco Item Number. If you don't know the Enesco Item Number or the Inspirational Title, use the ART CHART to obtain the Enesco Item Number.

Since mid-1981 Enesco has indicated when PRECIOUS MOMENTS collectibles were produced by including an annual symbol as part of the understamp. Pieces crafted prior to 1981 have no annual symbol and have become known as "No Marks."

The GREENBOOK lists the year of issue, issue price and a GREENBOOK Market Price for each change in annual symbol.

Knowing issue prices for each PRECIOUS MOMENTS collectible when it was first issued as well as the current issue price or suggested retail can also be important when investment potential is evaluated. Many PRECIOUS MOMENTS collectibles have been produced for years and collectors who purchased the piece earlier are enjoying an increase in value even though the piece is still being produced.

INTRODUCTION CONTINUED

A very common error made by collectors is to mistake the copyright date for the year of issue because the copyright date appears on the understamp written out as ©19XX. **In order to determine what year your piece was produced, you must refer to the annual symbol, not the © date.**

Another area of confusion for collectors also pertains to information found on the understamp. Prior to 1985, Jonathan & David was the licensor. Pieces produced prior to 1985 have the Jonathan & David logo on the bottom and "© 19XX Jonathan & David - Lic. Enesco Imports Corp. " Pieces which were in production prior to 1985 and are still in production today still bear the Jonathan & David information. In 1985, the Samuel J. Butcher Company became the licensor. Pieces introduced from that point on have the PRECIOUS MOMENTS logo on the bottom and "©19XX Samuel J. Butcher - Licensee Enesco Corp." It was at this time that the "Sam B" began being incised in the base of the pieces.

In addition to indicating when pieces were produced by an annual symbol on the understamp, Enesco periodically retires and suspends individual pieces. As a result, the GREENBOOK contains nine different classifications of Market Status. They are:

PRIMARY   Piece available from retailers at issue price.

SECONDARY   Piece *not* generally available from retailers at issue price.

RETIRED/PRIMARY   Piece with specific Enesco Item Number will never be produced again. Piece still available from retailers at issue price.

RETIRED/SECONDARY   Piece with specific Enesco Item Number will never be produced again. Piece *not* generally available from retailers at issue price.

SUSPENDED/PRIMARY   Piece with specific Enesco Item Number not currently being produced but may be re-sculpted and re-introduced in the future. Piece available from retailers at issue price.

SUSPENDED/SECONDARY   Piece with specific Enesco Item Number not currently being produced but may be re-sculpted and re-introduced in the future. Piece *not* generally available from retailers at issue price.

SUSPENDED/RETIRED/SECONDARY   Piece with specific Enesco Item Number was suspended, re-introduced, and subsequently retired. Piece *not* generally available from retailers at issue price.

DISCONTINUED/PRIMARY   Production ceased on piece with specific Enesco Item Number. Piece still available from retailers at issue price.

DISCONTINUED/SECONDARY   Production ceased on piece with specific Enesco Item Number. Piece *not* generally available from retailers at issue price.

The nine Market Status classifications have a major effect on the value of PM collectibles. This is reflected in the GREENBOOK Market Price.

Factors other than current availability that affect secondary market prices include rarity, year of issue, condition, and general appeal.

Because there are so many factors based on individual judgements, and because prices can vary from one section of the country to another, GREENBOOK Market Prices **are never an absolute number**.

Three questions that come up frequently in regard to their effect on GREEN-BOOK Market Prices are 1) boxes, 2) Sam Butcher's signature on the piece, and 3) variations.

In general, the newer the piece the more important it is to have the box. On hard-to-find, scarce, older pieces, not having a box usually does not subtract significantly from the GREENBOOK Market Price. On the other hand, pieces that are easier to come by are a tough sell without the box, because one with a box can always be found.

In the past we've said Sam Butcher signing a piece does not add appreciably to its GREENBOOK Market Price, but that it does vary with the rarity of the piece. Our experience is many collectors expect that a Sam Butcher signature will add hundreds or even thousands to the value of a piece. The fact is the value in most signed pieces to a collector is if it was signed by Mr. Butcher for you. To date, a Sam Butcher signature has added in the range of $20 to $75 to the market price, depending on the piece.

As with all things made by human hands, PRECIOUS MOMENTS porcelains exist with variations. Some differences occur naturally as a result of firing and painting. There are also pieces with variations caused by production changes or human error. Again, speaking in generalities, errors must be highly visible or be an announced production change before secondary market prices are affected appreciably.

The GREENBOOK GIFT GIVER'S GUIDE contains currently available pieces that are appropriate as gifts for special people and special occasions.

Because it is a "Collection within a Collection," the GREENBOOK Guide to SUGAR TOWN has been done as a "Guide within a Guide" with an entirely different set-up and format. Please see the SUGAR TOWN cover pages for an explanation of this section.

NOTES

GREENBOOK ART CHART

The GREENBOOK ART CHART contains authorized reproductions of 613 line drawings. In addition, it lists the Enesco Item Number for the figurine, plate, bell, musical, ornament, doll, thimble, frame, candle climber, box, night light, egg, plaque, wreath, medallion, stocking hanger, and tree topper derived from each drawing. Also, it is noted if each piece is a Dated Annual, an Annual, a Two-Year Collectible, a Limited Edition, Retired, Suspended, has a special Inspirational Title, or is derived from only a portion of the line drawing.

The ART CHART is designed to provide a graphic illustration of how individual pieces relate to each other and to the entire Collection as well as add to the fun of collecting PRECIOUS MOMENTS.

14

#	DESCRIPTIVE TITLE	FIG	PLT	BELL	MUSC	ORN	DOLL	THMBL	FRAME	CNDL CLMB	BOX	OTHER
1	Boy with Teddy	E-1372B E-9278	E-9275	E-5208		E-5631*			E-7170		E-9280	
2	Girl with Bunny	E-1372G E-9279 *104531*	E-9276	E-5209		E-5632*			E-7171		E-9281	
3	Boy with Black Eye	E-1373B										
4	Girl with Doll & Candle	E-1373G										
5	Girl with Goose	E-1374G *520322*	*E-7174*			522910						
6	Boy & Girl on Seesaw	E-1375A										
7	Boy & Girl with Bluebirds	**E-1375B**										
8	Boy & Girl Sitting/Stump	E-1376	*E-5215*			522929						
9	Boy Leading Lamb	**E-1377A**										
10	Boy Helping Lamb	**E-1377B**										
11	Boy with Turtle	**E-1379A**										
12	Boy with Report Card	**E-1379B**		E-5211								
13	Indian Boy	E-1380B										
14	Indian Girl	E-1380G										
15	Boy Patching World	**E-1381** (Also see ART CHART NUMBER 611)										
16	Boy Holding Lamb	**E-2010**		E-5620		E-6120						
17	Boy & Girl Playing Angels	**E-2012**			E-2809							
18	Boy & Girl Reading Book	**E-2013**			E-2808							
19	Boy with Dog	E-1374B										
20	Girl with Puppies	E-1378										

BOLD = Suspended   *Italics* = Limited Edition   Shaded Area = Retired   ◆ = Two-Year Collectible

Boxed = Dated Annual   Rounded Box = Annual   * = Special Inspirational Title or piece derived from a portion of the drawing

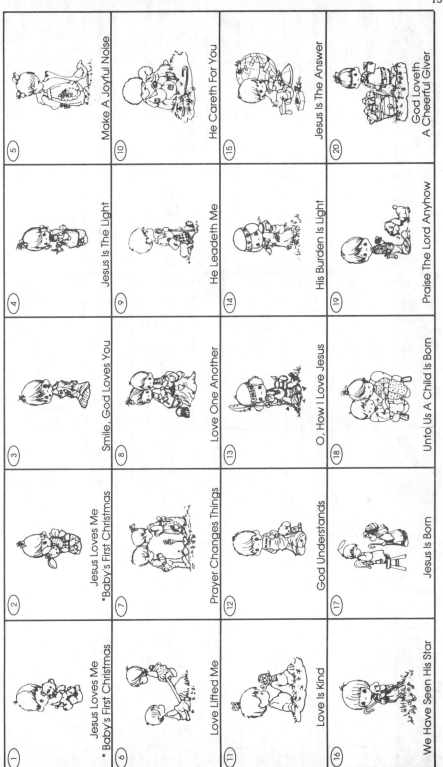

1 — Jesus Loves Me * Baby's First Christmas
2 — Jesus Loves Me *Baby's First Christmas
3
4 — Jesus Is The Light
5 — Make A Joyful Noise
6 — Love Lifted Me
7
8 — Smile, God Loves You
9 — He Leadeth Me
10 — He Careth For You
11 — Love Is Kind
12 — Prayer Changes Things
13 — Love One Another
14 — His Burden Is Light
15 — Jesus Is The Answer
16 — We Have Seen His Star
17 — Jesus Is Born
18 — Unto Us A Child Is Born
19 — Praise The Lord Anyhow
20 — God Loveth A Cheerful Giver

#	DESCRIPTIVE TITLE	FIG	PLT	BELL	MUSC	ORN	DOLL	THMBL	FRAME	CNDL CLMB	BOX	OTHER
21	Boy with Manger Baby	E-2011										
22	Nativity Set	E-2800	E-5646		E-2810*	E-5633*						
	E-2395 also includes a camel, donkey, and Three Kings											
23	Angels in Chariot	E-2801										
24	Boy Giving Toy Lamb	E-2802			E-2806							
25	Boy Kneel Manger/Crown	E-2803			E-2807							
26	Boy on Globe with Teddy	E-2804										
27	Boy in Santa Cap with Dog	E-2805										
28	Rocking Cradle	E-3104				E-0518 / E-5392			E-0521			
29	Boy with Bible/Crutches	E-3105										
30	Mother Needlepointing	E-3106	E-5217	E-7181	E-7182	E-0514	E-2850	13293	E-7241			
31	Boy Holding Cat/Dog	E-3107										
32	Girl Rocking Cradle	E-3108	E-9256		E-5204							
33	Grandma in Rocker	E-3109	E-7173	E-7183	E-7184	E-0516		13307	E-7242			
34	Boy Sharing with Puppy	E-3110B										
35	Girl Sharing with Puppy	E-3110G										
36	Girl Helper	E-3111										
37	Boy Writing in Sand/Girl	E-3113										
38	Bride and Groom	E-3114	E-5216	E-7179	E-7180	E-2385*			E-7166		E-7167	
39	Boy/Girl Angels on Cloud	E-3115 / E-0001									Plaques } E-0102 / E-0202 — Night Light I E-5207*	
40	Boy Carving/Tree for Girl	E-3116										

BOLD = Suspended *Italics* = Limited Edition Shaded Area = Retired

Boxed = Dated Annual (Rounded Box) = Annual * = Special Inspirational Title or piece derived from a portion of the drawing

♦ = Two-Year Collectible

(21) Come Let Us Adore Him

(22) Come Let Us Adore Him
*4 main pieces

(23) Jesus Is Born

(24) Christmas Is A Time
To Share

(25) Crown Him Lord Of All

(26) Peace On Earth

(27) Wishing You A Season
Filled With Joy

(28) Blessed Are The
Pure In Heart

(29)

(30) Mother Sew Dear

(31) Blessed Are
The Peacemakers

(32) The Hand That
Rocks The Future

(33) The Purr-fect Grandma

(34) He Watches Over Us All

(35)

(36) Be Not Weary
In Well Doing

(37) Thou Art Mine

(38) The Lord Bless You
And Keep You
*Our First Christmas Together

(39) Loving Is Sharing

(40) Loving Is Sharing
Thee I Love

But Love Goes On Forever
*My Guardian Angel

#	DESCRIPTIVE TITLE	FIG	PLT	BELL	MUSC	ORN	DOLL	THMBL	FRAME	CNDL CLMB	BOX	OTHER
41	Boy Pulling Wagon w/Girl	E-3117										
42	Boy with Books	**E-3119**										
43	Girl with Box of Kittens	**E-3120**				E-0534						
44	Boy Jogging with Dog	E-3112										
45	Girl with Fry Pan	E-3118										
46	Boy Graduate	**E-4720**		E-7175					E-7177			
47	Girl Graduate	E-4721		E-7176					E-7178			
48	Girl with Piggy Bank	**E-4722**										
49	Boy Reading Holy Bible	**E-4723**										
50	Christening	E-4724	E-7172									
51	Choir Boys w/Bandages	**E-4725**			E-4726							
52	Sad Boy with Teddy	**E-5200**										
53	Boy Helping Friend	**E-5201**										
54	Lemonade Stand	**E-5202**										
55	Boy with Dog on Stairs	**E-5203**										
56	Boy Angel on Cloud				**E-5205**	**E-5627***				**E-6118*** (set)	Plaque) **E-6901****	
57	Girl Angel on Cloud				**E-5206**	**E-5628***						
58	Girl Praying in Field	**E-7155***		E-5210		E-0515*						
59	Boy in Dad's Duds/Dog	E-5212										
60	Girl with Goose in Lap	**E-5213**										

BOLD = Suspended
Boxed = Dated Annual
Rounded Box = Annual
Italics = Limited Edition
Shaded Area = Retired
* = Special Inspirational Title or piece derived from a portion of the drawing
♦ = Two-Year Collectible

41	42	43	44	45
Walking By Faith	It's What's Inside That Counts	To Thee With Love	God's Speed	Eggs Over Easy

46	47	48	49	50
The Lord Bless You And Keep You	The Lord Bless You And Keep You	Love Cannot Break A True Friendship	Peace Amid The Storm	Rejoicing With You

51	52	53	54	55
Peace On Earth	Bear Ye One Another's Burdens	Love Lifted Me	Thank You For Coming To My Ade	Let Not The Sun Go Down Upon Your Wrath

56	57	58	59	60
My Guardian Angel *But Love Goes On Forever **Collection Plaque	My Guardian Angel *But Love Goes On Forever	Prayer Changes Things *Thanking Him For You	To A Special Dad *w/o dog	God Is Love

#	DESCRIPTIVE TITLE	FIG	PLT	BELL	MUSC	ORN	DOLL	THMBL	FRAME	CNDL CLMB	BOX	OTHER
61	Boy & Girl/Praying/Table	**E-5214**										
62	Manger with Child	**E-5619**										
63	Donkey	E-5621										
64	Shepherd			E-5623								
65	Three Kings on Camels	E-5624 108243				E-5630*						
66	Three Kings	E-5635	*E-0538*		**E-0520**	**E-5634**						
67	Angel with Trumpet	E-5636 520268			E-5645	113980						
68	Angel with Flashlight	E-5637										
69	Cow with Bell	E-5638										
70	Boy Angel Praying w/Harp	**E-5639**										
71	Girl Angel Praying w/Harp	**E-5640**										
72	Follow Me Angel w/3 Kings	**E-5641**										
73	Boy Angel and Knight				E-5642							
74	Two Section Wall	E-5644										
75	Mikey						E-6214B					
76	Debbie						E-6214G					
77	Praying Angel			E-5622		E-5629						
78	Boy on Telephone	PM-811										
79	Boy Angel Playing Trumpet					E-2343				E-2344 (pair)		
80	Boy in Pajamas w/Teddy	**E-2345**										

BOLD = Suspended   *Italics* = Limited Edition   Shaded Area = Retired

Boxed = Dated Annual   Rounded Box = Annual   * = Special Inspirational Title or piece derived from a portion of the drawing

◆ = Two-Year Collectible

61 Prayer Changes Things	**62** O Come Let Us Adore Him	**63** Donkey	**64** Jesus Is Born *Unto Us A Child Is Born	**65** They Followed The Star
66 Wee Three Kings	**67** Rejoice O Earth	**68** The Heavenly Light	**69** Cow	**70** Isn't He Wonderful
71 Isn't He Wonderful	**72** They Followed The Star	**73** Silent Knight	**74** Two Section Wall	**75** Mikey
76 Debbie	**77** Let The Heavens Rejoice	**78** Hello Lord, It's Me Again	**79** Joy To The World	**80** May Your Christmas Be Cozy

22

#	DESCRIPTIVE TITLE	FIG	PLT	BELL	MUSC	ORN	DOLL	THMBL	FRAME	CNDL CLMB	BOX	OTHER
81	Angel w/Friends Caroling		*E-2347*		**E-2346**	[E-0532*]						
82	Boy Next/Potbellied Stove	**E-2348**										
83	Girl w/Doll/Reading Book	**E-2349**	[15237]			**E-0533***						
84	Boy Ice Skater/Santa Cap	**E-2350**				E-2369						
85	Two Angels with Candles	E-2351										
86	Boy Carolling next to Lamp Post	E-2353			**E-2352**	**E-0531***						
87	Drummer Boy with Manger	**E-2356** E-2360* E-5384*	[E-2357]	[E-2358*]	**E-2355**	[E-2359*]						
88	Girl with Stocking	**E-2361**										
89	Baby in Christmas Stocking					**E-2362**						
90	Camel	E-2363										
91	Goat	**E-2364**										
92	Boy Angel with Candle	**E-2365**				**E-2367**						
93	Angel Praying	**E-2366**				E-2368						
94	Unicorn					E-2371						
95	Boy Holding Block					**E-2372**						
96	Girl with Presents	E-2374				(525057)						
97	Girl with Pie	E-2375				E-2376*						
98	Girl Knitting Tie for Boy	**E-2377**	**E-2378**									
99	Mouse with Cheese					**E-2381**						
100	Camel, Donkey, Cow					**E-2386**						

BOLD = Suspended   *Italics* = Limited Edition   Shaded Area = Retired   ◆ = Two-Year Collectible

Boxed = Dated Annual   Rounded Box = Annual   * = Special Inspirational Title or piece derived from a portion of the drawing

23

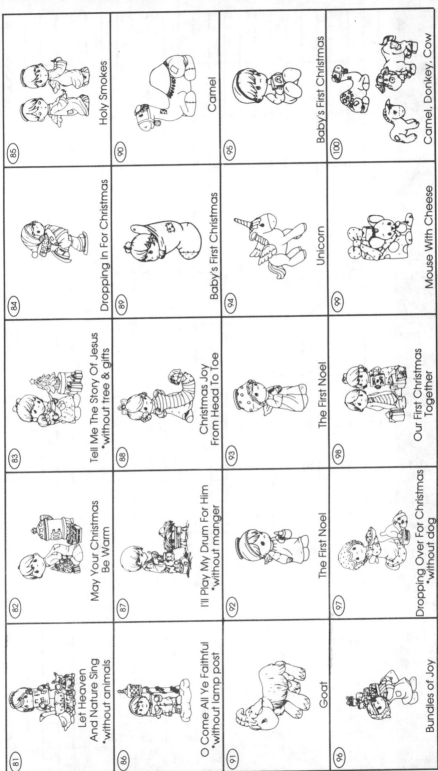

81 — Let Heaven And Nature Sing *without animals

82 — May Your Christmas Be Warm

83 — Tell Me The Story Of Jesus *without tree & gifts

84 — Dropping In For Christmas

85 — Holy Smokes

86 — O Come All Ye Faithful *without lamp post

87 — I'll Play My Drum For Him *without manger

88 — Christmas Joy From Head To Toe

89 — Baby's First Christmas

90 — Camel

91 — Goat

92 — The First Noel

93 — The First Noel

94 — Unicorn

95 — Baby's First Christmas

96 — Bundles of Joy

97 — Dropping Over For Christmas *without dog

98 — Our First Christmas Together

99 — Mouse With Cheese

100 — Camel, Donkey, Cow

#	DESCRIPTIVE TITLE	FIG	PLT	BELL	MUSC	ORN	DOLL	THMBL	FRAME	CNDL-CLMB	BOX	OTHER
101	Mini Houses w/Palm Tree	E-2387										
102	Boy Holding Heart	**E-7153**							12017*			
103	Girl Holding Heart	**E-7154**						100625	12025*			
104	Girl with Shopping Bag	E-0005 E-0105										
105	Boy Holding Chick	**E-7156**	*E-9257* (Also see ART CHART Number 374)									
106	Waitress Carrying Food	E-7157										
107	Nurse Giving Shot to Bear	E-7158										
108	Bandaged Boy by Sign	**E-7159**										
109	Grandpa in Rocking Chair	**E-7160**				E-0517*						
110	Shepherd Painting Lamb	E-7161										
111	Girl at School Desk	**E-7162**			E-7185							
112	Boy with Ice Bag on Head	**E-7163**										
113	Boy/Girl Paint'g Dog House	**E-7164**										
114	Boy/Girl Baptism Bucket	**E-7165**			E-7186							
115	Groom Doll						*E-7267B*					
116	Bride Doll						*E-7267G*					
117	Girl with Curlers	PM-821										
118	Boy Pushing Girl on Sled	**E-0501**			E-0519							
119	Boy w/Candle & Mouse	**E-0502**				E-0537*						
120	Girl/Snow Look'g Birdhouse	**E-0503**	523860*									

BOLD = Suspended   *Italics* = Limited Edition   Shaded Area = Retired   ◆ = Two-Year Collectible

Boxed = Dated Annual   (Rounded Box) = Annual   * = Special Inspirational Title or piece derived from a portion of the drawing

(101) House And Palm Tree	(102) God Is Love, Dear Valentine *Loving You	(103) God Is Love, Dear Valentine *Loving You	(104) Seek And Ye Shall Find	(105) I Believe In Miracles
(106) There Is Joy In Serving Jesus	(107) Love Beareth All Things	(108) Lord Give Me Patience	(109) The Perfect Grandpa *without dog	(110) His Sheep Am I
(111) Love Is Sharing	(112) God Is Watching Over You	(113) Bless This House	(114) Let The Whole World Know	(115) Cubby
(116) Tammy	(117) Smile, God Loves You	(118) Sharing Our Season Together	(119) Jesus Is The Light That Shines *without mouse	(120) Blessings From My House To Yours *Blessings From Me To Thee

#	DESCRIPTIVE TITLE	FIG	PLT	BELL	MUSC	ORN	DOLL	THMBL	FRAME	CNDL CLMB	BOX	OTHER
121	Boy Giving Teddy/Poor Boy	E-0504	E-0505									
122	Boy with Wreath	E-0506		E-0522		E-0513*						
123	Girl Looking into Manger	**E-0507**										
124	Boy/Girl Preparing Manger	**E-0508**										
125	Girl Angel Push Jesus/Cart	**E-0509**										
126	Rooster & Bird on Pig	E-0511 / 525278*										
127	Boy Angel/Red Cross Bag	**E-0512** / 525286*				102415*						
128	Knight in Armor	E-0523										
129	Boy & Dog Running Away	E-0525										
130	Angel Catch Falling Skater	**E-0526**										
131	Girl with Bird in Hand	E-0530										
132	Boy with Slate					**E-0535**						
133	Girl with Slate					**E-0536**						
134	Baby Collector's Doll						E-0539					
135	Boy Hold Board/Girl/Chalk	**E-9251**										
136	Boy & Girl with Bandage	**E-9252**										
137	Boy with Dog Rip'g Pants	**E-9253**										
138	Girl at Typewriter	E-9254										
139	Groom Carrying Bride	E-9255										
140	Bonnet Girl with Butterfly	E-9258 / 523879										525960 / Egg

BOLD = Suspended *Italics* = Limited Edition Shaded Area = Retired ◆ = Two-Year Collectible

Boxed = Dated Annual Rounded Box = Annual * = Special Inspirational Title or piece derived from a portion of the drawing

(121) Christmastime Is For Sharing	(122) Surrounded With Joy *Surround Us With Joy	(123) God Sent His Son	(124) Prepare Ye The Way Of The Lord	(125) Bringing God's Blessing To You
(126) Tubby's First Christmas *no bird	(127) It's A Perfect Boy *without manger	(128) Onward Christian Soldiers	(129) You Can't Run Away From God	(130) He Upholdeth Those Who Call
(131) His Eye Is On The Sparrow	(132) Love Is Patient	(133) Love Is Patient	(134) Katie Lynne	(135) Love Is Patient
(136) Forgiving Is Forgetting	(137) The End Is In Sight	(138) Praise The Lord Anyhow	(139) Bless You Two	(140) We Are God's Workmanship

#	DESCRIPTIVE TITLE	FIG	PLT	BELL	MUSC	ORN	DOLL	THMBL	FRAME	CNDL CLMB	BOX	OTHER
141	Boy with Piggy	**E-9259**										
142	Boy Angel Wind'g Rainbow	**E-9260**										
143	Boy Graduate with Scroll	**E-9261**										
144	Girl Graduate with Scroll	**E-9262**										
145	Boy & Girl/Horse Costume	**E-9263**										
146	Girl Ironing Clothes	E-9265										
147	Animals	**E-9267** (Also see ART CHART Numbers 407, 408, 409, 412, 413 & 414)										
148	Boy with Dunce Cap	E-9268										
149	Girl with Chicks in Umbrella	E-9273										
150	Girl Angel Making Food	E-9274										
151	Pig	**E-9282** **E-9282B**										
152	Bunny	**E-9282** **E-9282A**										
153	Lamb	**E-9282** **E-9282C**										
154	Boy at Pulpit	**E-9285**										
155	Girl with Lion & Lamb	**E-9287**										
156	Girl Angel w/Sprinkl'g Can	**E-9288**										
157	Boy Angel /Flying Lessons	**E-9289**										
158	Club Meeting	E-0103 E-0303										
159	Boy Clown Holding Mask	PM-822										
160	Girl Covering Kitten	PM-831										

BOLD = Suspended   *Italics* = Limited Edition   Shaded Area = Retired   ◆ = Two-Year Collectible

Boxed = Dated Annual   Rounded Box = Annual   * = Special Inspirational Title or piece derived from a portion of the drawing

29

141 We're In It Together

142 God's Promises Are Sure

143 Seek Ye The Lord

144 Seek Ye The Lord

145 How Can Two Walk Together Except They Agree

146 Press On

147 Animal Collection

148 Nobody's Perfect!

149 Let Love Reign

150 Taste And See That The Lord Is Good

151 You're Worth Your Weight In Gold

152 To Somebunny Special

153 Especially For Ewe

154 If God Be For Us, Who Can Be Against Us

155 Peace On Earth

156 Sending You A Rainbow

157 Trust In The Lord

158 Let Us Call The Club To Order

159 Put On A Happy Face

160 Dawn's Early Light

#	DESCRIPTIVE TITLE	FIG	PLT	BELL	MUSC	ORN	DOLL	THMBL	FRAME	CNDL CLMB	BOX	OTHER
161	Girl with String of Hearts	E-2821 *523283* 527661			112577 422282♦	112356	427527♦					
162	Girl Polishing Table	E-2822										
163	Boy Holding Picture Frame	**E-2823**										
164	Girl with Floppy Hat	E-2824										
165	Girl Put'g Bows/Sister's Hair	E-2825										
166	Girl at Table with Dolls	**E-2826**										
167	Girl with Bucket on Head	**E-2827**										
168	Girl/Trunk/Wedding Gown	E-2828										
169	Girl Mailing Snowball	E-2829	101834		112402	112372						
170	Bridesmaid	E-2831										
171	Bride with Flower Girl	E-2832										
172	Groomsman with Frog	E-2836										
173	Angel Helping Baby	**E-2840**										
174	Baby's First Photo	E-2841										
175	Boy & Girl on Swing		*E-2847*									
176	Mother Wrapping Bread		*E-2848*									
177	Baby Collector Doll						**E-2851**					
178	Baby Figurines	E-2852 (Also see ART CHART Numbers 401-406)										
179	Happy Anniversary	E-2853										
180	1st Anniversary	E-2854										

BOLD = Suspended *Italics* = Limited Edition Shaded Area = Retired ♦ = Two-Year Collectible

Boxed = Dated Annual (Rounded Box) = Annual * = Special Inspirational Title or piece derived from a portion of the drawing

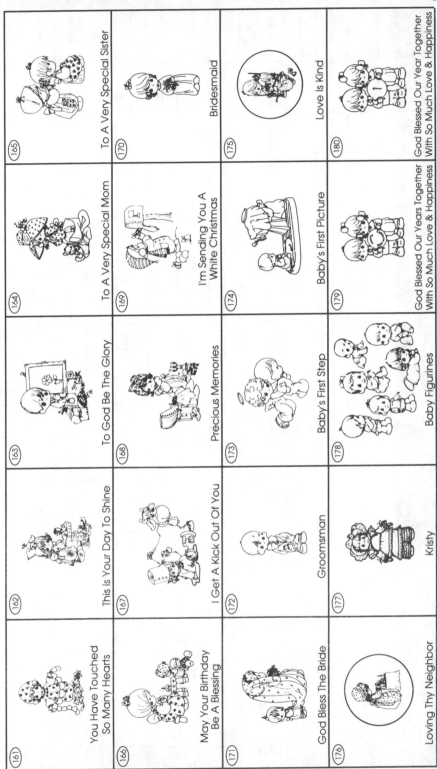

161	162	163	164	165
You Have Touched So Many Hearts	This Is Your Day To Shine	To God Be The Glory	To A Very Special Mom	To A Very Special Sister
166	167	168	169	170
May Your Birthday Be A Blessing	I Get A Kick Out Of You	Precious Memories	I'm Sending You A White Christmas	Bridesmaid
171	172	173	174	175
God Bless The Bride	Groomsman	Baby's First Step	Baby's First Picture	Love Is Kind
176	177	178	179	180
Loving Thy Neighbor	Kristy	Baby Figurines	God Blessed Our Years Together With So Much Love & Happiness	God Blessed Our Year Together With So Much Love & Happiness

#	DESCRIPTIVE TITLE	FIG	PLT	BELL	MUSC	ORN	DOLL	THMBL	FRAME	CNDL CLMB	BOX	OTHER
181	5th Anniversary	E-2855										
182	10th Anniversary	E-2856										
183	25th Anniversary	E-2857										
184	40th Anniversary	E-2859										
185	50th Anniversary	E-2860										
186	Girl w/Long Hair & Bible	**E-5376**										
187	Girl with Mouse	E-5377										
188	Boy with Harp	**E-5378**				E-5388						
189	Girl with Broom	E-5379 522988										
190	Boy w/Butterfly at Manger	**E-5380**										
191	Boys at Manger	**E-5381**										
192	Deluxe 4-Piece Nativity	**E-5382**										
193	"1984" Girl in Choir	E-5383		E-5393		E-5387						
194	Boy Angel with Candle	**E-5385**				**E-5389**						
195	Girl Angel Praying	**E-5386**				**E-5390**						
196	Boy in Choir					**E-5389**						
197	Girl in Scarf & Cap					**E-5390**						
198	Girl with Gift					**E-5391**						
199	Angel Behind Rainbow											**16020** Night Light
200	Carollers with Puppy				E-5394							

BOLD = Suspended *Italics* = Limited Edition Shaded Area = Retired ♦ = Two-Year Collectible

Boxed = Dated Annual Rounded Box = Annual * = Special Inspirational Title or piece derived from a portion of the drawing

32

181	182	183	184	185
God Blessed Our Years Together With So Much Love & Happiness 186 May Your Christmas Be Blessed	God Blessed Our Years Together With So Much Love & Happiness 187 Love Is Kind	God Blessed Our Years Together With So Much Love & Happiness 188 Joy To The World	God Blessed Our Years Together With So Much Love & Happiness 189 Isn't He Precious	God Blessed Our Years Together With So Much Love & Happiness 190 A Monarch Is Born
191 His Name Is Jesus	192 For God So Loved The World	193 Wishing You A Merry Christmas	194 Oh Worship The Lord	195 Oh Worship The Lord
196 Peace On Earth	197 May God Bless You With A Perfect Holiday Season	198 Love Is Kind	199 God Bless You With Rainbows	200 Wishing You A Merry Christmas

#	DESCRIPTIVE TITLE	FIG	PLT	BELL	MUSC	ORN	DOLL	THMBL	FRAME	CNDL CLMB	BOX	OTHER
201	Nativity Scene		*E-5395*									
202	Boy Pull Sled w/Girl & Tree		E-5396									
203	Boy Jogger						E-5397					
204	Girl with Present & Kitten	**E-6613**										
205	Girl with Dues Bank	E-0104										
		E-0404										
206	Boy Angel with Flashlight	PM-841										
207	Boy with Racing Cup	PM-842										
208	Ringbearer	E-2833										
209	Flower Girl	E-2835										
210	Junior Bridesmaid	E-2845										
211	Boy Sitting with Teddy	**100021**										
212	Boy/Bow & Arrow/Cloud	**100056**										
213	Girl Kneel/Church Window	100064										
214	Two Girls with Flowers	100072				113956						
215	Baseball Player with Bat	100110										
216	Ballerina	100129				102423*						
217	Mother with Babies	100137										
218	Tennis Girl	**100161**				102458*						
219	Kids in Boat	100250				522937						
220	Girl in Old Bath Tub	100277				112380						

BOLD = Suspended   *Italics* = Limited Edition   Shaded Area = Retired   ♦ = Two-Year Collectible

Boxed = Dated Annual   Rounded Box = Annual   * = Special Inspirational Title or piece derived from a portion of the drawing

35

201	202	203	204	205
Unto Us A Child Is Born	The Wonder Of Christmas	Timmy	God Sends The Gift Of His Love	Join In On The Blessings
206	207	208	209	210
God's Ray Of Mercy	Trust In The Lord To The Finish	Ringbearer	Flower Girl	Junior Bridesmaid
211	212	213	214	215
To My Favorite Paw	Sending My Love	Worship The Lord	To My Forever Friend	Lord I'm Coming Home
216	217	218	219	220
Lord. Keep Me On My Toes *without bar	The Joy Of The Lord Is My Strength	Serving The Lord *Serve With A Smile	Friends Never Drift Apart	He Cleansed My Soul

#	DESCRIPTIVE TITLE	FIG	PLT	BELL	MUSC	ORN	DOLL	THMBL	FRAME	CNDL CLMB	BOX	OTHER
221	Baby w/Bunny & Turtle	520934			100285							
222	Tennis Boy	**100293**				102431*						
223	Boy Kneel/Church Window	102229										
224	Girl Holding Cross	103632				522953						523534* Egg
225	Girl Making Heart Quilt	**12009**						12254				
226	Girl by Fence	(12068)	(12106)		408735♦		408786♦					
227	Girl with Crossed Arms	(12076)	(12114)		408743♦		408794♦					
228	Girl with Hands behind Her	(12084)	(12122)		408751♦		408808♦	(100641)				
229	Girl w/Scarf & Hat/Birds	(12092)	(12130)		408778♦		408816♦					
230	Angel Boy in Devil's Suit	**12149**										
231	Boy Playing Piano				12165							
232	Girl Playing Triangle	**12173**										
233	Nun	**12203**										
234	Angel Cutting Baby's Hair	**12211**										
235	Mini Clowns	12238 (Also see ART CHART Numbers 416-419)										
	*Girl Clown w/Balloon					15822*				100668 (Set of the two with balls)		
	**Boy Clown w/Cap & Ball					15830**						
236	Clown Holding Balloons	12262										
237	Policeman Writing Ticket	**12297**				102377*						
238	Teacher w/Report Card	12300										
239	Boy & Girl/Sandcastle	12319										
240	Mary Knitting Booties	**12343**										

BOLD = Suspended   *Italics* = Limited Edition   Shaded Area = Retired   ♦ = Two-Year Collectible

Boxed = Dated Annual   (Rounded Box) = Annual   * = Special Inspirational Title or piece derived from a portion of the drawing

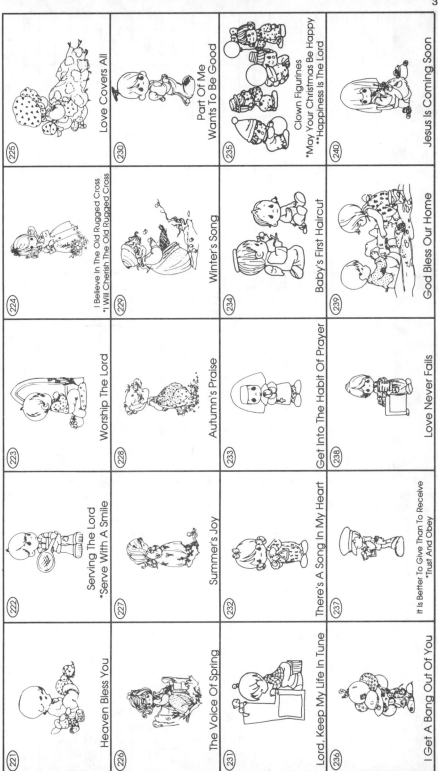

221) Heaven Bless You

222) Serving The Lord
*Serve With A Smile

223) Worship The Lord

224) I Believe In The Old Rugged Cross
*I Will Cherish The Old Rugged Cross

225) Love Covers All

226) The Voice Of Spring

227) Summer's Joy

228) Autumn's Praise

229) Winter's Song

230) Part Of Me
Wants To Be Good

231) Lord, Keep My Life In Tune

232) There's A Song In My Heart

233) Get Into The Habit Of Prayer

234) Baby's First Haircut

235) Clown Figurines
*May Your Christmas Be Happy
**Happiness Is The Lord

236) I Get A Bang Out Of You

237) It Is Better To Give Than To Receive
*Trust And Obey

238) Love Never Fails

239) God Bless Our Home

240) Jesus Is Coming Soon

#	DESCRIPTIVE TITLE	FIG	PLT	BELL	MUSC	ORN	DOLL	THMBL	FRAME	CNDL CLMB	BOX	OTHER
241	Angels Make Snowman	**12351**										
242	Boy Playing Banjo	**12378**										
243	Girl Playing Harmonica	**12386**										
244	Boy Playing Trumpet/Dog	**12394**										
245	Two Angels Sawing Star				12408							
246	Boy in Airplane					12416						
247	Boy Angel						**12424**					
248	Girl Angel						**12432**					
249	5th Anniversary Piece	12440										
250	Girl Clown w/Bskt/Goose	12459				112364						
251	Clown with Dog on Mud	12467										
252	Baby Boy						**12475**					
253	Baby Girl						**12483**					
254	Boy Tangled in Christmas Lights	15482				15849						
255	Mother Goose/Bonnet/Babes	15490				15857*						
256	Boy Clown Holding Jack-in-the-Box				15504	**113972**						
257	Baby Boy Holding Bottle	15539				15903						
258	Baby Girl Holding Bottle	15547				15911						
259	Angel with Holly Wreath	15881		15873		15768						
260	Mother with Cookie Sheet	15776						15865				

BOLD = Suspended *Italics* = Limited Edition Shaded Area = Retired ◆ = Two-Year Collectible

Boxed = Dated Annual Rounded Box = Annual * = Special Inspirational Title or piece derived from a portion of the drawing

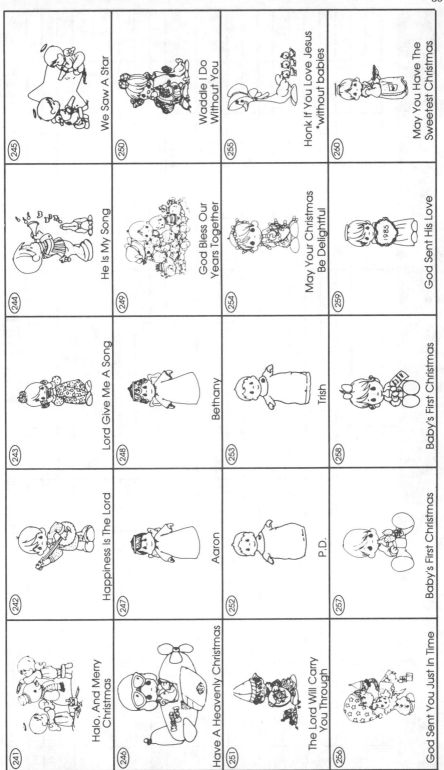

(241) Halo, And Merry Christmas	(242) Happiness Is The Lord	(243) Lord Give Me A Song	(244) He Is My Song	(245) We Saw A Star
(246) Have A Heavenly Christmas	(247) Aaron	(248) Bethany	(249) God Bless Our Years Together	(250) Waddle I Do Without You
(251) The Lord Will Carry You Through	(252) P.D.	(253) Trish	(254) May Your Christmas Be Delightful	(255) Honk If You Love Jesus *without babies
(256) God Sent You Just In Time	(257) Baby's First Christmas	(258) Baby's First Christmas	(259) God Sent His Love 1985	(260) May You Have The Sweetest Christmas

#	DESCRIPTIVE TITLE	FIG	PLT	BELL	MUSC	ORN	DOLL	THMBL	FRAME	CNDL CLMB	BOX	OTHER
261	Father Reading Bible	15784										
262	Boy Sitting Listen to Story	15792										
263	Girl with Ornament	15806										
264	Christmas Tree				15814							
265	Boy Angel								**E-7168**			
266	Girl Angel								**E-7169**			
267	Angel Pushing Buggy	**16012**										
268	Bridesmaid with Kitten	**E-2834**										
269	Groom	E-2837										
270	Clown Sitting on Ball	12270										
271	Boy Angel on Cloud	**12335**										
272	Mom & Dad w/Girl/ Adoption	**100145**										
273	Mom & Dad w/Boy/ Adoption	**100153**										
274	Boy with Football	100188				**111120**						
275	Boy Standing in Ink Spot	**100269**										
276	Pilgrim & Indian w/Turkey	**100544**										
277	Boy and Girl in Box				101702	102350 112399 520233						
278	Angel with Black Lamb	102261				102288						
279	Three Mini Animals	102296										
280	Girl with Muff	102342		102318		102326		102334				

BOLD = Suspended   *Italics* = Limited Edition   Shaded Area = Retired   ◆ = Two-Year Collectible

Boxed = Dated Annual   (Rounded Box) = Annual   * = Special Inspirational Title or piece derived from a portion of the drawing

261 The Story of God's Love	262 Tell Me A Story	263 God Gave His Best
266 My Guardian Angel	267 Baby's First Trip	268 Sharing Our Joy Together
271 You Can Fly	272 God Bless The Day We Found You	273 God Bless The Day We Found You
276 Brotherly Love	277 Our First Christmas Together	278 Shepherd Of Love

264 Silent Night	265 My Guardian Angel
269 Groom	270 Lord Keep Me On The Ball
274 I'm A Possibility	275 Help Lord, I'm In A Spot
279 Mini Animal Figurines	280 Wishing You A Cozy Christmas

#	DESCRIPTIVE TITLE	FIG	PLT	BELL	MUSC	ORN	DOLL	THMBL	FRAME	CNDL CLMB	BOX	OTHER
281	Fireman Holding Puppy	102393				102385						
282	Nurse with Potted Plant	102482				102407						
283	Rocking Horse					**102474**						
284	Husband/Wife/Puppy/ and Cookies	**102490**										
285	Baby Girl w/Candy Cane					102504						
286	Baby Boy w/Candy Cane					102512						
287	Clown on Elephant				102520							
288	Boy Angel w/B'day Cake	**102962**										
289	Boy Clown						*100455*					
290	Girl Clown						*100463*					
291	Doll with Stand						*102253*					
292	Uncle Sam Holding Bible with Dog	102938										
293	Girl Holding Lamb	PM-851										
294	Boy with Lamb and Book	PM-852										
295	Girl with Embroidery Hoop/ Bird	E-0006 E-0106				PM-864						
296	Teddy/Caboose - For Baby	15938										
297	Lamb - Age 1	15946										
298	Seal - Age 2	15962										
299	Pig - Age 3	15954										
300	Elephant - Age 4	15970										

BOLD = Suspended   *Italics* = Limited Edition   Shaded Area = Retired   ◆ = Two-Year Collectible

Boxed = Dated Annual   Rounded Box = Annual   * = Special Inspirational Title or piece derived from a portion of the drawing

281	282	283	284	285
Love Rescued Me	Angel Of Mercy	Rocking Horse	Sharing Our Christmas Together	Baby's First Christmas
286	287	288	289	290
Baby's First Christmas	Let's Keep In Touch	It's The Birthday Of A King	Bong Bong	Candy
291	292	293	294	295
Connie	God Bless America	The Lord Is My Shepherd	I Love To Tell The Story	Birds Of A Feather Collect Together
296	297	298	299	300
May Your Birthday Be Warm	Happy Birthday Little Lamb	God Bless You On Your Birthday	Heaven Bless Your Special Day	May Your Birthday Be Gigantic

#	DESCRIPTIVE TITLE	FIG	PLT	BELL	MUSC	ORN	DOLL	THMBL	FRAME	CNDL CLMB	BOX	OTHER
301	Lion - Age 5	15989										
302	Giraffe - Age 6	15997										
303	Clown with Pull Rope	16004										
304	Clown with Drum	B-0001										
305	Praying Grandma	PM-861										
306	1986 Dated Reindeer					102466						
307	Nativity Set with Cassette	104000										
308	Lamb and Bunny / Lamb and Skunk										E-9266	
309	Dog (A) / Cat (B)										E-9283	
310	Baby Boy								12033			
311	Baby Girl								12041			
312	Complete Wedding Party	(E-2838)										
313	Bride	E-2846						100633*				
314	Birthday Boy	**12157**										
315	Girl with Piano				12580							
316	Girl with Flowers & Deer	100048										
317	Girl/Boy Bandaging Heart	100080										
318	Girl Graduate	106208										
319	Girl/Crutches/Bible	(107999)										
320	Boy in Car	PM-862										

BOLD = Suspended *Italics* = Limited Edition Shaded Area = Retired

Boxed = Dated Annual Rounded Box = Annual * = Special Inspirational Title or piece derived from a portion of the drawing

◆ = Two-Year Collectible

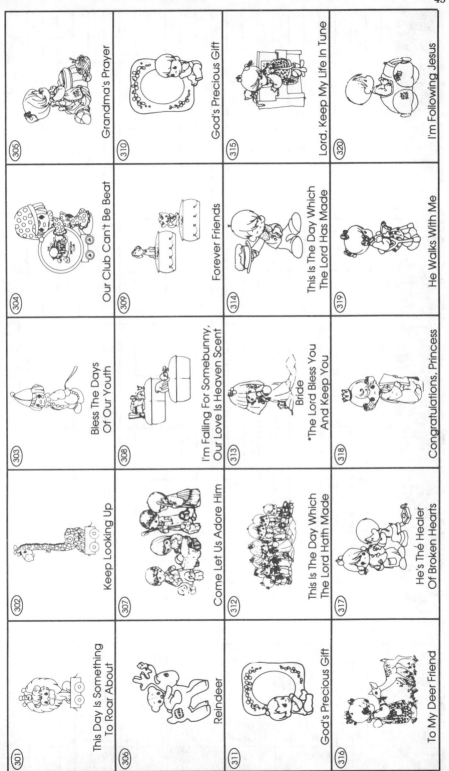

301 This Day Is Something To Roar About

302 Keep Looking Up

303 Bless The Days Of Our Youth

304 Our Club Can't Be Beat

305 Grandma's Prayer

306 Reindeer

307 Come Let Us Adore Him

308 I'm Falling For Somebunny, Our Love Is Heaven Scent

309 Forever Friends

310 God's Precious Gift

311 God's Precious Gift

312 This Is The Day Which The Lord Hath Made

313 Bride *The Lord Bless You And Keep You

314 This Is The Day Which The Lord Has Made

315 Lord, Keep My Life In Tune

316 To My Deer Friend

317 He's Thé Healer Of Broken Hearts

318 Congratulations, Princess

319 He Walks With Me

320 I'm Following Jesus

#	DESCRIPTIVE TITLE	FIG	PLT	BELL	MUSC	ORN	DOLL	THMBL	FRAME	CNDL CLMB	BOX	OTHER
321	Boy Painting Valentine	PM-873										
322	Girl w/Crayon/Valentine	PM-874										
323	Girl with Sick Bear	100102										
324	Girl on Scale	100196										
325	Parents of the Groom	100498										
326	Parents of the Bride	100501										
327	Girl with Skunk	100528										
328	Boy w/Gardening Mother	100536										
329	Girl at Gate to Heaven	101826										
330	Clown Balancing	101842					113964*						
331	Clowns on Unicycle	101850										
332	Bridal Arch	102369										
333	Boy with Hat & Fish	103497					**114006**						
334	Boy Graduate	106194										
335	Raccoon Holding Fish	BC-861										
336	Girl Sending Package to Friend	E-0007 / E-0107										
337	Nativity w/Backdrop/Video	104523										
338	Shepherd and Lambs	103004										
339	Nurse Doll							*12491*				
340	Girl/Cat/Bird Cage	100226										

BOLD = Suspended   *Italics* = Limited Edition   [Boxed] = Dated Annual   (Rounded Box) = Annual   Shaded Area = Retired   * = Special Inspirational Title or piece derived from a portion of the drawing   ◆ = Two-Year Collectible

(325) God Bless Our Family	(324) The Spirit Is Willing But The Flesh Is Weak	(323) Make Me A Blessing	(322) Loving You Dear Valentine	(321) Loving You Dear Valentine
(330) Smile Along The Way *without base & ball	(329) No Tears Past The Gate	(328) I Picked A Very Special Mom	(327) Scent From Above	(326) God Bless Our Family
(335) Fishing For Friends	(334) God Bless You Graduate	(333) My Love Will Never Let You Go	(332) Wedding Arch	(331) Lord Help Us Keep Our Act Together
(340) The Lord Giveth & The Lord Taketh Away	(339) Angie, The Angel Of Mercy	(338) We Belong To The Lord	(337) Dealer's Only Nativity	(336) Sharing Is Universal

#	DESCRIPTIVE TITLE	FIG	PLT	BELL	MUSC	ORN	DOLL	THMBL	FRAME	CNDL CLMB	BOX	OTHER
341	Kids w/Pup, Kitten, Bird		102954		109746*/**	523062*						
342	Baby Boy/Tub	102970										
343	Boy Giving Girl Ring	104019										
344	Boy Mending Hobby Horse	**104027**										
345	Girl Cheerleader	104035				**113999**						
346	Girl Clown with Books	**104396**										
347	Bear on a Sled					104515						
348	Baby Boy/Wood Tub	104817										
349	Girl Angel on Stool	**104825**										
350	Boy Reading Scroll	**105635**										
351	Dentist/Patient/Pull Tooth	**105813**										
352	Elephant Showering Mouse	105945										
353	Boy with Donkey	**106151**										
354	Schoolboy Clown	**106216**										
355	Baby Boy/Dog	109231										
356	Baby Girl/Rocking Horse					109401						
357	Baby Boy/Rocking Horse					109428						
358	Girl with Ice Cream	109754	523801*									
359	Family Thanksgiving Set	109762										
360	Girl with Present	110930		109835		109770		109843				

BOLD = Suspended   *Italics* = Limited Edition   Shaded Area = Retired

(Rounded Box) = Annual   Dated Annual

* = Special Imprint/used Title or piece derived from a portion of the drawing
♦ = Two-Year Collectible

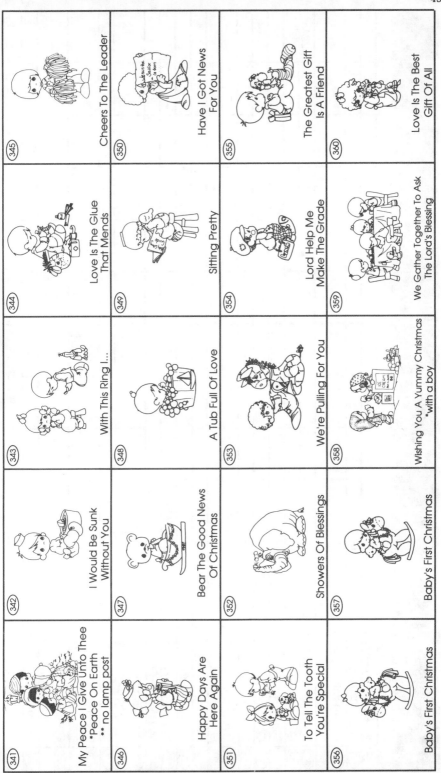

341

My Peace I Give Unto Thee
*Peace On Earth
** no lamp post

342

I Would Be Sunk
Without You

343

With This Ring I...

344

Love Is The Glue
That Mends

345

Cheers To The Leader

346

Happy Days Are
Here Again

347

Bear The Good News
Of Christmas

348

A Tub Full Of Love

349

Sitting Pretty

350

Have I Got News
For You

351

To Tell The Tooth
You're Special

352

Showers Of Blessings

353

We're Pulling For You

354

Lord Help Me
Make The Grade

355

The Greatest Gift
Is A Friend

356

Baby's First Christmas

357

Baby's First Christmas

358

Wishing You A Yummy Christmas
*with a boy

359

We Gather Together To Ask
The Lord's Blessing

360

Love Is The Best
Gift Of All

#	DESCRIPTIVE TITLE	FIG	PLT	BELL	MUSC	ORN	DOLL	THMBL	FRAME	CNDL CLMB	BOX	OTHER
361	Grandma on a Sled	109819										
362	4 Piece Large Nativity	**111333**										
363	Baby Girl/Wood Tub	112313										
364	Clown with Cymbals	B-0102 B-0002										
365	'84 Giveaway Medallion											12246 Medallion
366	Girl Feeding Lamb	PM-871										
367	Girl/Doll/Sleigh	109983				521574*						
368	Girl/Plant in Snow	109991										
369	Girl with Kite	110019										
370	Girl with Umbrella	110027										
371	Girl with Potted Plant	110035										
372	Girl/Dress Up as Bride	110043										
373	Girl With Pearl	(102903)										
374	Boy Holding Bluebird	E-7156R	(Also see ART CHART Number 105)									
375	Boy Waiting /Seed/Grow	PM-872										
376	Brass Filigree Giveaway Ornament/Kids					PM-009						
377	Cowboy/Fence/Guitar	105821										
378	Groom/Trunk/Bride	106755				522945* 528870*						
379	Couple on Couch with Wedding Album	106763										
380	Anniversary Couple w/Dog	106798										

BOLD = Suspended *Italics* = Limited Edition Shaded Area = Retired ◆ = Two-Year Collectible

* = Special Inscription. These pieces are designed from a section of the piece.

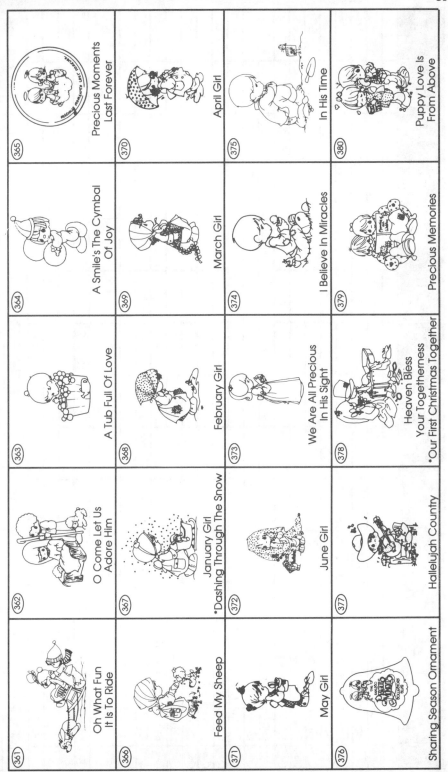

361. Oh What Fun It Is To Ride

362. O Come Let Us Adore Him

363. A Tub Full Of Love

364. A Smile's The Cymbal Of Joy

365. Precious Moments Last Forever

366. Feed My Sheep

367. January Girl *Dashing Through The Snow

368. February Girl

369. March Girl

370. April Girl

371. May Girl

372. June Girl

373. We Are All Precious In His Sight

374. I Believe In Miracles

375. In His Time

376. Sharing Season Ornament

377. Hallelujah Country

378. Heaven Bless Your Togetherness *Our First Christmas Together

379. Precious Memories

380. Puppy Love Is From Above

#	DESCRIPTIVE TITLE	FIG	PLT	BELL	MUSC	ORN	DOLL	THMBL	FRAME	CNDL CLMB	BOX	OTHER
381	Girl Holding Poppy Plant	106836										
382	Girl Sewing Boy's Pants	106844										
383	Boy with Barbells	**109487**										
384	Clown Angel with Flowers	109584										
385	Boy/Basket/Chick	109924										
386	Girl with Hearts in Cloud	109967										
387	Boy with Flower	109975										
388	Girl Holding Bunny	109886										
389	Girl with Plunger	111155										
390	Girl with Flower	112143										
391	Boy with Broken Heart	114014										
392	Couple w/Dog & Puppies	(114022)										
393	Leopard - Age 7	109479										
394	Ostrich - Age 8	109460										
395	Skunk & Mouse	105953										
396	Boy with Braces & Dog	(115479)										
397	Girl/Balloons/Satchel	(115231)										
398	Mouse in Sugar Bowl	BC-871										
399	Girl/Flowerpot/Sunflower	E-0108 / E-0008				520349						
400	Kitten Hanging on Wreath					520292						

BOLD = Suspended   *Italics* = Limited Edition   Shaded Area = Retired   ◆ = Two-Year Collectible

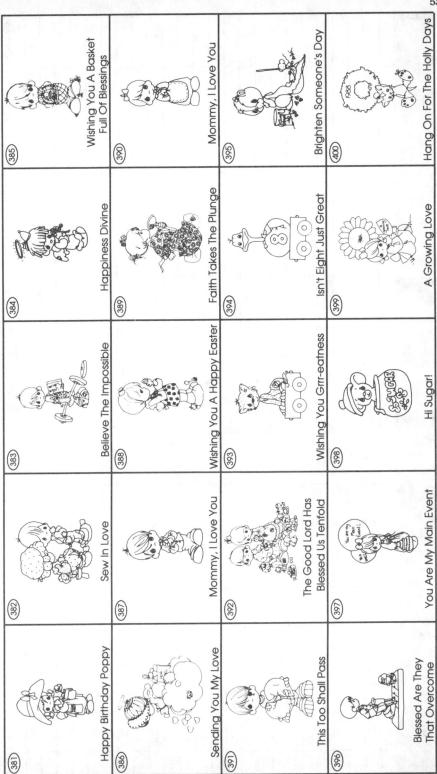

381 Happy Birthday Poppy

382 Sew In Love

383 Believe The Impossible

384 Happiness Divine

385 Wishing You A Basket Full Of Blessings

386 Sending You My Love

387 Mommy, I Love You

388 Wishing You A Happy Easter

389 Faith Takes The Plunge

390 Mommy, I Love You

391 This Too Shall Pass

392 The Good Lord Has Blessed Us Tenfold

393 Wishing You Grrr-eatness

394 Isn't Eight Just Great

395 Brighten Someone's Day

396 Blessed Are They That Overcome

397 You Are My Main Event

398 Hi Sugar!

399 A Growing Love

400 Hang On For The Holly Days

#	DESCRIPTIVE TITLE	FIG	PLT	BELL	MUSC	ORN	DOLL	THMBL	FRAME	CNDL CLMB	BOX	OTHER
401	Baby Boy Standing	E-2852A										
402	Baby Girl/Bow Hair	E-2852B										
403	Baby Boy Sitting	E-2852C										
404	Baby Girl Clapping Hands	E-2852D	(Also see ART CHART Number 178)									
405	Baby Boy Crawling	E-2852E										
406	Baby Girl Lying Down	E-2852F										
407	Dog with Slippers	**E-9267B**										
408	Bunny with Carrot	**E-9267C**	(Also see ART CHART Number 147)									
409	Lamb with Bird on Back	**E-9267E**										
410	Christmas Wreath											111465 Wreath
411	Kids on Cloud under Dome	E-7350										
412	Pig with Patches	**E-9267F**										
413	Cat with Bow Tie	**E-9267D**	(Also see ART CHART Number 147)									
414	Teddy Bear	**E-9267A**										
415	Retailer's Wreath Bell			112348								
416	Boy Balancing Ball	12238A										
417	Girl Holding Balloon	12238B										
418	Boy Bending over Ball	12238C	(Also see ART CHART Number 235)									
419	Girl with Flower Pot	12238D										
420	Rhino with Bird	104418										

BOLD = Suspended   *Italics* = Limited Edition   Shaded Area = Retired   ♦ = Two-Year Collectible

Boxed = Dated Annual   Rounded Box = Annual   * = Special Inspirational Title or piece derived from a portion of the drawing

55

401 Baby Figurine	402 Baby Figurine	403 Baby Figurine	404 Baby Figurine	405 Baby Figurine
406 Baby Figurine		407 409 408		410 Retailer's Wreath
411 Retailer's Dome	412 413 414 Animal Collection			415 Retailer's Wreath Bell
416 Clown Figurine	417 Clown Figurine	418 Clown Figurine	419 Clown Figurine	420 Friends To The End

#	DESCRIPTIVE TITLE	FIG	PLT	BELL	MUSC	ORN	DOLL	THMBL	FRAME	CNDL CLMB	BOX	OTHER
421	Girl Holding Doll with Dog	**105643**										
422	Wreath Contestant Orn.					PM-008						
423	Girl with Kitten	109800										
424	Girl with Puppy in Basket	110051										
425	Girl in Swimming Pool	110078										
426	Girl Balancing Books	110086										
427	Girl with Pumpkins	110094										
428	Girl in Pilgrim Suit	110108										
429	Girl with Christmas Candle	110116										
430	Girl Adding Seasoning	111163										
431	Bunnies	111274 522996*										
432	Baby Boy in Sleigh					115282 523194						
433	Couple with Gifts	**115290**										
434	Girl with Calendar & Clock	115339		115304		115320		115312				
435	Baby Girl in Sleigh					520241 523208						
436	Puppy in Stocking					520276						
437	Angel w/Newspaper/Dog	520357										
438	Girl Decorating Reindeer	522317	520284									
439	Girl Painting Butterfly	PM-881										
440	Pippin Popping out of a Birthday Cake	B-0003 B-0103										

BOLD = Suspended   *Italics* = Limited Edition   Shaded Area = Retired   ◆ = Two-Year Collectible

Boxed = Dated Annual   (Rounded Box) = Annual   * = Special Inspirational Title or piece derived from a portion of the drawing

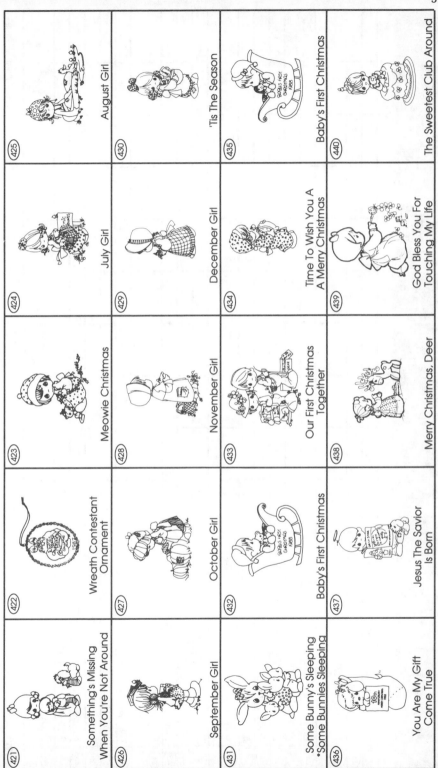

421 Something's Missing
When You're Not Around

422 Wreath Contestant
Ornament

423 Meowie Christmas

424 July Girl

425 August Girl

426 September Girl

427 October Girl

428 November Girl

429 December Girl

430 'Tis The Season

431 Some Bunny's Sleeping
*Some Bunnies Sleeping

432 Baby's First Christmas

433 Our First Christmas
Together

434 Time To Wish You A
A Merry Christmas

435 Baby's First Christmas

436 You Are My Gift
Come True

437 Jesus The Savior
Is Born

438 Merry Christmas, Deer

439 God Bless You For
Touching My Life

440 The Sweetest Club Around

#	DESCRIPTIVE TITLE	FIG	PLT	BELL	MUSC	ORN	DOLL	THMBL	FRAME	CNDL CLMB	BOX	OTHER
441	Bunny with Stuffed Carrot	BC-881										
442	Boy/Dog/Trash Can	PM-882										
443	Girl with Lily	522376										
444	Girl/Puppies/Box	C-0109 C-0009				522961						
445	Boy Tangled in Lights											558125 Artplas Stock'g Hngr
446	Bride Holding Up Dress	520799										
447	Boy Angel w/Butterfly Net	520640										
448	Girl Holding Trophy	520829										
449	Mouse Wiping Clown's Tear	520632										
450	Boy with Newspaper over Head	520683										
451	Kangaroo/Baby in Pouch	521175										
452	Grandpa/Cane/Dog	**520810**										
453	Two Girls Having Tea Party	520748										
454	Boy Holding Girl up to Fountain	520675										
455	Girl with Hen & Easter Egg	520667										
456	Dog Pulling Boy's Fish'g Line	520721										
457	Indian Couple in Canoe	520772										
458	Nurse X-raying Boy's Heart	520624										
459	Boy Proposing to Girl	520845										
460	Bride & Groom in Car	520780				521558* 525324*						

BOLD = Suspended   *Italics* = Limited Edition   Shaded Area = Retired   ◆ = Two-Year Collectible

Boxed = Dated Annual   Rounded Box = Annual   * = Special Inspirational Title or piece derived from a portion of the drawing

59

(441) Somebunny Cares

(442) You Just Cannot Chuck A Good Friendship

(443) His Love Will Shine On You

(444) Always Room For One More

(445) Stocking Hanger

(446) Someday My Love

(447) I'm So Glad You Fluttered Into My Life

(448) You Are My Number One

(449) A Friend Is Someone Who Cares

(450) Sending You Showers Of Blessings

(451) Hello World!

(452) We Need A Good Friend Through The Ruff Times

(453) Friendship Hits The Spot

(454) Your Love Is So Uplifting

(455) Eggspecially For You

(456) Just A Line To Wish You A Happy Day

(457) Many Moons In Same Canoe, Blessum You

(458) My Heart Is Exposed With Love

(459) Wishing You A Perfect Choice

(460) Wishing You Roads Of Happiness *Our First Christmas Together

#	DESCRIPTIVE TITLE	FIG	PLT	BELL	MUSC	ORN	DOLL	THMBL	FRAME	CNDL CLMB	BOX	OTHER
461	Boy w/Baby Feeding Dog	520705										
462	Girl w/Paint & Ladder	**520802**										
463	Orphan Girl	**520853**										
464	Boy at Crossroads	520756										
465	Two Puppies	520764										
466	Bridal Couple/Candle	520837										
467	Girl with Chalkboard	520861										
468	Angel w/ Baby Name Book	523097										
469	Teddy in Rocker	522856										
470	Puppy Resting on Elbow					520462						
471	Boy/Fallen Christmas Tree	522112				521590*						
472	Boy Dining with Turkey	522031										
473	Boy Playing Football/Dog	522023										
474	Boy & Girl on Motorcycle	522201										
475	Girl with Lamp Post				521507							
476	Girl on Telephone	521477										
477	Girl w/Snowball Tied with Ribbon					521302						
478	Boy/Pkg/Puppy & Bat	522120										
479	Family Christmas Scene		523003			523704						
480	Boy by Tree Stump	521949										

BOLD = Suspended *Italics* = Limited Edition Shaded Area = Retired ◆ = Two-Year Collectible

Boxed = Dated Annual (Rounded Box) = Annual * = Special Inspirational Title or piece derived from a portion of the drawing

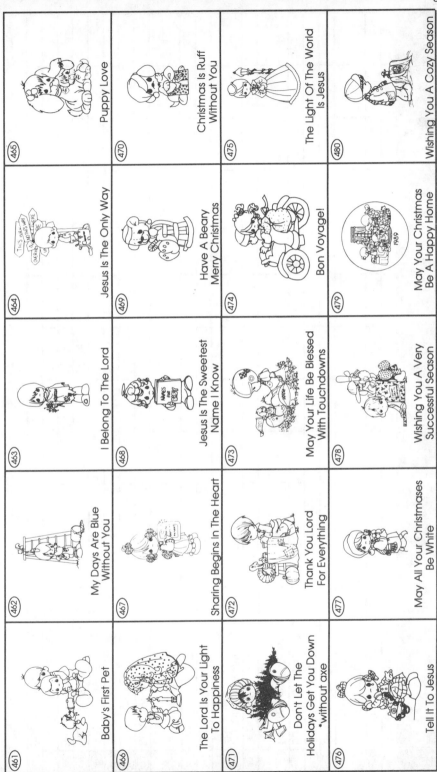

461 Baby's First Pet

462 My Days Are Blue Without You

463 I Belong To The Lord

464 Jesus Is The Only Way

465 Puppy Love

466 The Lord Is Your Light To Happiness

467 Sharing Begins In The Heart

468 Jesus Is The Sweetest Name I Know

469 Have A Beary Merry Christmas

470 Christmas Is Ruff Without You

471 Don't Let The Holidays Get You Down *without axe

472 Thank You Lord For Everything

473 May Your Life Be Blessed With Touchdowns

474 Bon Voyage!

475 The Light Of The World Is Jesus

476 Tell It To Jesus

477 May All Your Christmases Be White

478 Wishing You A Very Successful Season

479 May Your Christmas Be A Happy Home

480 Wishing You A Cozy Season

#	DESCRIPTIVE TITLE°	FIG	PLT	BELL	MUSC	ORN	DOLL	THMBL	FRAME	CNDL CLMB	BOX	OTHER
481	Angel on Cloud w/Manger	522252										
482	Girl Playing Violin	522546		522821		522848						
483	Angel Holding Commandments	**521868**						522554				
484	Giraffe with Baby Bear	522260										
485	Girl with Ballot Box	PM-891										
486	Boy Pushing Lawn Mower	PM-892										
487	Teddy Bear with Balloon	B-0104										
		B-0004										
488	Teddy w/ Bee & Beehive	BC-891										
489	Girl at Table with Figurine	C-0110				PM-904						
		C-0010										
490	Girl with Fan	523526										
491	Angel outside Chapel	523011										
492	Girls with Flower	521817										
		525049										
493	Ballerina	520551										
494	Girl on Hobby Horse	521205				523224*						
495	B&G Kiss'g under Mistletoe	523747										
496	Girl Wearing Boxing Gloves	521396										
497	Mom-To-Be w/Baby Book	523453				527165						
498	Boy with Kite	521957										
499	Girl on Roller Skates	521280				521566*						
500	Boy & Girl in Garden	522090										

BOLD = Suspended   *Italics* = Limited Edition   Shaded Area = Retired   ◆ = Two-Year Collectible

Boxed = Dated Annual   Rounded Box = Annual   * = Special Inspirational Title or piece derived from a portion of the drawing

62

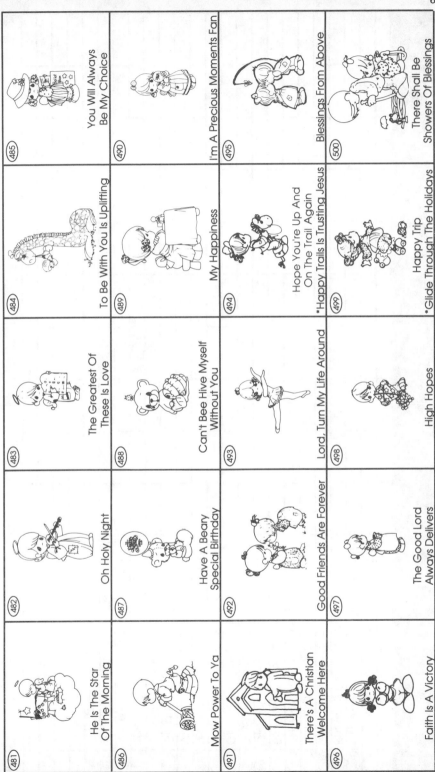

63

481 He Is The Star
Of The Morning

482 Oh Holy Night

483 The Greatest Of
These Is Love

484 To Be With You Is Uplifting

485 You Will Always
Be My Choice

486 Mow Power To Ya

487 Have A Beary
Special Birthday

488 Can't Bee Hive Myself
Without You

489 My Happiness

490 I'm A Precious Moments Fan

491 There's A Christian
Welcome Here

492 Good Friends Are Forever

493 Lord, Turn My Life Around

494 Hope You're Up And
On The Trail Again
*Happy Trails Is Trusting Jesus

495 Blessings From Above

496 Faith Is A Victory

497 The Good Lord
Always Delivers

498 High Hopes

499 Happy Trip
*Glide Through The Holidays

500 There Shall Be
Showers Of Blessings

#	DESCRIPTIVE TITLE	FIG	PLT	BELL	MUSC	ORN	DOLL	THMBL	FRAME	CNDL CLIMB	BOX	OTHER
501	Gorilla and Parrot	521043										
502	Girl Sweep Dust under Rug	521779										
503	Girl w/Account Bks & Glue	521450										
504	Kneeling Girl w/Bouquet *	522287										
505	Girl with Apple	521310										
506	Girl Holding Bible & Cross	523496			523682							
507	Girl/Sleep'g Chick in Egg	(524522)										
508	Boy Pull Wagon/Lily & Girl	521892										
509	Girl/Valentine behind Back	523518										
510	Boy Whispering to Girl	521841										
511	Girl w/Letters "Y" "O" "U"	521418										
512	Fireplace with Stockings	524883										
513	Teddy Bear in Package	524875										
514	Mouse on Cheese/Kitten	524484										
515	Girl and Melting Snowman	524913										
516	Baby Girl with Pie					523771						
517	Baby Boy with Pie					523798						
518	Nurse at Desk w/Clock	523739										
519	Girl with Book and Candle	523836		523828		523852		523844				
520	Crying Girls Hugging	521183										

BOLD = Suspended *Italics* = Limited Edition Shaded Area = Retired ◆ = Two-Year Collectible

Boxed = Dated Annual Rounded Box = Annual * = Special Inspirational Title or piece derived from a portion of the drawing

(501) To My Favorite Fan	(502) Sweep All Your Worries Away	(503) Lord, Help Me Stick To My Job	(504) Thinking Of You Is What I Really Like To Do	(505) Yield Not To Temptation
(506) This Day Has Been Made In Heaven	(507) Always In His Care	(508) Easter's On Its Way	(509) God Is Love Dear Valentine	(510) Love Is From Above
(511) I'll Never Stop Loving You	(512) Christmas Fireplace	(513) Happy Birthday Dear Jesus	(514) Not A Creature Was Stirring	(515) We're Going To Miss You
(516) Baby's First Christmas	(517) Baby's First Christmas	(518) Time Heals	(519) Once Upon A Holy Night	(520) That's What Friends Are For

#	DESCRIPTIVE TITLE	FIG	PLT	BELL	MUSC	ORN	DOLL	THMBL	FRAME	CNDL CLMB	BOX	OTHER
521	Kitten with Ornament					520497						
522	Baby Boy on Pillow				429570							
523	Baby Girl on Pillow				429589							
524	Ballerina on Pointe	520543										
525	Ballerina at Barre				520691							
526	Girl and Boy Hugging	521299										
527	Girl/Bunny/Candle/Log	521485										
528	Girl Hammers Boy's Thumb	521698										
529	Girl Collecting Eggs/Frog	521906										
530	Boy/Bee/Flower Pot	521965										
531	Girl and Bird at Bird Bath	522279										
532	Stork Deliver'g Baby/Mom	523178										
533	Boy/Dog/Blocks/"Success"	523763										
534	Baby in Highchair w/Bowl	524077										
535	Girl Holding Flower	(524263)										
536	Girl w/Cake and Candles	524301										
537	Girl Holding Net/Butterfly	524425										
538	Bird on Cage Door/Kitten	524492										
539	Girl Helping Bird to Fly	(527114)										
540	Girl in Race Car	PM-901										

BOLD = Suspended *Italics* = Limited Edition Shaded Area = Retired ◆ = Two-Year Collectible

Boxed = Dated Annual (Rounded Box) = Annual * = Special Inspirational Title or piece derived from a portion of the drawing

521 Wishing You A Purr-fect Holiday

522 The Eyes Of The Lord Are Upon You

523 The Eyes Of The Lord Are Upon You

524 In The Spotlight Of His Grace

525 Lord, Keep My Life In Balance

526 Hug One Another

527 There's A Light At The End Of The Tunnel

528 Thumb-Body Loves You

529 Hoppy Easter Friend

530 To A Special Mum

531 A Reflection Of His Love

532 Joy On Arrival

533 I Can't Spell Success Without You

534 Baby's First Meal

535 HE Loves Me

536 May Your Birthday Be A Blessing

537 May Only Good Things Come Your Way

538 Can't Be Without You

539 Sharing A Gift Of Love

540 Ten Years And Still Going Strong

#	DESCRIPTIVE TITLE	FIG	PLT	BELL	MUSC	ORN	DOLL	THMBL	FRAME	CNDL CLMB	BOX	OTHER
541	Girl Sew'g Patch on Teddy	PM-902										
542	Chapel Stained Glass Window Replicas				PM-890 (Set of 7) (Also individually #'d PM-190, PM-290, PM-390, PM-490, PM-590, PM-690, PM-790)							
543	Clown/Puppy thru Drum	B-0105 B-0005										
544	Skunk with Flowers	BC-901										
545	Angel											617334 Tree Topper
546	Girl Holding Puppy	527122										
547	Squirrel/Mesh Bag/Nuts	BC-902										
548	Christmas Girl in Plaid Dress				417777◆		417785◆					
549	Rabbit on Skates					520438						
550	Boy on Rocking Horse	521272										
551	Girl Holding Picture Frame	521434										
552	Girl with Baby	521493										
553	Boy Decorating Globe	522082										
554	Girl Climbing Ladder	523615				524131						
555	Girl in Snowsuit/Bunny	524123				524174 526940						
556	Girl Holding Bird	524166		524182				524190				
557	Two Angels on Stool	524921										
558	Elephant/String/Tied/Trunk	526924										
559	Three Penguins	526959										
560	Boy with Drum					527084						

BOLD = Suspended *Italics* = Limited Edition Shaded Area = Retired ◆ = Two-Year Collectible

Boxed = Dated Annual Rounded Box = Annual * = Special Inspirational Title or piece derived from a portion of the drawing

541 You Are A Blessing To Me

542 Beatitude Ornament Series

543 Our Club Is A Tough Act To Follow

544 Collecting Makes Good Scents

545 Rejoice, O Earth

546 You Can Always Bring A Friend

547 I'm Nuts Over My Collection

548 May You Have An Old Fashioned Christmas

549 Sno-Bunny Falls For You Like I Do

550 Take Heed When You Stand

551 To A Very Special Mom And Dad

552 A Special Delivery

553 May Your World Be Trimmed With Joy

554 Good News Is So Uplifting

555 Good Friends Are For Always

556 May Your Christmas Be Merry

557 Angels We Have Heard On High

558 How Can I Ever Forget You

559 We Have Come From Afar

560 Baby's First Christmas

#	DESCRIPTIVE TITLE	FIG	PLT	BELL	MUSC	ORN	DOLL	THMBL	FRAME	CNDL CLMB	BOX	OTHER
561	Girl with Drum					527092						
562	Girl at Mailbox/Newsletter	C-0011				PM-037						
		C-0111										
563	Sam Draws/Paints Animals	523038										
564	Child Tak'g First Steps/Mom	PM-911										
565	Indian Boy Hold'g Spinach	PM-912										
566	Baby Monkey w/Pacifier	BC-911										
567	Pup & Kitten Share Paint'g	BC-912										
568	Jester Jack-in-the-Box Playing Concertina	B-0106										
		B-0006										
569	Girl in Spacesuit Holding Space Helmet	C-0112										
		C-0012										
570	Squirrel Decorat'g Tree/Log					520411						
571	Ballerina on Pointe	520535										
572	Ballerina on Pointe	520578										
573	Whale Riding Wave (10)	521825										
574	Curly Maned Pranc'g Pony	521833										
575	Hens Laugh/Egg on Pup	522104										
576	Boy Peek'g into Present				522244							
577	Girl Typing Message	523542										
578	Bird Watching Girl Swing	524085										
579	Girl Watering Seedling	524271										
580	Praying Girl/Globe	524352										

BOLD = Suspended   *Italics* = Limited Edition   Shaded Area = Retired   ◆ = Two-Year Collectible

Boxed = Dated Annual   Rounded Box = Annual   * = Special Inspirational Title or piece derived from a portion of the drawing

(561) Baby's First Christmas

(562) Sharing The Good News Together

(563) He Is My Inspiration

(564) One Step At A Time

(565) Lord, Keep Me In Teepee Top Shape

(566) Love Pacifies

(567) True Blue Friends

(568) Jest To Let You Know You're Tops

(569) The Club That's Out Of This World

(570) I'm Nuts About You

(571) The Lord Turned My Life Around

(572) You Deserve An Ovation

(573) May Your Birthday Be Mammoth

(574) Being Nine Is Just Divine

(575) It's No Yolk When I Say I Love You

(576) Do Not Open Till Christmas

(577) You Are The Type I Love

(578) My Warmest Thoughts Are You

(579) Friendship Grows When You Plant A Seed

(580) What The World Needs Now

#	DESCRIPTIVE TITLE	FIG	PLT	BELL	MUSC	ORN	DOLL	THMBL	FRAME	CNDL CLMB	BOX	OTHER
581	Girl on Skis Start'd by Jump	524905										
582	Ballerina on Pointe					525332						
583	Angels Ring'g Bell & Pray'g	525898										
584	Angel Tak'g Child/Heaven	525979										
585	Girl Cuddling Kitten	*526010*										
586	Girl Checking Roadmap	526142										
587	Girl Holding Roses/Bluebird	(526185)										
588	Boy in Sailor Suit and Hat	526568										
589	Boy in Dress Uniform Salut'g	526576										
590	Boy in Dress Uniform/Duffel	526584										
591	Seated Child Sign'g Mes'g'	(527173)										
592	Baby Talking into Mike	527238										
593	Two Pups Hug Each Other	527270										
594	Girl Soldier in Dress Uniform	527289										
595	African-American Soldier	527297										
596	Girl Wades to Duck w/Eggs	(527319)										
597	B/Day Bird Blows Candle	527343										
598	Girl Puts Star on Boy's Head	527378										
599	Explorer/Animal Crew/Sail	527386										
600	Girl Sitting on Candy Cane					527475						

BOLD = Suspended *Italics* = Limited Edition Shaded Area = Retired

Boxed = Dated Annual (Rounded Box) = Annual ◆ = Two-Year Collectible

* = Special Inspirational Title or piece derived from a portion of the drawing

581	**582**	**583** Ring Those Christmas Bells	**584** Going Home
It's So Uplifting To Have A Friend Like You	**585** You Are Such A Purr-fect Friend		
586 I Would Be Lost Without You	**587** Lord Keep Me On My Toes	**588** Bless Those Who Serve Their Country - Navy	**589** Bless Those Who Serve Their Country - Army
			590 Bless Those Who Serve Their Country - Air Force
591 A Universal Love	**592** Baby's First Word	**593** Let's Be Friends	**594** Bless Those Who Serve Their Country - Girl Soldier
			595 Bless Those Who Serve Their Country - African-American Soldier
596 An Event Worth Wading For	**597** Happy Birdie	**598** You Are My Favorite Star	**599** This Land Is Our Land
			600 Baby's First Christmas - Girl

#	DESCRIPTIVE TITLE	FIG	PLT	BELL	MUSC	ORN	DOLL	THMBL	FRAME	CNDL CLMB	BOX	OTHER
601	Boy Sitting on Candy Cane					527483						
602	Boy/Full Dress at Attention	527521										
603	Mom/Wordless Book/Kids	527556										
604	Uncle Sam Kneeling/Prayer	(527564)										
605	Boy Santa/Pup w/Whiskers	527629										
606	Girl Holding List to Santa	527688	527742	527726		527696 527734		527718				
607	Angel Holding Blanket	527750										
608	Explorer Hold'g Flag/Teddy	(527777)										
609	Girl Crying over Spilled Milk										Wall Hangings	523380
610	Princess Wash Servant Feet											523437
611	Boy/Stethoscope to World	E-1381R (Also see ART CHART NUMBER 15)										
612	Engineer Rid'g Locomotive	B-0107 B-0007										
613	Mr. Webb Build'g Birdhome	PM-921										

BOLD = Suspended   *Italics* = Limited Edition   Shaded Area = Retired   ◆ = Two-Year Collectible

Boxed = Dated Annual   (Rounded Box) = Annual   * = Special Inspirational Title or piece derived from a portion of the drawing

601	602	603	604	605
Baby's First Christmas - Boy	Bless Those Who Serve Their Country - Marine	Bring The Little Ones To Jesus	God Bless The USA	Wishing You A Ho Ho Ho
606	607	608	609	610
But The Greatest Of These Is Love	Wishing You A Comfy Christmas	This Land Is Our Land	Blessed Are The Ones Who Mourn	Blessed Are The Humble
611	612	613		
Jesus Is The Answer	All Aboard For Birthday Club Fun	Only Love Can Make A Home		

NOTES

GREENBOOK ALPHA-LOG

The GREENBOOK ALPHA-LOG lists PRECIOUS MOMENTS Inspirational Titles alphabetically, cross-referencing the Descriptive Title, GREENBOOK ART CHART Number, and Enesco Item Number for each figurine, plate, bell, musical, ornament, doll, thimble, frame, candle climber, box, night light, egg, plaque, wreath, medallion, stocking hanger, and tree topper with that Inspirational Title. In addition, it is noted if each piece is a Dated Annual, an Annual, a Two-Year Collectible, a Limited Edition, Retired, or Suspended.

INSPIRATIONAL TITLE	DESCRIPTIVE TITLE	#	FIG	PLT	BELL	MUSC	ORN	DOLL	THMBL	FRAME	CNDL CLMB	BOX	OTHER
A Friend Is Someone Who Cares	Mouse Wiping Tears	449	520632										
A Growing Love	Girl/Flowerpot/Sunflwr	399	E-0108 / E-0008				520349						
A Monarch Is Born	Boy/Butterfly/Manger	190	**E-5380**										
A Reflection Of His Love	Girl/Bird/Bird Bath	531	522279										
A Smile's The Cymbal Of Joy	Clown with Cymbals	364	B-0102 / B-0002										
A Special Delivery	Girl with Baby	552	521493										
A Tub Full Of Love	Baby Girl/Wood Tub	363	112313										
A Tub Full Of Love	Baby Boy/Wood Tub	348	104817										
A Universal Love	Child Signing Message	591	527173										
Aaron	Boy Angel	247						12424					
All Aboard For Birthday Club Fun	Engineer Riding Locomotive	612	B-0107 / B-0007										
Always In His Care	Girl/Chick in Egg	507	524522										
Always Room For One More	Girl/Box/Puppies	444	C-0009 / C-0109				522961						
An Event Worth Wading For	Girl Wading to Ducks	596	527319										
Angel Of Mercy	Nurse w/Potted Plant	282	102482				102407						
Angels We Have Heard On High	Two Angels on Stool	557	524921										
Angie, The Angel Of Mercy	Nurse Doll	339						12491					
Animal Collection	Animals	147	**E-9267** (For A-F see ART CHART Numbers 407, 408, 409, 412, 413, & 414.)										
April Girl	Girl with Umbrella	370	110027										
August Girl	Girl in Swimming Pool	425	110078										
Autumn's Praise	Girl/Hands behind Her	228	12084	12122		408751 ◆		408808 ◆					
Baby Figurines		178	E-2852 (For A-F see ART CHART Numbers 401-406.)										
Baby's First Christmas	Baby Boy Hold Bottle	257	15539				15903						
Baby's First Christmas	Boy w/Candy Cane	286					102512						
Baby's First Christmas	Boy Holding Block	95					**E-2372**						
Baby's First Christmas	Baby Girl w/Bottle	258	15547				15911						
Baby's First Christmas	Baby/Chrstms Stock'g	89					**E-2362**						
Baby's First Christmas	Girl w/Candy Cane	285					102504						
Baby's First Christmas	Boy with Teddy	1					**E-5631**						
Baby's First Christmas	Girl with Bunny	2					**E-5632**						

Name	Description	No.	Item No.	Other No.
Baby's First Christmas	Boy/Rocking Horse	357		109428
Baby's First Christmas	Boy in Sleigh	432		115282 / 523194
Baby's First Christmas	Girl in Sleigh	435		520241 / 523208
Baby's First Christmas	Baby Girl with Pie	516		523771
Baby's First Christmas	Baby Boy with Pie	517		523798
Baby's First Christmas	Baby Boy with Drum	560		527084
Baby's First Christmas	Baby Girl with Drum	561		527092
Baby's First Christmas	Boy Sit/Candy Cane	601		527483
Baby's First Christmas	Girl Sit/Candy Cane	600		527475
Baby's First Haircut	Angel Cut Baby's Hair	234	12211	
Baby's First Meal	Baby/Highchair/Bowl	534	524077	
Baby's First Pet	Boy/Baby/Feed Dog	461	520705	
Baby's First Picture	Angel Tak'g Baby Pic	174	E-2841	
Baby's First Step	Angel Helping Baby	173	E-2840	
Baby's First Trip	Angel Pushing Buggy	267	16012	
Baby's First Word	Baby/Footed Sleepers	597	527238	
Be Not Weary In Well Doing	Girl Helper	36	E-3111	
Bear The Good News Of Christmas	Bear on Sled	347		104515
Bear Ye One Another's Burdens	Sad Boy with Teddy	52	E-5200	
Beatitude Ornament Series	Chapel Stained Glass Window Replicas	542		PM-890 (Set of 7) (Also individually numbered PM-190 through PM-790.)
Being Nine Is Just Divine	Prancing Pony	574	521833	
Believe The Impossible	Boy with Barbells	383	109487	
Bethany	Girl Angel	248		12432
Birds Of A Feather Collect Together	Girl with Embroidery Hoop/Bird	295	E-0006 / E-0106	PM-864
Bless The Days Of Our Youth	Clown with Pull Rope	303	16004	
Bless This House	B&G Paint Dog House	113	E-7164	
Bless Those Who Serve Their Country	African-American	595	527297	
	Air Force	590	526584	
	Army	589	526576	
	Girl Soldier	594	527289	
	Marine	602	527521	
	Navy	588	526568	

BOLD = Suspended   Italics = Limited Edition   [Shaded Area] = Retired   Boxed = Dated / Annual   (Rounded Box) = Annual   ♦ = Two Year Collectible

INSPIRATIONAL TITLE	DESCRIPTIVE TITLE	#	FIG	PLT	BELL	MUSC	ORN	DOLL	THMBL	FRAME	CNDL CLMB	BOX	OTHER
Bless You Two	Groom Carrying Bride	139	E-9255										
Blessed Are The Humble	Princess Washes Feet	610											523437 Wall Hanging
Blessed Are The Peacemakers	Boy Hold'g Cat & Dog	31	E-3107										
Blessed Are The Pure In Heart	Rocking Cradle	28	E-3104				E-0518 / E-5392			E-0521			523380 Wall Hanging
Blessed Are The Ones Who Mourn	Girl Crying/Kitten/Spilled Milk	609											
Blessed Are They That Overcome	Boy w/Braces & Dog	396	115479										
Blessings From Above	B&G Kissing/Mistletoe	495	523747										
Blessings From Me To Thee	Girl at Birdhouse	120		523860									
Blessings From My House To Yours	Girl at Birdhouse	120	E-0503										
Bon Voyage!	B&G on Motorcycle	474	522201										
Bong Bong	Boy Clown	289	E-2846					100455					
Bride	Bride	313	E-2831										
Bridesmaid	Bridesmaid	170	E-2831										
Brighten Someone's Day	Skunk and Mouse	395	105953										
Bring The Little Ones To Jesus	Mom/Wordless Bk/Kids	603	527556										
Bringing God's Blessing To You	Girl Angel Push'g Jesus	125	E-0509										
Brotherly Love	Pilgrim/Indian/Turkey	276	100544										
Bundles Of Joy	Girl with Presents	96	E-2374										
But Love Goes On Forever	B/G Angels on Cloud	39	E-3115 / E-0001				525057					Plaques {	E-0102 / E-0202
But Love Goes On Forever	Boy Angel on Cloud	56					E-5627						
But Love Goes On Forever	Girl Angel on Cloud	57					E-5628				E-6118		
But The Greatest Of These Is Love	Girl Holding Her List to Santa	600	527688	527742	527726		527696 / 527734		527718				
Camel	Camel	90	E-2363										
Camel, Donkey, Cow	Camel, Donkey, Cow	100					E-2386						
Candy	Girl Clown	280						100463					
Can't Be Without You	Kitty/open Cage/Bird	534	524492										
Can't Bee Hive Myself Without You	Teddy w/Bee & Hive	488	BC-891										
Cheers To The Leader	Girl Cheerleader	345	104035				113999						
Christmas Fireplace	Fireplace w/Stockings	512	524883										

Inspirational Title	No.	Figurine	Product Number(s)
Christmas Is A Little To Share			
Boy Giving Toy Lamb / ...			E-2002
Christmas Is Ruff Without You	(470)	Puppy Rest'g on Elbow	520462
Christmas Joy From Head To Toe	(88)	Girl with Stocking	**E-2361**
Christmastime Is For Sharing	(121)	Boy Giving Teddy	E-0504	E-0505
Clown Figurines/Thimbles	(235)	Mini Clowns	12238(/A-D) (Also see ART CHART Numbers 416-419.) 100668
Collecting Makes Good Scents	(544)	Skunk with Flowers	BC-901
Collection Plaque	(56)	Plaque	**E-6901**
Come Let Us Adore Him	(21)	Boy Angel on Cloud	**E-2011**
Come Let Us Adore Him	(62)	Boy w/Manger Baby	**E-5619**
Come Let Us Adore Him	(307)	Manger w/Child	104000
Come Let Us Adore Him	(22)	Nativity Set/Cassette	E-2800 E-2395 *E-5646* E-2810 **E-5633** E-2800
Congratulations, Princess	(318)	Girl Graduate	106208
Connie	(29)	Doll with Stand	*102253*
Cow	(69)	Cow with Bell	E-5638
Crown Him Lord Of All	(25)	Boy/Manger/Crown	**E-2803** **E-2807**
Cubby	(115)	Groom Doll	*E-7267B*
Dashing Through The Snow	(367)	Girl/Doll/Sleigh	521574
Dawn's Early Light	(160)	Girl Covering Kitten	PM-831
"Dealers Only" Nativity	(337)	Nativity w/Backdrop	104523
Debbie	(76)	Debbie Doll	E-6214G
December Girl	(429)	Girl/Christmas Candle	110116
Do Not Open Till Christmas	(576)	Boy Peeking into Pkg	522244
Donkey	(63)	Donkey	E-5621
Don't Let The Holidays Get You Down	(471)	Boy w/Christmas Tree	522112 521590
Dropping In For Christmas	(84)	Boy Ice Skater/Cap	**E-2350** E-2369
Dropping Over For Christmas	(97)	Girl with Pie	**E-2375** E-2376
Easter's On Its Way	(508)	Boy/Wagon/Lily/Girl	521892
Eggs Over Easy	(45)	Girl with Fry Pan	**E-3118**
Eggspecially For You	(455)	Girl/Hen/Easter Egg	520667
Especially For Ewe	(153)	Lamb	**E-9282 (/C)**

BOLD = Suspended   *Italics* = Limited Edition   Shaded Area = Retired   Boxed = Dated / Annual   (Rounded Box) = Annual   ◆ = Two Year Collectible

INSPIRATIONAL TITLE	DESCRIPTIVE TITLE	#	FIG	PLT	BELL	MUSC	ORN	DOLL	THMBL	FRAME	CNDL CLMB	BOX	OTHER
Faith Is A Victory	Girl/Boxing Gloves	496	521396										
Faith Takes The Plunge	Girl with Plunger	389	111155										
February Girl	Girl/Plant in Snow	368	109991										
Feed My Sheep	Girl Feeding Lamb	366	PM-871										
Fishing For Friends	Raccoon Holding Fish	335	BC-861										
Flower Girl	Flower Girl	209	E-2835										
For God So Loved The World	Deluxe Nativity	192	**E-5382**										
Forever Friends	Dog and Cat (2)	309										E-9283	
Forgiving Is Forgetting	B&G with Bandage	136	**E-9252**										
Four Seasons	Four Seasons Thimbles	226		227 228 229						100641				
Friends Never Drift Apart	Kids in Boat	219	100250				522937						
Friends To The End	Rhino with Bird	420	104418										
Friendship Grows When You Plant A Seed	Girl Watering Seedling	573	524271										
Friendship Hits The Spot	Two Girls/Tea Party	453	520748										
Get Into The Habit Of Prayer	Nun	233	**12203**										
Glide Through The Holidays	Girl on Roller Skates	499					521566						
Goat	Goat	91	**E-2364**										
God Bless America	Uncle Sam/Bible/Dog	292	102938										
God Bless Our Family	Parents of the Groom	325	100498										
God Bless Our Family	Parents of the Bride	326	100501										
God Bless Our Home	B&G/Sandcastle	239	12319										
God Bless Our Years Together	Family/Birthday Cake	249	12440										
God Bless The Bride	Bride with Flower Girl	171	E-2832										
God Bless The Day We Found You	Mom/Dad/Girl w/Adoption	272	**100145**										
God Bless The Day We Found You	Mom/Dad/Boy w/Adoption	273	**100153**										
God Bless The USA	Uncle Sam Praying	404	527564										
God Bless You For Touching My Life	Girl Painting Butterfly	439	PM-881										
God Bless You Graduate	Boy Graduate	334	106194										
God Bless You On Your Birthday	Seal - Age 2	288	15962										
God Bless You With Rainbows	Angel/Rainbow	199											Night Light	**16020**

Name	Description	Item No.	Other numbers (year columns)
God Blessed Our Year — Together With So Much Love And Happiness	1st Anniversary	E-2854	
God Blessed Our Years — Together With So Much Love And Happiness	Happy Anniversary	(179) E-2853	
	5th Anniversary	(181) E-2855	
	10th Anniversary	(182) E-2856	
	25th Anniversary	(183) E-2857	
	40th Anniversary	(184) E-2859	
	50th Anniversary	(185) E-2860	
God Gave His Best	Girl with Ornament	(263) 15806	
God Is Love	Girl w/Goose in Lap	(60) **E-5213**	
God Is Love, Dear Valentine	Boy Holding Heart	(102) **E-7153**	
God Is Love, Dear Valentine	Girl Holding Heart	(103) **E-7154**	100625
God Is Love Dear Valentine	Girl w/Valentine	(509) 523518	
God Is Watching Over You	Boy w/Ice Bag/Head	(112) **E-7163**	
God Loveth A Cheerful Giver	Girl with Puppies	(20) E-1378	
God Sends The Gift Of His Love	Girl/Present/Kitten	(204) **E-6613**	15865
God Sent His Love	Angel w/Holly Wreath	(259) 15881	15873, 15768
God Sent His Son	Girl Look'g in Manger	(123) **E-0507**	15504, 113972
God Sent You Just In Time	Clown/Jack-in-Box	(256)	E-5211
God Understands	Boy w/Report Card	(12) **E-1379B**	12033
God's Precious Gift	Baby Boy	(310)	12041
God's Precious Gift	Baby Girl	(311)	
God's Promises Are Sure	Ang'l Wind'g Rainbow	(142) **E-9260**	
God's Ray Of Mercy	Boy Angel/Flashlight	(206) PM-841	
God's Speed	Boy Jogging w/Dog	(44) **E-3112**	
Going Home	Angel/Child/Heaven	(584) 525979	
Good Friends Are For Always	Girl in Snowsuit/Bunny	(555) 524123	524131
Good Friends Are Forever	Girls with Flower	(492) 521817 / (525049)	
Good News Is So Uplifting	Girl on Ladder	(654) 523615	
Grandma's Prayer	Praying Grandma	(305) PM-861	
Groom	Groom	(269) E-2837	
Groomsman	Groomsman w/Frog	(172) E-2836	

BOLD = Suspended *Italics* = Limited Edition Shaded Area = Retired Boxed = Dated Annual (Rounded Box) = Annual ◆ = Two Year Collectible

INSPIRATIONAL TITLE	DESCRIPTIVE TITLE	#	FIG	PLT	BELL	MUSC	ORN	DOLL	THMBL	FRAME	CNDL CLMB	BOX	OTHER
Hallelujah Country	Cowboy/Guitar	377	105821										
Halo, & Merry Christmas	Angels/Snowman	241	12351										
Hang On For The Holly Days	Kitten Hang'g/Wreath	400					520292						
Happiness Divine	Clown Angel/Flowers	384	109584										
Happiness Is The Lord	Boy Playing Banjo	242	12378										
Happiness Is The Lord	Boy Clown w/Ball	235					15830						
Happy Birdie	Bird Blow'g out Candle	597	527343										
Happy Birthday Dear Jesus	Teddy Bear in Pkg	513	524875										
Happy Birthday Little Lamb	Lamb - Age 1	297	15946										
Happy Birthday Poppy	Girl Holding Poppy	381	106836										
Happy Days Are Here Again	Girl Clown w/Books	346	104396										
Happy Trails Is Trusting Jesus	Girl on Hobby Horse	494					523224						
Happy Trip	Girl on Roller Skates	499	521280										
Have A Beary Merry Christmas	Teddy in Rocker	469	522856										
Have A Beary Special Birthday	Teddy Bear w/Balloon	487	B-0104 B-0004										
Have A Heavenly Christmas	Boy in Airplane	246					12416						
Have I Got News For You	Boy Reading Scroll	350	105635										
He Careth For You	Boy Helping Lamb	10	E-1377B										
He Cleansed My Soul	Girl in Old Bath Tub	220	100277				112380						
He Is My Inspiration	Sam Butcher as Artist	563	523038										
He Is My Song	Boy/Trumpet/Dog	244	12394										
He Is The Star Of The Morning	Angel/Cloud/Manger	481	522252										
He Leadeth Me	Boy Leading Lamb	9	E-1377A										
HE Loves Me	Girl Holding Flower	535	524263										
He Upholdeth Those Who Call	Angel Catch'g Skater	130	E-0526										
He Walks With Me	Girl/Crutches/Bible	319	107999										
He Watches Over Us All	Boy/Bible/Crutches	29	E-3105										
Heaven Bless You	Baby w/Bunny/Turtle	221	520934			100285							
Heaven Bless Your Special Day	Pig - Age 3	299	15954										
Heaven Bless Your Togetherness	Groom/Trunk/Bride	378	106755										
Hello, Lord It's Me Again	Boy on Telephone	78	PM-811										
Hello World!	Kangaroo with Baby	451	521175										
Help Lord, I'm In A Spot	Boy Stand'g in Ink Spot	275	100269										
He's The Healer Of Broken Hearts	B/G Bandaging Heart	317	100080										

Title	Description	No.	Code			
Hi Sugar!	Mouse in Sugar Bowl	(398)	BC-871			
High Hopes	Boy with Kite	(498)	521957			
His Burden Is Light	Indian Girl	(14)	E-1380G			
His Eye Is On The Sparrow	Girl w/Bird in Hand	(31)	E-0530			
His Love Will Shine On You	Girl with Lily	(443)	522376			
His Name Is Jesus	Boys at Manger	(191)	**E-5381**			
His Sheep Am I	Shepherd Paint Lamb	(110)	**E-7161**			
Holy Smokes	Two Angels/Candles	(85)	E-2351			
Honk If You Love Jesus	Mother Goose/Babes	(255)	15490	15857		
Hope You're Up And On The Trail Again	Girl on Hobby Horse	(494)	521205			
Hoppy Easter Friend	Girl Collect Eggs/Frog	(529)	521906			
Houses And Palm Tree	Mini Houses w/Palms	(101)	E-2387			
How Can I Ever Forget You	Elephant/Knot in Trunk	(558)	526924			
How Can Two Walk Together Except They Agree	B/G Horse Costume	(145)	**E-9263**			
Hug One Another	B&G Hugging	(526)	521299			
I Believe In Miracles	Boy Holding Chick	(105)	**E-7156**			*E-9257*
I Believe In Miracles	Boy Holding Bluebird	(374)	**E-7156R**			
I Believe In The Old Rugged Cross	Girl Holding Cross	(224)	103632	522953		
I Belong To The Lord	Orphan Girl	(463)	**520853**			
I Can't Spell Success Without You	Boy and Dog Using Blocks to Spell	(533)	523763			
I Get A Bang Out Of You	Clown Hold'g Balloons	(236)	12262			
I Get A Kick Out Of You	Girl/Bucket on Head	(167)	**E-2827**			
I Love To Tell The Story	Boy w/Lamb & Book	(292)	PM-852			
I Picked A (Very) Special Mom	Boy w/Garden'g Mom	(328)	100536			
I Will Cherish The Old Rugged Cross	Girl Holding Cross	(224)			523534 Egg	
I Would Be Lost Without You	Girl Check Roadmap	(886)	526142			
I Would Be Sunk Without You	Baby Boy/Tub	(342)	102970			
If God Be For Us, Who Can Be Against Us	Boy at Pulpit	(154)	**E-9285**			
I'll Never Stop Loving You	Girl/Letters "Y""O""U"	(511)	521418			

BOLD = Suspended   *Italics* = Limited Edition   Shaded Area = Retired   Boxed = Dated Annual   (Rounded Box) = Annual   ◆ = Two Year Collectible

INSPIRATIONAL TITLE	DESCRIPTIVE TITLE	#	FIG	PLT	BELL	MUSC	ORN	DOLL	THMBL	FRAME	CNDL CLMB	BOX	OTHER
I'll Play My Drum For Him	Drummer Boy/Manger	87	E-2356 / E-2360 / E-5384	E-2357	E-2358	E-2355	E-2359						
I'm A Possibility	Boy with Football	274	100188				111120						
I'm A PRECIOUS MOMENTS Fan	Girl with Fan	490	523526									E-9266	
I'm Falling For Somebunny	Lamb and Bunny	308											
I'm Following Jesus	Boy in Car	320	PM-862				520411						
I'm Nuts About You	Squirrel Decorat'g Tree	570											
I'm Nuts Over My Collection	Squirrel/Bag of Nuts	547	BC-902										
I'm Sending You A White Christmas	Girl Mailing Snowball	169	E-2829	101834		112402	112372						
I'm So Glad You Fluttered Into My Life	Boy Angel with Butterfly Net	447	520640										
In His Time	Boy/Wait/Seed/Grow	375	PM-872										
In The Spotlight Of His Grace	Ballerina on Pointe	524	520543										
Isn't Eight Just Great	Ostrich - Age 8	394	109460										
Isn't He Precious?	Girl with Broom	189	E-5379 / 522988										
Isn't He Wonderful	Boy Angel Pray'g/Harp	70	E-5639										
Isn't He Wonderful	Girl Angel/Pray'g/Harp	71	E-5640										
It Is Better To Give Than To Receive	Policeman Writing Ticket	237	12297										
It's A Perfect Boy	Boy Angel/Red Cross	127	E-0512 / 525286				102415						
It's No Yolk When I Say I Love You	Hens Laugh/Girl Drops Egg on Pup's Head	575	522104										
It's So Uplifting To Have A Friend Like You	Girl on Skis Startled by Ski Jump	581	524905										
It's The Birthday Of A King	Boy Angel/B'day Cake	288	102962										
It's What's Inside That Counts	Boy with Books	42	E-3119										
January Girl	Girl/Doll/Sleigh	367	109983										
Jest To Let You Know You're Tops	Clown Pop'g out/Box	568	B-0106 / B-0006										
Jesus Is Born	Angels in Chariot	23	E-2801										

Name	Description	No.	Item Numbers (left → right)
Jesus Is Born	B&G Playing Angels	1	**E-2012**, E-2809
Jesus Is Born	Shepherd	64	**E-5623**
Jesus Is Coming Soon	Mary Knitting Booties	240	**12343**
Jesus Is The Answer	Boy Patching World	15	**E-1381**
Jesus Is The Answer	Boy/Steth'sc'pe/World	611	E-1381R
Jesus Is The Light	Girl w/Doll & Candle	4	E-1373G
Jesus Is The Light That Shines	Boy/Candle/Mouse	119	**E-0502**, E-0537
Jesus Is The Only Way	Boy at Crossroads	464	520756
Jesus Is The Sweetest Name I Know	Angel w/Baby Book	468	523097
Jesus Loves Me	Boy with Teddy	1	E-1372B, E-9278, **E-9275**, E-5208, E-7170, E-9280
Jesus Loves Me	Girl with Bunny	2	E-1372G, E-9279, 104531, **E-9276**, E-5209, E-7171, E-9281
Jesus The Savior Is Born	Angel/Newspaper	437	520357
Join In On The Blessings	Girl w/Dues Bank	205	E-0104, E-0404
Joy On Arrival	Stork Delivering Baby	532	523178
Joy To The World	Boy Angel/Trumpet	79	E-2343, E-2344
Joy To The World	Boy Playing Harp	188	**E-5378**, E-5388
July Girl	Girl w/Puppy/Basket	424	110051
June Girl	Girl Dress Up/Bride	372	110043
Junior Bridesmaid	Junior Bridesmaid	210	E-2845
Just A Line To Wish You A Happy Day	Dog Pulling Boy's Fishing Line	456	520721
Katie Lynne	Baby Collector's Doll	134	E-0539
Keep Looking Up	Giraffe - Age 6	302	**15997**
Kristy	Baby Collector's Doll	177	E-2851
Let Heaven And Nature Sing	Angel/Friends Carol'g	81	E-2347, E-2346, E-0532
Let Love Reign	Girl/Chicks/Umbrella	149	E-9273
Let Not The Sun Go Down Upon Your Wrath	Boy w/Dog on Stairs	55	E-5203
Let The Heavens Rejoice	Praying Angel	77	E-5622
Let The Whole World Know	B/G Baptism Bucket	14	**E-7165**, E-5629, E-7186

BOLD = Suspended   *Italics* = Limited Edition   Shaded Area = Retired   Boxed = Dated/Annual   (Rounded Box) = Annual   ◆ = Two Year Collectible

INSPIRATIONAL TITLE	DESCRIPTIVE TITLE	#	FIG	PLT	BELL	MUSC	ORN	DOLL	THMBL	FRAME	CNDL CLMB	BOX	OTHER
Let Us Call The Club To Order	Club Meeting	(158)	E-0103 E-0303										
Let's Be Friends	Pups Hug Each Other	(593)	527270										
Let's Keep In Touch	Clown on Elephant	(287)				102520							
Lord Give Me A Song	Girl Play'g Harmonica	(245)	12386										
Lord Give Me Patience	Bandaged Boy/Sign	(108)	E-7159										
Lord, Help Me Make The Grade	Schoolboy Clown	(354)	106216										
Lord, Help Me Stick To My Job	Girl w/Account Books	(563)	521450										
Lord, Help Us Keep Our Act Together	Clowns on Unicycle	(331)	101850										
Lord I'm Coming Home	Baseball Player/Bat	(215)	100110										
Lord, Keep Me In Teepee Top Shape	Indian Boy with Can of Spinach	(565)	PM-912										
Lord Keep Me On My Toes	Ballerina	(216)	100129				102423						
Lord Keep Me On My Toes	Ballerina	(582)					525332						
Lord Keep Me On The Ball	Clown Sitting on Ball	(270)	12270										
Lord, Keep My Life In Balance	Ballerina at Barre	(525)				520691							
Lord, Keep My Life In Tune	Boy Playing Piano	(231)				12165							
Lord, Keep My Life In Tune	Girl with Piano	(315)				12580							
Lord, Turn My Life Around	Ballerina	(493)	520551										
Love Beareth All Things	Nurse Give Shot/Bear	(107)	E-7158										
Love Cannot Break A True Friendship	Girl w/Piggy Bank	(48)	E-4722										
Love Covers All	Girl/Heart Quilt	(225)	12009										
Love Is From Above	Boy Whisper'g to Girl	(510)	521841						12254				
Love Is Kind	Boy w/Turtle	(11)	E-1379A										
Love Is Kind	Girl with Gift	(198)											
Love Is Kind	Girl with Mouse	(187)	E-5377				E-5391						
Love Is Kind	B/G on Swing	(175)		E-2847									
Love Is Patient	Teacher/Boy/Blkboard	(335)	E-9251										
Love Is Patient	Girl with Slate	(133)					E-0536						
Love Is Patient	Boy with Slate	(132)					E-0535						
Love Is Sharing	Girl at School Desk	(111)	E-7162			E-7185							
Love Is The Best Gift Of All	Girl with Present	(360)	110930		109835		109770						
Love Is The Glue That Mends	Boy Mending Horse	(344)	104027						109843				

No.	Title	Description	Item #			
⑤③	Love Lifted Me	Boy Helping Friend	**E-5201**			
⑥	Love Lifted Me	B/G on Seesaw	E-1375A			
②③⑧	Love Never Falls	Teacher/Report Card	12300			
⑧	Love One Another	B/G Sitting on Stump	*E-5215* / E-1376	522929		
⑤⑥⑥	Love Pacifies	Monkey with Pacifier	BC-911			
②⑧	Love Rescued Me	Fireman Hold Puppy	102393	102385		
③④	Loving Is Sharing	Boy Sharing w/Puppy	E-3110B			
③⑤	Loving Is Sharing	Girl Sharing w/Puppy	E-3110G			
①⑦⑥	Loving Thy Neighbor	Mother Wrap Bread			E-2848	
①⓪②	Loving You	Boy Holding Heart				**12017**
①⓪③	Loving You	Girl Holding Heart				**12025**
③②	Loving You Dear Valentine	Boy Paint'g Valentine	PM-873			
③②②	Loving You Dear Valentine	Girl/Valentine	PM-874			
⑤	Make A Joyful Noise	Girl with Goose	E-1374G / *520322*	522910	*E-7174*	
③②③	Make Me A Blessing	Girl with Sick Bear	100102 [shaded]			
④⑤⑦	Many Moons In Same Canoe, Blessum You	Indians in Canoe	520772 [shaded]			
③⑥⑨	March Girl	Girl with Kite	110019			
④⑦⑦	May All Your Christmases Be White	Girl/Snowball		521302		
③⑦	May Girl	Girl/Potted Plant	110035			
①⑨⑦	May God Bless You With A Perfect Holiday Season	Girl In Scarf/Cap		**E-5390**		
⑤③⑦	May Only Good Things Come Your Way	Girl Holding Net for Butterfly	524425			
⑤④⑧	May You Have An Old Fashioned Christmas	Christmas Girl in Plaid Dress		417777◆		417785◆
②⑥⓪	May You Have The Sweetest Christmas	Mother with Cookie Sheet	15776			
①⑥⑥	May Your Birthday Be A Blessing	Girl at Table with Dolls	**E-2826**			
⑤③⑥	May Your Birthday Be A Blessing	Girl with Cake with Candles	524301			
③⓪⓪	May Your Birthday Be Gigantic	Elephant - Age 4	15970			

BOLD = Suspended   *Italics* = Limited Edition   Shaded Area = Retired   Boxed = Annual   Dated = Annual   (Rounded Box) = Annual   ◆ = Two Year Collectible

INSPIRATIONAL TITLE	DESCRIPTIVE TITLE	#	FIG	PLT	BELL	MUSC	ORN	DOLL	THMBL	FRAME	CNDL CLMB	BOX	OTHER
May Your Birthday Be Mammoth	Whale - Age 10	573	521825										
May Your Birthday Be Warm	Teddy/Caboose	296	15938										
May Your Christmas Be A Happy Home	Family Christmas Scene	479		523003			523704						
May Your Christmas Be Blessed	Girl with Bible	186	E-5376										
May Your Christmas Be Cozy	Boy/PJ's/Teddy	80	E-2345										
May Your Christmas Be Delightful	Boy Tangled in Chirstmas Lights	254	15482				15849						
May Your Christmas Be Happy	Girl Clown/Balloon	235					**15822**						
May Your Christmas Be Merry	Girl Holding Bird	556	524166		524182		524174 526940		524190				
May Your Christmas Be Warm	Boy/Potbellied Stove	82	E-2348										
May Your Life Be Blessed With Touchdowns	Boy Playing Football	473	522023										
May Your World Be Trimmed With Joy	Boy Decorating Globe	553	522082										
Meowie Christmas	Girl with Kitten	423	109800										
Merry Christmas, Deer	Girl/Reindeer	438	522317	520284									
Mikey	Mikey	75						E-6214B					
Mini Animal Figurines	3 Mini Animals	279	102296										
Mommy, I Love You	Girl with Flower	390	112143										
Mommy, I Love You	Boy with Flower	387	109975										
Mother Sew Dear	Mother Needlepoint'g	30	E-3106	E-5217	**E-7181**	E-7182	E-0514	E-2850	13293	E-7241			
Mouse With Cheese	Mouse with Cheese	99					**E-2381**						
Mow Power To Ya	Boy Push Lawn Mower	486	PM-892										
My Days Are Blue Without You	Girl/Paint/Ladder	462	**520802**										
My Guardian Angel	Boy Angel on Cloud	56				**E-5205**							
My Guardian Angel	Girl Angel on Cloud	57				**E-5206**							
My Guardian Angel	Boy Angel	265								**E-7168**			
My Guardian Angel	Girl Angel	266								**E-7169**			
My Guardian Angels	B/G Angels/Cloud	39											
My Happiness	Girl at Table with Figurine	489	C-0110 C-0010				PM-904					Night Light **E-5207**	
My Heart Is Exposed With Love	Nurse/Xray/Heart	458	520624										
My Love Will Never Let You Go	Boy w/Hat & Fish	333	103497				**114006**						

Title	Description	Ref	C1	C2	C3	C4	C5	C6	C7	C8
My Peace I Give Unto Thee	Kids/Lamp Post	341								102954
My Warmest Thoughts Are You	Girl on Tree Swing	578							524085	
No Tears Past The Gate	Girl/Gate to Heaven	329						101826		
Nobody's Perfect!!	Boy w/Dunce Cap	148						E-9268		
Not A Creature Was Stirring	Mouse/Cheese/Kitten	516						524484		
November Girl	Girl in Pilgrim Suit	428						110108		
O Come All Ye Faithful	Boy Carolling	86	E-2353		E-2352	E-0531				
O Come Let Us Adore Him	4 Piece Nativity	362	**111333**							
O, How I Love Jesus	Indian Boy	13	E-1380B							
October Girl	Girl with Pumpkins	427	110094							
Oh Holy Night	Girl Playing Violin	482	522546		522821	522848	522554			
Oh What Fun It Is To Ride	Grandma on a Sled	361	109819							
Oh Worship The Lord	Boy Angel/Candle	194	**E-5385**							
Oh Worship The Lord	Girl Angel Praying	195	**E-5386**							
Once Upon A Holy Night	Girl w/Book & Candle	519	523836		523828	523852	523844			
One Step At A Time	Child Tak'g First Steps	664	PM-911							
Only Love Can Make A Home	Mr. Webb/Bird Home	613	PM-921							
Onward Christian Soldiers	Knight in Armor	128	E-0523							
Our Club Can't Be Beat	Clown with Drum	304	B-0001							
Our Club Is A Tough Act To Follow	Clown/Puppy/Drum	543	B-0005 / B-0105							
Our First Christmas Together	Boy and Girl in Box	277			101702	102350 / 112399 / 520233				
Our First Christmas Together	Girl Knitting Tie	98	**E-2377**	E-2378						
Our First Christmas Together	Bride and Groom	38				E-2385				
Our First Christmas Together	Couple with Gifts	433	**115290**							
Our First Christmas Together	Bride/Groom in Car	460				521558 / 525324				
Our First Christmas Together	Groom/Trunk/Bride	378				522945 / 528870				
Our Love Is Heaven Scent	Lamb and Skunk	308					E-9266			
P.D.		252								
Part Of Me Wants To Be Good	Boy Angel/Devil Suit	230	**12149**			12475				

INSPIRATIONAL TITLE	DESCRIPTIVE TITLE	#	FIG	PLT	BELL	MUSC	ORN	DOLL	THMBL	FRAME	CNDL CLMB	BOX	OTHER
Peace Amid The Storm	Boy Reading Bible	49	E-4723										
Peace On Earth	Boy In Choir	196					E-5389						
Peace On Earth	Boy/Globe/Teddy	26	E-2804										
Peace On Earth	Choir Boys/Bandages	51	E-4725			E-4726							
Peace On Earth	Girl w/Lion & Lamb	155	E-9287										
Peace On Earth	Kids/Pup/Kitten/Bird	341				109746	523062						
Praise The Lord Anyhow	Boy with Dog	19	E-1374B										
Praise The Lord Anyhow	Girl at Typewriter	138	E-9254										
Prayer Changes Things	B & G Praying @ Table	61	E-5214										
Prayer Changes Things	B & G with Bluebirds	7	E-1375B										
Prayer Changes Things	Girl Praying in Field	58			E-5210								
Precious Memories	Girl/Trunk/Wedding	168	E-2828										
Precious Memories	Couple/Album	379	106763										
Precious Moments Last Forever	Giveaway Medallion	365											12246 Medallion
Prepare Ye The Way Of The Lord	Angels Prep Manger	124	E-0508										
Press On	Girl Ironing Clothes	146	E-9265										
Puppy Love	Two Puppies	465	520764										
Puppy Love Is From Above	Anniversary Couple	380	106798										
Put On A Happy Face	Boy Clown/Mask	159	PM-822										
Reindeer	Reindeer	306					102466						
Rejoice O Earth	Angel with Trumpet	67	E-5636 520268			E-5645	113980						
Rejoice, O Earth	Angel	545											Tree Topper	617334
Rejoicing With You	Christening	50	E-4724	E-7172									
Retailer's Dome	Kids on Cloud/Dome	411	E-7350										
Retailer's Wreath	Wreath w/Ornaments	410											Wreath	111465
Retailer's Wreath Bell	Retailer's Wreath Bell	415			112348								
Ring Those Christmas Bells	Angels Ring Bell/Pray	683	525898										
Ringbearer	Ringbearer	208	E-2833										
Rocking Horse	Rocking Horse	283					102474						
Scent From Above	Girl with Skunk	327	100528										

Name	No.	Description	No.	Item No.	Item No. 2
Seek And Ye Shall Find		Girl/Shopping Bag	(104)	E-0005 / E-0105	
Seek Ye The Lord		Boy Grad/Scroll	(143)	**E-9261**	
Seek Ye The Lord		Girl Grad/Scroll	(144)	**E-9262**	
Sending My Love		Boy/Bow and Arrow	(212)	**100056**	
Sending You A Rainbow		Girl Angel/Spr'k'g Can	(150)	**E-9288**	
Sending You My Love		Girl w/Hearts/Cloud	(386)	109967	
Sending You Showers Of Blessings		Boy/Newspapers over Head	(450)	520683	
September Girl		Girl Balancing Books	(426)	110086	
Serve With A Smile		Tennis Boy	(222)		102431
Serve With A Smile		Tennis Girl	(218)		102458
Serving The Lord		Tennis Boy	(222)	**100293**	
Serving The Lord		Tennis Girl	(218)	**100161**	
Sew In Love		Girl Sewing Pants	(382)	106844	
Sharing A Gift Of Love		Girl Help Bird to Fly	(539)	527114 (rounded box)	
Sharing Begins In The Heart		Girl with Chalkboard	(467)	520861 (rounded box)	
Sharing Is Universal		Girl/Package/Friend	(336)	E-0007 / E-0107	
Sharing Our Christmas Together		Husband/Wife/Puppy	(284)	**102490**	
Sharing Our Joy Together		Bridesmaid w/Kitten	(268)	**E-2834**	
Sharing Our Season Together		Boy & Girl/Sled	(118)	**E-0501**	E-0519
Sharing Season Ornament		Brass Filagree/Kids	(376)		
Sharing The Good News Together		Girl at Mailbox with Club Newsletter	(562)	C-0011 / C-0111	PM-009 / PM-037
Shepherd Of Love		Angel w/Black Lamb	(278)	102261	102288
Showers Of Blessings		Elephant /Mouse	(352)	105945	
Silent Knight		Boy Angel/Knight	(73)		E-5642
Silent Night		Christmas Tree	(264)	15814	15814
Sitting Pretty		Girl Angel/Stool	(349)	**104825**	
Smile Along The Way		Clown Balancing	(330)	101842	113964
Smile, God Loves You		Boy with Black Eye	(3)	E-1373B	
Smile, God Loves You		Girl with Curlers	(117)	PM-821	
Sno-Bunny Falls For You Like I Do		Rabbit on Skates	(549)	520438 (boxed)	
Some Bunnies Sleeping		Bunnies	(431)	522996	
Some Bunny's Sleeping		Bunnies	(431)	115274	
Somebunny Cares		Bunny/Stuffed Carrot	(441)	BC-881	

BOLD = Suspended   *Italics* = Limited Edition   Shaded Area = Retired   Boxed = Dated / Annual   Rounded Box = Annual   ♦ = Two Year Collectible

INSPIRATIONAL TITLE	DESCRIPTIVE TITLE	#	FIG	PLT	BELL	MUSC	ORN	DOLL	THMBL	FRAME	CNDL CLMB	BOX	OTHER
Someday My Love	Bride with Dress	446	520799										
Something's Missing When You're Not Around	Girl Holding Doll with Dog	421	105643										
Stocking Hanger	Boy Tangled in Lights	445	558125										
Summer's Joy	Girl w/Crossed Arms	227	12076			408743◆		408794◆					
Surround Us With Joy	Boy with Wreath	122	E-0506				E-0513						
Surrounded With Joy	Boy with Wreath	122	E-0506		E-0522								
Sweep All Your Worries Away	Girl/Dust under Rug	502	521779										
Take Heed When You Stand	Boy on Rocking Horse	550	521272										
Tammy	Bride Doll	116						E-7267G					
Taste And See That The Lord Is Good	Girl Angel Making Food	150	E-9274										
Tell It To Jesus	Girl on Telephone	476	521477										
Tell Me A Story	Boy Sit Listen/Story	262	15792										
Tell Me The Story Of Jesus	Girl/Doll/Book	83	E-2349	15237			E-0533						
Ten Years And Still Going Strong	Girl in Race Car	540	PM-901										
Thank You For Coming To My Ade	Lemonade Stand	54	E-5202										
Thank You Lord For Everything	Boy/Turkey/Dine	472	522031										
Thanking Him For You	Girl Praying in Field	58	E-7155										
That's What Friends Are For	Crying Girls Hugging	520	521183										
The Club That's Out Of This World	Girl in Spacesuit	569	C-0112 C-0012										
The End Is In Sight	Dog Rip'g Boy's Pants	137	E-9253										
The Eyes Of The Lord Are Upon You	Baby Girl on Pillow	523				429589							
The Eyes Of The Lord Are Upon You	Baby Boy on Pillow	522				429570							
The First Noel	Boy Angel/Candle	92	E-2365				E-2367						
The First Noel	Girl Angel Praying	93	E-2366				E-2368						
The Good Lord Always Delivers	Mom-To-Be/Baby Bk	497	523453				527165						
The Good Lord Has Blessed Us Ten Fold	Couple w/ Dog & Puppies	392	114022										
The Greatest Gift Is A Friend	Baby Boy/Dog	355	109231										

Two Year Collectibles

	Subject	#							
The Greatest Of These Is Love	Commandments	483	**521868**		E-9256		E-5204		
The Hand That Rocks The Future	Girl Rocking Cradle	32	**E-3108**						
The Heavenly Light	Angel with Flashlight	68	E-5637						
The Joy Of The Lord Is My Strength	Mother with Babies	217	100137						
The Light Of The World Is Jesus	Girl with Lamppost	475			521507				
The Lord Bless You And Keep You	Boy Graduate	46	**E-4720**	**E-7175**			E-7177		
The Lord Bless You And Keep You	Bride and Groom	38	E-3114	**E-5216**	E-7179	E-7180	E-7166		E-7167
The Lord Bless You And Keep You	Girl Graduate	47	E-4721	**E-7176**			E-7178		
The Lord Bless You And Keep You	Bride	313						100633	
The Lord Giveth And The Lord Taketh Away	Girl with Cat and Birdcage	340	100226						
The Lord Is My Shepherd	Girl Holding Lamb	293	PM-851						
The Lord Is Your Light To Happiness	Bridal Couple Lighting Candle	466	520837						
The Lord Turned My Life Around	Ballerina on Pointe	577	520535						
The Lord Will Carry You Through	Clown w/Dog/Mud	251	12467						
The Perfect Grandpa	Grandpa in Rocker	109	**E-7160**				E-0517		
The Purr-fect Grandma	Grandma in Rocker	33	E-3109	_E-7173_	**E-7183**	E-7184	E-0516	13307	E-7242
The Spirit Is Willing But The Flesh Is Weak	Girl/Candy/Scale	324	100196						
The Story Of God's Love	Father Reading Bible	263	15784						
The Sweetest Club Around	Pippin/Pop/Cake	440	B-0003 / B-0103						
The Voice Of Spring	Girl by Fence	226	12068	12106					
The Wonder Of Christmas	Boy/Sled/Girl/Tree	202	E-5396			408735◆		408786◆	
Thee I Love	Boy Carving Tree	40	E-3116						
There Is Joy In Serving Jesus	Waitress Carry'g Food	106	E-7157						
There Shall Be Showers Of Blessings	Boy and Girl in Garden	500	522090						
There's A Christian Welcome Here	Angel outside Chapel	497	523011						

BOLD = Suspended   _Italics_ = Limited Edition   Shaded Area = Retired   Boxed = Dated / Annual   Rounded Box = Annual   ◆ = Two Year Collectibles

INSPIRATIONAL TITLE	DESCRIPTIVE TITLE	#	FIG	PLT	BELL	MUSC	ORN	DOLL	THMBL	FRAME	CNDL CLMB	BOX	OTHER
There's A Light At The End Of The Tunnel	Girl Peek thru Log at Bunny with Candle	527	521485										
There's A Song In My Heart	Girl Playing Triangle	232	**12173**										
They Followed The Star	Angel/3 Kings	72	**E-5641**										
They Followed The Star	3 Kings/Camels	65	E-5624 108243										
Thinking Of You Is What I Really Like To Do	Kneel'g Girl/Bouquet	504	522287										
This Day Has Been Made In Heaven	Girl/Bible/Cross	506	523496			523682							
This Day Is Something To Roar About	Lion - Age 5	301	15989										
This Is The Day Which The Lord Has Made	Birthday Boy	314	**12157**										
This Is The Day Which The Lord Hath Made	Complete Wedding Party	162	E-2838										
This Is Your Day To Shine	Girl Polishing Table	162	E-2822										
This Land Is Our Land	Explorer/Animal Crew	599	527386										
This Land Is Our Land	Explorer w/Flag/Teddy	608	527777										
This Too Shall Pass	Boy w/Broken Heart	391	114014										
Thou Art Mine	B/G Writing in Sand	37	E-3113										
Thumb-body Loves You	Girl Nails Boy's Thumb	528	521698										
Time Heals	Nurse at Desk w/Clock	518	523739										
Time To Wish You A Merry Christmas	Girl/Calendar/Clock/Mouse	434	115339		115304		115320		115312				
Timmy	Boy Jogger	203						E-5397					
'Tis The Season	Girl Adding Seasoning	430	111163										
To A Special Dad	Boy in Dad's Duds	59	E-5212										
To A Special Mum	Boy/Bee/Flower Pot	530	521965				E-0515						
To A Very Special Mom	Girl with Floppy Hat	164	E-2824										
To A Very Special Mom & Dad	Girl Hold'g Picture Frm	551	521434										
To A Very Special Sister	Bows/Sister's Hair	165	E-2825										
To Be With You Is Uplifting	Giraffe/Baby Bear	484	522260										
To God Be The Glory	Boy Holding Frame	163	**E-2823**										
To My Deer Friend	Girl w/Flowers/Deer	316	100048										

Item	Description	No.					
To My Favorite Fan	Santa and Parrot						
To My Favorite Paw	Boy Sitting w/Teddy	211	100021				
To My Forever Friend	Two Girls w/Flowers	214	100072		113956		
To Somebunny Special	Bunny	152	**E-9282 (/A)**				
To Tell The Tooth You're Special	Dentist/Patient Pulled Tooth	351	**105813**				
To Thee With Love	Girl w/Box/Kittens	43	**E-3120**	**E-0534**			
Trish	Baby Girl	253			12463		
True Blue Friends	Pup/Kit'n Share Paint'g	567	BC-912				
Trust And Obey	Policeman Writing Tkt	237		102377			
Trust In The Lord	Angel/Fly Lessons	157	**E-9289**				
Trust In The Lord To The Finish	Boy w/Racing Cup	207	PM-842				
Tubby's First Christmas	Rooster & Bird on Pig	126	E-0511 / 525278				
Two Section Wall	Two Section Wall	74	E-5644				
Unicorn	Unicorn	94					E-2371
Unto Us A Child Is Born	B/G Reading Book	18	**E-2013**		E-2808		
Unto Us A Child Is Born	Nativity Scene	20		*E-5395*			
Unto Us A Child Is Born	Shepherd	64			E-5630		
Waddle I Do Without You	Clown/Basket/Goose	250	12459			112364	
Walking By Faith	Boy Pull'g Wagon/Girl	41	E-3117				
We Are All Precious In His Sight	Girl with Pearl	373	102903				
We Are God's Workmanship	Bonnet Girl/Butterfly	140	E-9258 / *523879*				525960 Egg
We Belong To The Lord	Boy with Staff/Lambs	338	103004				
We Gather Together To Ask The Lord's Blessing	Thanksgiving Set	359	109762				
We Have Come From Afar	Penguins	559	526959				
We Have Seen His Star	Boy Holding Lamb	16	**E-2010**	E-5620		E-6120	
We Need A Good Friend Through The Ruff Times	Grandpa/Cane/Dog	462	**520810**				
We Saw A Star	2 Angels Sawing Star	245		12408			
Wedding Arch	Bridal Arch	332	102369				

BOLD = Suspended Italics = Limited Edition Shaded Area = Retired Boxed = Dated/Annual (Rounded Box) = Annual ◆ = Two Year Collectible

INSPIRATIONAL TITLE	DESCRIPTIVE TITLE	#	FIG	PLT	BELL	MUSC	ORN	DOLL	THMBL	FRAME	CNDL CLMB	BOX	OTHER
Wee Three Kings	Three Kings	(66)	E-5635	E-0538		E-0520	E-5634						
We're Going To Miss You	Girl/Melting Snowman	(515)	524913										
We're In It Together	Boy with Piggy	(141)	**E-9259**										
We're Pulling For You	Boy with Donkey	(353)	**106151**										
What The World Needs Now	Girl/Globe/Praying	(680)	524352										
Winter's Song	Girl Feeding Birds	(229)	(12092)	(12130)		408778 ◆		408816 ◆					
Wishing You A Basket Full Of Blessings	Boy/Basket/Chick	(385)	109924										
Wishing You A Comfy Christmas	Angel Hold'g Blanket	(607)	527750										
Wishing You A Cozy Christmas	Girl with Muff	(280)	[102342]		102318		102326		102334				
Wishing You A Cozy Season	Boy by Stump	(480)	521949										
Wishing You A Happy Easter	Girl Holding Bunny	(388)	109886										
Wishing You A Ho Ho Ho	Boy Santa/Pup/Whskrs	(605)	527629										
Wishing You A Merry Christmas	Carollers with Puppy	(200)				E-5394							
Wishing You A Merry Christmas	Girl in Choir	(193)	E-5383		E-5393		E-5387						
Wishing You A Perfect Choice	Boy Propose to Girl	(452)	520845										
Wishing You A Purr-fect Holiday	Kitten with Ornament	(521)					520497						
Wishing You A Season Filled With Joy	Boy/Santa Cap/Dog	(27)	E-2805										
Wishing You A Very Successful Season	Boy/Package/Puppy	(478)	522120										
Wishing You A Yummy Christmas	Girl w/Ice Cream/Boy	(358)	109754	523801									
Wishing You Grrr-eatness	Leopard - Age 7	(393)	109479										
Wishing You Roads Of Happiness	Bride & Groom in Car	(460)	520780										
With This Ring I...	Boy Giving Girl Ring	(343)	104019										
Worship The Lord	Boy Kneeling/Church	(223)	102229										
Worship The Lord	Girl Kneeling/Church	(213)	100064										
Wreath Contestant Ornament	Boy/Girl/Cloud/ w/PM Logo	(422)					PM-008						
Yield Not To Temptation	Girl with Apple	(505)	521310										
You Are A Blessing To Me	Girl/Patch Teddy Bear	(541)	PM-902										
You Are My Favorite Star	Girl/Star/Boy's Head	(598)	527378										

Title	Description	No.	Item Number			
You Are My Happiness	Girl Hold'g Roses/Bird	587	526185			
You Are My Main Event	Girl/Balloons/Satchel	397	115231			
You Are My Number One	Girl Holding Trophy	448	520829			
You Are Such A Purr-fect Friend	Girl Cuddling Kitten	585	526010			
You Are The Type I Love	Girl Typing Message	577	523542			
You Can Always Bring A Friend	Girl Holding Puppy	546	527122			
You Can Fly	Boy Angel on Cloud	271	12335			
You Can't Run Away From God	Boy & Dog Run Away	129	E-0525			
You Deserve An Ovation	Ballerina on Toe-point	572	520578			
You Have Touched So Many Hearts	Girl with Hearts	161	E-2821 / 523283 / 527661	112577 / 422282◆	112356	427527◆
You Just Cannot Chuck A Good Friendship	Boy/Dog/Trash	442	PM-882			
You Will Always Be My Choice	Girl with Ballot Box	485	PM-891			
Your Love Is So Uplifting	Boy Hold Girl/Fountain	454	520675			
You're Worth Your Weight In Gold	Pig	151	E-9282 (/B)			

BOLD = Suspended   *Italics* = Limited Edition   Shaded Area = Retired   Boxed = Dated Annual   (Rounded Box) = Annual   ◆ = Two Year Collectible

QUICK REFERENCE SECTION

Many times certain pieces become important as part of a group. PRECIOUS MOMENTS groups that have become important are included in this QUICK REFERENCE SECTION. Groups included are The "Original 21," Limited Editions, Retired pieces, Suspended pieces, Re-introduced pieces, pieces that have moved from the Suspended List to the Retired List, Dated Annuals, Annuals - Not Dated, Two-Year Collectibles, The Enesco PRECIOUS MOMENTS Birthday Club pieces, and The Enesco PRECIOUS MOMENTS Collectors' Club pieces.

In addition, the OUTLINE OF ANNUALS Section groups annual collectibles by series and product type. The OUTLINE OF THE SERIES Section itemizes the individual pieces that comprise each series.

There's a QUICK REFERENCE CALENDAR as well. It's a summary, by year, of Retired, Suspended, and Annual pieces.

QUICK REFERENCE LISTS

THE "ORIGINAL 21"

E-1372B	Figurine	Jesus Loves Me
E-1372G	Figurine	Jesus Loves Me
E-1373B	Figurine	Smile, God Loves You
E-1373G	Figurine	Jesus Is The Light
E-1374B	Figurine	Praise The Lord Anyhow
E-1374G	Figurine	Make A Joyful Noise
E-1375A	Figurine	Love Lifted Me
E-1375B	Figurine	Prayer Changes Things
E-1376	Figurine	Love One Another
E-1377A	Figurine	Love Leadeth Me
E-1377B	Figurine	He Careth For You
E-1378	Figurine	God Loveth A Cheerful Giver
E-1379A	Figurine	Love Is Kind
E-1379B	Figurine	God Understands
E-1380B	Figurine	O, How I Love Jesus
E-1380G	Figurine	His Burden Is Light
E-1381	Figurine	Jesus Is The Answer
E-2010	Figurine	We Have Seen His Star
E-2011	Figurine	Come Let Us Adore Him
E-2012	Figurine	Jesus Is Born
E-2013	Figurine	Unto Us A Child Is Born

LIMITED EDITIONS

E-0538	Plate	15,000	Wee Three Kings
E-2347	Plate	15,000	Let Heaven And Nature Sing
E-2847	Plate	15,000	Love Is Kind
E-2848	Plate	15,000	Loving Thy Neighbor
E-5215	Plate	15,000	Love One Another
E-5217	Plate	15,000	Mother Sew Dear
E-5395	Plate	15,000	Unto Us A Child Is Born
E-5646	Plate	15,000	Come Let Us Adore Him
E-7173	Plate	15,000	The Purr-fect Grandma
E-7174	Plate	15,000	Make A Joyful Noise
E-7267B	Doll	5,000	Cubby
E-7267G	Doll	5,000	Tammy
E-9256	Plate	15,000	The Hand That Rocks The Future
E-9257	Plate	15,000	I Believe In Miracles
12491	Doll	12,500	Angie, The Angel Of Mercy
100455	Doll	12,000	Bong Bong
100463	Doll	12,000	Candy
102253	Doll	7,500	Connie
104531	Figurine	1,000	Jesus Loves Me
520322	Figurine	1,500	Make A Joyful Noise
523283	Figurine	2,000	You Have Touched So Many Hearts
523879	Figurine	2,000	We Are God's Workmanship
526010	Figurine	2,000	You Are Such A Purr-fect Friend

} 9" Easter Seal Figurines are a sub-set of the Limited Editions.

QUICK REFERENCE LISTS

RETIRED

E-0504	Figurine	1990	Christmastime Is For Sharing
E-0506	Figurine	1989	Surrounded With Joy
E-0519	Musical	1986	Sharing Our Season Together
E-0525	Figurine	1989	You Can't Run Away From God
E-0530	Figurine	1987	His Eye Is On The Sparrow
E-0532	Ornament	1986	Let Heaven And Nature Sing
E-0534	Ornament	1989	To Thee With Love
E-1373B	Figurine	1984	Smile God Loves You
E-1373G	Figurine	1988	Jesus Is The Light
E-1374B	Figurine	1982	Praise The Lord Anyhow
E-1378	Figurine	1981	God Loveth A Cheerful Giver
E-1380G	Figurine	1984	His Burden Is Light
E-1380B	Figurine	1984	O, How I Love Jesus
E-2011	Figurine	1981	Come Let Us Adore Him
E-2351	Figurine	1987	Holy Smokes
E-2353	Figurine	1986	O Come All Ye Faithful
E-2368	Ornament	1984	The First Noel
E-2369	Ornament	1986	Dropping In For Christmas
E-2371	Ornament	1988	Unicorn
E-2375	Figurine	1991	Dropping Over For Christmas
E-2376	Ornament	1985	Dropping Over For Christmas
E-2805	Figurine	1985	Wishing You A Season Filled With Joy
E-2806	Musical	1984	Christmas Is A Time To Share
E-2822	Figurine	1988	This Is Your Day To Shine
E-2841	Figurine	1986	Baby's First Picture
E-2850	Doll	1985	Mother Sew Dear
E-3107	Figurine	1985	Blessed Are The Peacemakers
E-3111	Figurine	1985	Be Not Weary In Well Doing
E-3112	Figurine	1983	God's Speed
E-3118	Figurine	1983	Eggs Over Easy
E-5211	Bell	1984	God Understands
E-5377	Figurine	1987	Love Is Kind
E-5388	Ornament	1987	Joy To The World
E-5645	Musical	1988	Rejoice O Earth
E-6120	Ornament	1984	We Have Seen His Star
E-7156	Figurine	1992	I Believe In Miracles
E-7156R	Figurine	1992	I Believe In Miracles
E-7157	Figurine	1986	There Is Joy In Serving Jesus
E-7185	Musical	1985	Love Is Sharing
E-9268	Figurine	1990	Nobody's Perfect!
E-9273	Figurine	1987	Let Love Reign
E-9274	Figurine	1986	Taste And See That The Lord Is Good
12459	Figurine	1989	Waddle I Do Without You
12467	Figurine	1988	The Lord Will Carry You Through
15504	Musical	1989	God Sent You Just In Time
100102	Figurine	1990	Make Me A Blessing
100129	Figurine	1988	Lord Keep Me On My Toes
100196	Figurine	1991	The Spirit Is Willing But The Flesh Is Weak
100269	Figurine	1989	Help Lord, I'm In A Spot
100528	Figurine	1991	Scent From Above
101842	Figurine	1991	Smile Along The Way
101850	Figurine	1992	Lord, Help Us Keep Our Act Together
102423	Ornament	1990	Lord, Keep Me On My Toes

RETIRED CONTINUED

113980	Ornament	1991	Rejoice O Earth
520640	Figurine	1991	I'm So Glad You Fluttered Into My Life
520772	Figurine	1990	Many Moons In Same Canoe, Blessum You

From the Enesco Dictionary -

RETIRED - A figurine or collectible that has been permanently removed from production and the molds destroyed. It is regarded as an honor for a figurine to be chosen for Retired status. Pieces are Retired from time to time to make room in the Collection for new introductions.

QUICK REFERENCE LISTS

SUSPENDED

E-0501	Figurine	1986	Sharing Our Season Together
E-0502	Figurine	1986	Jesus Is The Light That Shines
E-0503	Figurine	1986	Blessings From My House To Yours
E-0507	Figurine	1987	God Sent His Son
E-0508	Figurine	1986	Prepare Ye The Way Of The Lord
E-0509	Figurine	1987	Bringing God's Blessing To You
E-0512	Figurine	1990	It's A Perfect Boy
E-0515	Ornament	1988	To A Special Dad
E-0517	Ornament	1990	The Perfect Grandpa
E-0520	Musical	1986	Wee Three Kings
E-0521	Frame	1987	Blessed Are The Pure In Heart
E-0526	Figurine	1985	He Upholdeth Those Who Call
E-0531	Ornament	1986	O Come All Ye Faithful
E-0533	Ornament	1988	Tell Me The Story Of Jesus
E-0535	Ornament	1986	Love Is Patient
E-0536	Ornament	1986	Love Is Patient
E-0537	Ornament	1985	Jesus Is The Light
E-0539	Doll	1988	Katie Lynne
E-1375B	Figurine	1984	Prayer Changes Things
E-1377A	Figurine	1984	He Leadeth Me
E-1377B	Figurine	1984	He Careth For You
E-1379A	Figurine	1984	Love Is Kind
E-1379B	Figurine	1984	God Understands
E-1381	Figurine	1984	Jesus Is The Answer
E-2010	Figurine	1984	We Have Seen His Star
E-2012	Figurine	1984	Jesus Is Born
E-2013	Figurine	1984	Unto Us A Child Is Born
E-2343	Ornament	1988	Joy To The World
E-2344	Cndl Clmb	1985	Joy To The World
E-2345	Figurine	1984	May Your Christmas Be Cozy
E-2346	Musical	1989	Let Heaven And Nature Sing
E-2348	Figurine	1988	May Your Christmas Be Warm
E-2349	Figurine	1985	Tell Me The Story Of Jesus
E-2350	Figurine	1984	Dropping In For Christmas
E-2352	Musical	1984	O Come All Ye Faithful
E-2355	Musical	1984	I'll Play My Drum For Him
E-2356	Figurine	1985	I'll Play My Drum For Him
E-2361	Figurine	1986	Christmas Joy From Head To Toe
E-2362	Ornament	1988	Baby's First Christmas
E-2364	Figurine	1989	Goat
E-2365	Figurine	1984	The First Noel
E-2366	Figurine	1984	The First Noel
E-2367	Ornament	1984	The First Noel
E-2372	Ornament	1985	Baby's First Christmas
E-2377	Figurine	1985	Our First Christmas Together
E-2378	Plate	1985	Our First Christmas Together
E-2381	Ornament	1984	Mouse With Cheese
E-2385	Ornament	1991	Our First Christmas Together
E-2386	Ornaments	1984	Camel, Donkey, Cow
E-2801	Figurine	1984	Jesus Is Born
E-2802	Figurine	1984	Christmas Is The Time To Share
E-2803	Figurine	1984	Crown Him Lord Of All
E-2804	Figurine	1984	Peace On Earth
E-2807	Musical	1984	Crown Him Lord Of All

SUSPENDED CONTINUED

E-2808	Musical	1984	Unto Us A Child Is Born
E-2809	Musical	1985	Jesus Is Born
E-2823	Figurine	1987	To God Be The Glory
E-2826	Figurine	1986	May Your Birthday Be A Blessing
E-2827	Figurine	1986	I Get A Kick Out Of You
E-2834	Figurine	1991	Sharing Our Joy Together
E-2840	Figurine	1988	Baby's First Step
E-2851	Doll	1989	Kristy
E-3104	Figurine	1991	Blessed Are The Pure In Heart
E-3105	Figurine	1984	He Watches Over Us All
E-3108	Figurine	1984	The Hand That Rocks The Future
E-3119	Figurine	1984	It's What's Inside That Counts
E-3120	Figurine	1986	To Thee With Love
E-4720	Figurine	1987	The Lord Bless You And Keep You
E-4722	Figurine	1985	Love Cannot Break A True Friendship
E-4723	Figurine	1984	Peace Amid The Storm
E-4725	Figurine	1984	Peace On Earth
E-4726	Musical	1984	Peace On Earth
E-5200	Figurine	1984	Bear Ye One Another's Burdens
E-5201	Figurine	1984	Love Lifted Me
E-5202	Figurine	1984	Thank You For Coming To My Ade
E-5203	Figurine	1984	Let Not The Sun Go Down Upon Your Wrath
E-5205	Musical	1985	My Guardian Angel
E-5206	Musical	1988	My Guardian Angel
E-5207	Night Light	1984	My Guardian Angel
E-5208	Bell	1985	Jesus Loves Me
E-5209	Bell	1985	Jesus Loves Me
E-5210	Bell	1984	Prayer Changes Things
E-5213	Figurine	1989	God Is Love
E-5214	Figurine	1984	Prayer Changes Things
E-5216	Plate	1987	The Lord Bless You And Keep You
E-5376	Figurine	1986	May Your Christmas Be Blessed
E-5378	Figurine	1989	Joy To The World
E-5380	Figurine	1986	A Monarch Is Born
E-5381	Figurine	1987	His Name Is Jesus
E-5382	Figurines	1986	For God So Loved The World
E-5385	Figurine	1986	Oh Worship The Lord
E-5386	Figurine	1986	Oh Worship The Lord
E-5389	Ornament	1986	Peace On Earth
E-5390	Ornament	1989	May God Bless You With A Perfect Holiday Season
E-5391	Ornament	1989	Love Is Kind
E-5394	Musical	1986	Wishing You A Merry Christmas
E-5397	Doll	1991	Timmy
E-5619	Figurine	1985	Come Let Us Adore Him
E-5620	Bell	1985	We Have Seen His Star
E-5623	Bell	1984	Jesus Is Born
E-5627	Ornament	1985	But Love Goes On Forever
E-5628	Ornament	1985	But Love Goes On Forever
E-5630	Ornament	1985	Unto Us A Child Is Born
E-5631	Ornament	1985	Baby's First Christmas
E-5632	Ornament	1985	Baby's First Christmas
E-5633	Ornaments	1984	Come Let Us Adore Him
E-5634	Ornaments	1984	Wee Three Kings
E-5639	Figurine	1985	Isn't He Wonderful

QUICK REFERENCE LISTS

SUSPENDED CONTINUED

E-5640	Figurine	1985	Isn't He Wonderful
E-5641	Figurine	1985	They Followed The Star
E-5642	Musical	1985	Silent Knight
E-6118	Cndl Clmb	1988	But Love Goes On Forever
E-6214B	Doll	1985	Mikey
E-6214G	Doll	1985	Debbie
E-6613	Figurine	1987	God Sends The Gift Of His Love
E-6901	Plaque	1986	Collection Plaque
E-7153	Figurine	1986	God Is Love, Dear Valentine
E-7154	Figurine	1986	God Is Love, Dear Valentine
E-7155	Figurine	1984	Thanking Him For You
E-7159	Figurine	1985	Lord Give Me Patience
E-7160	Figurine	1986	The Perfect Grandpa
E-7161	Figurine	1984	His Sheep Am I
E-7162	Figurine	1984	Love Is Sharing
E-7163	Figurine	1984	God Is Watching Over You
E-7164	Figurine	1984	Bless This House
E-7165	Figurine	1987	Let The Whole World Know
E-7167	Box	1985	The Lord Bless You And Keep You
E-7168	Frame	1984	My Guardian Angel
E-7169	Frame	1984	My Guardian Angel
E-7170	Frame	1985	Jesus Loves Me
E-7171	Frame	1985	Jesus Loves Me
E-7172	Plate	1985	Rejoicing With You
E-7175	Bell	1985	The Lord Bless You And Keep You
E-7176	Bell	1985	The Lord Bless You And Keep You
E-7177	Frame	1987	The Lord Bless You And Keep You
E-7178	Frame	1987	The Lord Bless You And Keep You
E-7181	Bell	1988	Mother Sew Dear
E-7183	Bell	1988	The Purr-fect Grandma
E-7186	Musical	1986	Let The Whole World Know
E-7241	Frame	1986	Mother Sew Dear
E-7242	Frame	1988	The Purr-fect Grandma
E-9251	Figurine	1985	Love Is Patient
E-9252	Figurine	1989	Forgiving Is Forgetting
E-9253	Figurine	1985	The End Is In Sight
E-9259	Figurine	1990	We're In It Together
E-9260	Figurine	1987	God's Promises Are Sure
E-9261	Figurine	1986	Seek Ye The Lord
E-9262	Figurine	1986	Seek Ye The Lord
E-9263	Figurine	1985	How Can Two Walk Together Except They Agree
E-9266	Box	1988	I'm Falling For Somebunny
E-9266	Box	1988	Our Love Is Heaven-Scent
E-9267	Figurines	1991	Animal Collection
E-9267A	Figurine	1991	Teddy Bear
E-9267B	Figurine	1991	Dog
E-9267C	Figurine	1991	Bunny
E-9267D	Figurine	1991	Cat
E-9267E	Figurine	1991	Lamb
E-9267F	Figurine	1991	Pig
E-9275	Plate	1984	Jesus Loves Me
E-9276	Plate	1984	Jesus Loves Me
E-9280	Box	1985	Jesus Loves Me
E-9281	Box	1985	Jesus Loves Me

SUSPENDED CONTINUED

E-9282A	Figurine	1990	To Somebunny Special
E-9282B	Figurine	1990	You're Worth Your Weight In Gold
E-9282C	Figurine	1990	Especially For Ewe
E-9283A	Box	1984	Forever Friends - Dog
E-9283B	Box	1984	Forever Friends - Cat
E-9285	Figurine	1985	If God Be For Us, Who Can Be Against Us
E-9287	Figurine	1986	Peace On Earth
E-9288	Figurine	1986	Sending You A Rainbow
E-9289	Figurine	1987	Trust In The Lord
12009	Figurine	1991	Love Covers All
12017	Frame	1987	Loving You
12025	Frame	1987	Loving You
12033	Frame	1987	God's Precious Gift
12149	Figurine	1989	Part Of Me Wants To Be Good
12157	Figurine	1990	This Is The Day Which The Lord Has Made
12165	Musical	1989	Lord, Keep My Life In Tune
12173	Figurine	1990	There's A Song In My Heart
12203	Figurine	1986	Get Into The Habit Of Prayer
12211	Figurine	1987	Baby's First Haircut
12254	Thimble	1990	Love Covers All
12297	Figurine	1987	It Is Better To Give Than To Receive
12335	Figurine	1988	You Can Fly
12343	Figurine	1986	Jesus Is Coming Soon
12351	Figurine	1988	Halo, And Merry Christmas
12378	Figurine	1990	Happiness Is The Lord
12386	Figurine	1990	Lord Give Me A Song
12394	Figurine	1990	He Is My Song
12408	Musical	1987	We Saw A Star
12424	Doll	1986	Aaron
12432	Doll	1986	Bethany
12475	Doll	1986	P.D.
12483	Doll	1986	Trish
12580	Musical	1990	Lord Keep My Life In Tune
15822	Ornament	1989	May Your Christmas Be Happy
15830	Ornament	1989	Happiness Is The Lord
16012	Figurine	1989	Baby's First Trip
16020	Night Light	1989	God Bless You With Rainbows
100021	Figurine	1988	To My Favorite Paw
100056	Figurine	1991	Sending My Love
100145	Figurine	1990	God Bless The Day We Found You (Daughter)
100153	Figurine	1990	God Bless The Day We Found You (Son)
100161	Figurine	1990	Serving The Lord (Girl)
100293	Figurine	1990	Serving The Lord (Boy)
100544	Figurine	1989	Brotherly Love
100625	Thimble	1989	God Is Love, Dear Valentine
100633	Thimble	1991	The Lord Bless You And Keep You
100668	Thimbles	1988	Clown Thimbles
102415	Ornament	1989	It's A Perfect Boy
102431	Ornament	1988	Serve With A Smile
102458	Ornament	1988	Serve With A Smile
102474	Ornament	1991	Rocking Horse
102490	Figurine	1988	Sharing Our Christmas Together
102962	Figurine	1989	It's The Birthday Of A King
104027	Figurine	1990	Love Is The Glue That Mends

SUSPENDED CONTINUED

104396	Figurine	1990	Happy Days Are Here Again
104825	Figurine	1990	Sitting Pretty
105635	Figurine	1991	Have I Got News For You
105643	Figurine	1991	Something's Missing When You're Not Around
105813	Figurine	1990	To Tell The Tooth You're Special
106151	Figurine	1991	We're Pulling For You
106216	Figurine	1990	Lord Help Me Make The Grade
109487	Figurine	1991	Believe The Impossible
111120	Ornament	1990	I'm A Possibility
111333	Figurine	1991	O Come Let Us Adore Him
113972	Ornament	1991	God Sent You Just In Time
113999	Ornament	1991	Cheers To The Leader
114006	Ornament	1991	My Love Will Never Let You Go
115290	Figurine	1991	Our First Christmas Together
520802	Figurine	1991	My Days Are Blue Without You
520810	Figurine	1991	We Need A Good Friend Through The Ruff Times
520853	Figurine	1991	I Belong To The Lord
521868	Figurine	1991	The Greatest Of These Is Love

From the Enesco Dictionary -

SUSPENDED - A figurine or collectible that has been removed from production for an unspecified period of time. A piece designated as Suspended cannot be moved to Retired status without first being "re-introduced" to the Collection. There is no time limit on how long a collectible may be Suspended from the Collection.

RE-INTRODUCED

E-7156 as E-7156R　　　Figurine　　　1987　　　I Believe In Miracles
Both subsequently retired in 1992.

E-1381 as E-1381R　　　Figurine　　　1992　　　Jesus Is The Answer

From the Enesco Dictionary -

RE-INTRODUCED - A figurine re-activated from Suspended status into the Collection is said to be "re-introduced." As of this printing, only two figurines, E-7156 and E-1381, have been removed from Suspended status and Re-introduced to the Collection as E-7156R and E-1381R. When a figurine is Re-introduced, it is re-sculptured to differentiate it from the **original**, pre-Suspended version.

MOVED FROM SUSPENDED LIST TO RETIRED LIST

E-7156　　I Believe In Miracles
Suspended 1985, Re-introduced 1987, Retired 1992

QUICK REFERENCE LISTS

DATED ANNUALS

E-0505	Plate	1983	Christmastime Is For Sharing
E-0513	Ornament	1983	Surround Us With Joy
E-0518	Ornament	1983	Blessed Are The Pure In Heart
E-0522	Bell	1983	Surrounded With Joy
E-2357	Plate	1982	I'll Play My Drum For Him
E-2358	Bell	1982	I'll Play My Drum For Him (only prototypes were dated)
E-2359	Ornament	1982	I'll Play My Drum For Him
E-5383	Figurine	1984	Wishing You A Merry Christmas
E-5387	Ornament	1984	Wishing You A Merry Christmas
E-5392	Ornament	1984	Blessed Are The Pure In Heart
E-5393	Bell	1984	Wishing You A Merry Christmas
E-5396	Plate	1984	The Wonder Of Christmas
E-5622	Bell	1981	Let The Heavens Rejoice
E-5629	Ornament	1981	Let The Heavens Rejoice
15237	Plate	1985	Tell Me The Story Of Jesus
15539	Figurine	1985	Baby's First Christmas
15547	Figurine	1985	Baby's First Christmas
15768	Ornament	1985	God Sent His Love
15865	Thimble	1985	God Sent His Love
15873	Bell	1985	God Sent His Love
15881	Figurine	1985	God Sent His Love
15903	Ornament	1985	Baby's First Christmas
15911	Ornament	1985	Baby's First Christmas
101834	Plate	1986	I'm Sending You A White Christmas
102318	Bell	1986	Wishing You A Cozy Christmas
102326	Ornament	1986	Wishing You A Cozy Christmas
102334	Thimble	1986	Wishing You A Cozy Christmas
102342	Figurine	1986	Wishing You A Cozy Christmas
102350	Ornament	1986	Our First Christmas Together
102466	Ornament	1986	Reindeer Ornament
102504	Ornament	1986	Baby's First Christmas
102512	Ornament	1986	Baby's First Christmas
102954	Plate	1987	My Peace I Give Unto Thee
104515	Ornament	1987	Bear The Good News Of Christmas
109401	Ornament	1987	Baby's First Christmas
109428	Ornament	1987	Baby's First Christmas
109770	Ornament	1987	Love Is The Best Gift Of All
109835	Bell	1987	Love Is The Best Gift Of All
109843	Thimble	1987	Love Is The Best Gift Of All
110930	Figurine	1987	Love Is The Best Gift Of All
112399	Ornament	1987	Our First Christmas Together
115282	Ornament	1988	Baby's First Christmas
115304	Bell	1988	Time To Wish You A Merry Christmas
115312	Thimble	1988	Time To Wish You A Merry Christmas
115320	Ornament	1988	Time To Wish You A Merry Christmas
115339	Figurine	1988	Time To Wish You A Merry Christmas
520233	Ornament	1988	Our First Christmas Together
520241	Ornament	1988	Baby's First Christmas
520276	Ornament	1988	You Are My Gift Come True
520284	Plate	1988	Merry Christmas, Deer
520292	Ornament	1988	Hang On For The Holly Days
520411	Ornament	1992	I'm Nuts About You
520438	Ornament	1991	Sno-Bunny Falls For You Like I Do
520462	Ornament	1989	Christmas Is Ruff Without You

DATED ANNUALS CONTINUED

520497	Ornament	1990	Wishing You A Purr-fect Holiday
521558	Ornament	1989	Our First Christmas Together
522546	Figurine	1989	Oh Holy Night
522554	Thimble	1989	Oh Holy Night
522821	Bell	1989	Oh Holy Night
522848	Ornament	1989	Oh Holy Night
522945	Ornament	1991	Our First Christmas Together
523003	Plate	1989	May Your Christmas Be A Happy Home
523062	Ornament	1989	Peace On Earth
523194	Ornament	1989	Baby's First Christmas
523208	Ornament	1989	Baby's First Christmas
523534	Egg	1991	I Will Cherish The Old Rugged Cross
523704	Ornament	1990	May Your Christmas Be A Happy Home
523771	Ornament	1990	Baby's First Christmas
523798	Ornament	1990	Baby's First Christmas
523801	Plate	1990	Wishing You A Yummy Christmas
523828	Bell	1990	Once Upon A Holy Night
523836	Figurine	1990	Once Upon A Holy Night
523844	Thimble	1990	Once Upon A Holy Night
523852	Ornament	1990	Once Upon A Holy Night
523860	Plate	1991	Blessings From Me To Thee
524166	Figurine	1991	May Your Christmas Be Merry
524174	Ornament	1991	May Your Christmas Be Merry
524182	Bell	1991	May Your Christmas Be Merry
524190	Thimble	1991	May Your Christmas Be Merry
525324	Ornament	1990	Our First Christmas Together
525960	Egg	1992	We Are God's Workmanship
526940	Ornament	1991	May Your Christmas Be Merry
527084	Ornament	1991	Baby's First Christmas
527092	Ornament	1991	Baby's First Christmas
527475	Ornament	1992	Baby's First Christmas
527483	Ornament	1992	Baby's First Christmas
527688	Figurine	1992	But The Greatest Of These Is Love
527696	Ornament	1992	But The Greatest Of These Is Love
527718	Thimble	1992	But The Greatest Of These Is Love
527726	Bell	1992	But The Greatest Of These Is Love
527734	Ornament	1992	But The Greatest Of These Is Love
527742	Plate	1992	But The Greatest Of These Is Love
528870	Ornament	1992	Our First Christmas Together

QUICK REFERENCE LISTS

ANNUALS - NOT DATED

E-2838	Figurine	1987	This Is The Day Which The Lord Hath Made
12068	Figurine	1985	The Voice Of Spring
12076	Figurine	1985	Summer's Joy
12084	Figurine	1986	Autumn's Praise
12092	Figurine	1986	Winter's Song
12106	Plate	1985	The Voice Of Spring
12114	Plate	1985	Summer's Joy
12122	Plate	1986	Autumn's Praise
12130	Plate	1986	Winter's Song
100536	Figurine	1987	I Picked A Very Special Mom
100641	Thimbles	1986	Four Seasons
102903	Figurine	1987	We Are All Precious In His Sight
102938	Figurine	1986	God Bless America
107999	Figurine	1987	He Walks With Me
114022	Figurine	1988	The Good Lord Has Blessed Us Tenfold
115231	Figurine	1988	You Are My Main Event
115479	Figurine	1988	Blessed Are They That Overcome
520861	Figurine	1989	Sharing Begins In The Heart
522376	Figurine	1989	His Love Will Shine On You
523380	Wall Hanging	1992	Blessed Are The Ones Who Mourn
523437	Wall Hanging	1992	Blessed Are The Humble
523526	Figurine	1990	I'm A PRECIOUS MOMENTS Fan
524263	Figurine	1991	HE Loves Me
524522	Figurine	1990	Always In His Care
525049	Figurine	1990	Good Friends Are Forever
525057	Ornament	1990	Bundles Of Joy
526185	Figurine	1992	You Are My Happiness
527114	Figurine	1991	Sharing A Gift Of Love
527122	Figurine	1991	You Can Always Bring A Friend
527173	Figurine	1992	A Universal Love
527319	Figurine	1992	An Event Worth Wading For
527564	Figurine	1992	God Bless The USA
527777	Figurine	1992	This Land Is Our Land
617334	Tree Topper	1990	Rejoice O Earth

TWO-YEAR COLLECTIBLES

408735	Musical Jack-in-the-Box	1990, 1991	The Voice Of Spring
408743	Musical Jack-in-the-Box	1990, 1991	Summer's Joy
408751	Musical Jack-in-the-Box	1990, 1991	Autumn's Praise
408778	Musical Jack-in-the-Box	1990, 1991	Winter's Song
408786	Doll	1990. 1991	The Voice Of Spring
408794	Doll	1990, 1991	Summer's Joy
408808	Doll	1990, 1991	Autumn's Praise
408816	Doll	1990, 1991	Winter's Song
417777	Musical Jack-in-the-Box	1991, 1992	May You Have An Old Fashioned Christmas
417785	Doll	1991, 1992	May You Have An Old Fashioned Christmas
422282	Musical Jack-in-the-Box	1991, 1992	You Have Touched So Many Hearts
427527	Doll	1991, 1992	You Have Touched So Many Hearts

QUICK REFERENCE OUTLINE OF THE ANNUALS

(✓ indicates a completed series)

✓ JOY OF CHRISTMAS PLATE SERIES   (Series of 4, Dated)

E-2357	1982	I'll Play My Drum For Him
E-0505	1983	Christmastime Is For Sharing
E-5396	1984	The Wonder Of Christmas
15237	1985	Tell Me The Story Of Jesus

✓ THE FOUR SEASONS PLATES   (Set of 4, Unnumbered Certificate)

12106	1985	The Voice Of Spring
12114	1985	Summer's Joy
12122	1986	Autumn's Praise
12130	1986	Winter's Song

✓ THE FOUR SEASONS FIGURINES   (Set of 4, Unnumbered Certificate)

12068	1985	The Voice Of Spring
12076	1985	Summer's Joy
12084	1986	Autumn's Praise
12092	1986	Winter's Song

✓ THE FOUR SEASONS THIMBLES   (Set of 4)

100641	1986	Four Seasons Thimbles

✓ CHRISTMAS LOVE PLATE SERIES   (Series of 4, Dated)

101834	1986	I'm Sending You A White Christmas
102954	1987	My Peace I Give To Thee
520284	1988	Merry Christmas, Deer
523003	1989	May Your Christmas Be A Happy Home

SPECIAL EASTER SEAL FIGURINES

107999	1987	He Walks With Me
115479	1988	Blessed Are They That Overcome
522376	1989	His Love Will Shine On You
524522	1990	Always In His Care
527114	1991	Sharing A Gift Of Love
527173	1992	A Universal Love

SPECIAL EVENTS FIGURINES

115231	1988	You Are My Main Event
520861	1989	Sharing Begins In The Heart
523526	1990	I'm A PRECIOUS MOMENTS Fan
525049	1990	Good Friends Are Forever (Rosebud Understamp)
527122	1991	You Can Always Bring A Friend
527319	1992	An Event Worth Wading For

CHRISTMAS BLESSINGS PLATE SERIES   (Dated)

523801	1990	Wishing You A Yummy Christmas
523860	1991	Blessings From Me To Thee
527742	1992	But The Greatest Of These Is Love

CHAPEL WINDOW COLLECTION - BEATITUDE SERIES   (Announced Series of 7)

523437	1992	Blessed Are The Humble
523380	1992	Blessed Are The Ones Who Mourn

QUICK REFERENCE OUTLINE OF THE ANNUALS CONTINUED

MASTERPIECE ORNAMENT SERIES   (Dated)

523062	1989	Peace On Earth
523704	1990	May Your Christmas Be A Happy Home
526940	1991	May Your Christmas Be Merry
527734	1992	But The Greatest Of These Is Love

ANNUAL FIGURINES   (Dated)

E-5383	1984	Wishing You A Merry Christmas
15539	1985	Baby's First Christmas (Boy)
15547	1985	Baby's First Christmas (Girl)
15881	1985	God Sent His Love
102342	1986	Wishing You A Cozy Christmas
110930	1987	Love Is The Best Gift Of All
115339	1988	Time To Wish You A Merry Christmas
522546	1989	Oh Holy Night
523836	1990	Once Upon A Holy Night
524166	1991	May Your Christmas Be Merry
527688	1992	But The Greatest Of These Is Love

ANNUAL BELLS   (Dated)

E-5622	1981	Let The Heavens Rejoice
E-2358	1982	I'll Play My Drum For Him
E-0522	1983	Surrounded With Joy
E-5393	1984	Wishing You A Merry Christmas
15873	1985	God Sent His Love
102318	1986	Wishing You A Cozy Christmas
109835	1987	Love Is The Best Gift Of All
115304	1988	Time To Wish You A Merry Christmas
522821	1989	Oh Holy Night
523828	1990	Once Upon A Holy Night
524182	1991	May Your Christmas Be Merry
527726	1992	But The Greatest Of These Is Love

ANNUAL ORNAMENTS   (Dated)

E-5629	1981	Let The Heavens Rejoice
E-2359	1982	I'll Play My Drum For Him
E-0513	1983	Surround Us With Joy
E-5387	1984	Wishing You A Merry Christmas
15768	1985	God Sent His Love
102326	1986	Wishing You A Cozy Christmas
109770	1987	Love Is The Best Gift Of All
115320	1988	Time To Wish You A Merry Christmas
520276	1988	You Are My Gift Come True
522848	1989	Oh Holy Night
523852	1990	Once Upon A Holy Night
524174	1991	May Your Christmas Be Merry
527696	1992	But The Greatest Of These Is Love

ANNUAL BABY'S FIRST CHRISTMAS ORNAMENTS – UNISEX   (Dated)

E-0518	1983	Blessed Are The Pure In Heart
E-5392	1984	Blessed Are The Pure In Heart

QUICK REFERENCE OUTLINE OF THE ANNUALS CONTINUED

ANNUAL BABY'S FIRST CHRISTMAS ORNAMENTS – GIRL   (Dated)

15911	1985	Baby's First Christmas
102504	1986	Baby's First Christmas
109401	1987	Baby's First Christmas
520241	1988	Baby's First Christmas
523208	1989	Baby's First Christmas
523771	1990	Baby's First Christmas
527092	1991	Baby's First Christmas
527475	1992	Baby's First Christmas

ANNUAL BABY'S FIRST CHRISTMAS ORNAMENTS – BOY   (Dated)

15903	1985	Baby's First Christmas
102512	1986	Baby's First Christmas
109428	1987	Baby's First Christmas
115282	1988	Baby's First Christmas
523194	1989	Baby's First Christmas
523798	1990	Baby's First Christmas
527084	1991	Baby's First Christmas
527483	1992	Baby's First Christmas

ANNUAL OUR FIRST CHRISTMAS TOGETHER ORNAMENTS   (Dated)

102350	1986	Our First Christmas Together
112399	1987	Our First Christmas Together
520233	1988	Our First Christmas Together
521558	1989	Our First Christmas Together
525324	1990	Our First Christmas Together
522945	1991	Our First Christmas Together
528870	1992	Our First Christmas Together

BIRTHDAY COLLECTION ANNUAL ORNAMENTS   (Dated)

102466	1986	Reindeer
104515	1987	Bear The Good News Of Christmas
520292	1988	Hang On For The Holly Days
520462	1989	Christmas Is Ruff Without You
520497	1990	Wishing You A Purr-fect Holiday
520438	1991	Sno-Bunny Falls For You Like I Do
520411	1992	I'm Nuts About You

ANNUAL THIMBLES   (Dated)

15865	1985	God Sent His Love
102334	1986	Wishing You A Cozy Christmas
109843	1987	Love Is The Best Gift Of All
115312	1988	Time To Wish You A Merry Christmas
522554	1989	Oh Holy Night
523844	1990	Once Upon A Holy Night
524190	1991	May Your Christmas Be Merry
527718	1992	But The Greatest Of These Is Love

ANNUAL EGGS   (Dated)

523534	1991	I Will Cherish The Old Rugged Cross
525960	1992	We Are God's Workmanship

QUICK REFERENCE OUTLINE OF THE SERIES

(✔ indicates a completed series)

✔MOTHER'S LOVE PLATE SERIES   (Series of 4, Individually Numbered)
E-5217	Mother Sew Dear
E-7173	The Purr-Fect Grandma
E-9256	The Hand That Rocks The Future
E-2848	Loving Thy Neighbor

✔INSPIRED THOUGHTS PLATE SERIES   (Series of 4, Individually Numbered)
E-5215	Love One Another
E-7174	Make A Joyful Noise
E-9257	I Believe In Miracles
E-2847	Love Is Kind

✔CHRISTMAS COLLECTION PLATE SERIES   (Series of 4, Individually Numbered)
E-5646	Come Let Us Adore Him
E-2347	Let Heaven And Nature Sing
E-0538	Wee Three Kings
E-5395	Unto Us A Child Is Born

✔BRIDAL SERIES   (Series of 8)
E-2831	Bridesmaid
E-2836	Groomsman
E-2835	Flower Girl
E-2833	Ringbearer
E-2845	Junior Bridesmaid
E-2837	Groom
E-2846	Bride
E-2838	This Is The Day Which The Lord Hath Made

✔HEAVENLY HALOS SERIES   (Series of 4)
E-9260	God's Promises Are Sure
E-9274	Taste And See That The Lord Is Good
E-9288	Sending You A Rainbow
E-9289	Trust In The Lord

✔CLOWN SERIES   (Series of 4)
12262	I Get A Bang Out Of You
12459	Waddle I Do Without You
12467	The Lord Will Carry You Through
12270	Lord Keep Me On The Ball

✔REJOICE IN THE LORD BAND SERIES   (Series of 6)
12165	Lord, Keep My Life In Tune
12173	There's A Song In My Heart
12378	Happiness Is The Lord
12386	Lord Give Me A Song
12394	He Is My Song
12580	Lord, Keep My Life In Tune

✓CALENDAR GIRL SERIES   (Series of 12)
109983   January Girl
109991   February Girl
110019   March Girl
110027   April Girl
110035   May Girl
110043   June Girl
110051   July Girl
110078   August Girl
110086   September Girl
110094   October Girl
110108   November Girl
110116   December Girl

✓BLESS THOSE WHO SERVE THEIR COUNTRY   (Series of 6)
526568   Navy
526576   Army
526584   Air Force
527521   Marines
527289   Girl Soldier
527297   African-American Soldier

"BABY'S FIRST" SERIES   (Announced Series of 8)
E-2840   Baby's First Step
E-2841   Baby's First Picture
12211   Baby's First Haircut
16012   Baby's First Trip
520705   Baby's First Pet
524077   Baby's First Meal
527238   Baby's First Word

THE FAMILY CHRISTMAS SCENE SERIES
15776   May You Have The Sweetest Christmas
15784   The Story Of God's Love
15792   Tell Me A Story
15806   God Gave His Best
15814   Silent Night
522856   Have A Beary Merry Christmas
524883   Christmas Fireplace

THE BIRTHDAY CIRCUS TRAIN SERIES
15938   May Your Birthday Be Warm (Baby)
15946   Happy Birthday Little Lamb (Age 1)
15962   God Bless You On Your Birthday (Age 2)
15954   Heaven Bless Your Special Day (Age 3)
15970   May Your Birthday Be Gigantic (Age 4)
15989   This Day Is Something To Roar About (Age 5)
15997   Keep Looking Up (Age 6)
109479   Wishing You Grrr-eatness (Age 7)
109460   Isn't Eight Just Great (Age 8)
521833   Being Nine Is Just Divine (Age 9)
521825   May Your Birthday Be Mammoth (Age 10)
16004   Bless The Days Of Our Youth

THE CLUBS

"Symbols of Membership" are received with enrollment in the Club. Charter members who renew receive "Symbols of Charter Membership." All members have the option to purchase "Membership Pieces" that are crafted exclusively for Club Members.

The Enesco PRECIOUS MOMENTS Collectors' Club is on a calendar year basis. Collectors renewing or joining by December 31 receive that year's Symbol of Membership. Order forms for the Membership Pieces must be taken to an authorized Enesco PRECIOUS MOMENTS Retailer by March 31 of the following year.

The Enesco PRECIOUS MOMENTS Birthday Club's year runs from July 1 to June 30. Order forms for the Membership Pieces must be redeemed by September 30.

Currently The Enesco PRECIOUS MOMENTS Collectors' Club membership fees are: new one year $25.00, new two year $48.00, one year renewal $22.50, and two year renewal $43.00. The Enesco PRECIOUS MOMENTS Birthday Club membership fees are: new one year $16.00, new two year $29.00, and one year renewal $15.00.

THE ENESCO PRECIOUS MOMENTS BIRTHDAY CLUB

SYMBOLS OF CHARTER MEMBERSHIP

B-0001	1986	Our Club Can't Be Beat
B-0102	1987	A Smile's The Cymbal Of Joy
B-0103	1988	The Sweetest Club Around
B-0104	1989	Have A Beary Special Birthday
B-0105	1990	Our Club Is A Tough Act To Follow
B-0106	1991	Jest To Let You Know You're Tops
B-0107	1992	All Aboard For Birthday Club Fun

SYMBOLS OF MEMBERSHIP

B-0002	1987	A Smile's The Cymbal Of Joy
B-0003	1988	The Sweetest Club Around
B-0004	1989	Have A Beary Special Birthday
B-0005	1990	Our Club Is A Tough Act To Follow
B-0006	1991	Jest To Let You Know You're Tops
B-0007	1992	All Aboard For Birthday Club Fun

MEMBERSHIP PIECES

BC-861	Fishing For Friends
BC-871	Hi Sugar!
BC-881	Somebunny Cares
BC-891	Can't Bee Hive Myself Without You
BC-901	Collecting Makes Good Scents
BC-902	I'm Nuts Over My Collection
BC-911	Love Pacifies
BC-912	True Blue Friends

THE ENESCO PRECIOUS MOMENTS COLLECTORS' CLUB

SYMBOLS OF CHARTER MEMBERSHIP

E-0001	1981	But Love Goes On Forever
E-0102	1982	But Love Goes On Forever
E-0103	1983	Let Us Call The Club To Order
E-0104	1984	Join In On The Blessings
E-0105	1985	Seek And Ye Shall Find
E-0106	1986	Birds Of A Feather Collect Together
E-0107	1987	Sharing Is Universal
E-0108	1988	A Growing Love
C-0109	1989	Always Room For One More
C-0110	1990	My Happiness
C-0111	1991	Sharing The Good News Together
C-0112	1992	The Club That's Out Of This World

SYMBOLS OF MEMBERSHIP

E-0202	1982	But Love Goes On Forever
E-0303	1983	Let Us Call The Club To Order
E-0404	1984	Join In On The Blessings
E-0005	1985	Seek And Ye Shall Find
E-0006	1986	Birds Of A Feather Collect Together
E-0007	1987	Sharing Is Universal
E-0008	1988	A Growing Love
C-0009	1989	Always Room For One More
C-0010	1990	My Happiness
C-0011	1991	Sharing The Good News Together
C-0012	1992	The Club That's Out Of This World

COMMEMORATIVE MEMBERSHIP PIECES

12440	God Bless Our Years Together
527386	This Land Is Our Land

MEMBERSHIP PIECES

PM-811	Hello Lord, It's Me Again
PM-821	Smile, God Loves You
PM-822	Put On A Happy Face
PM-831	Dawn's Early Light
PM-841	God's Ray Of Mercy
PM-842	Trust In The Lord To The Finish
PM-851	The Lord Is My Shepherd
PM-852	I Love To Tell The Story
PM-861	Grandma's Prayer
PM-862	I'm Following Jesus
PM-871	Feed My Sheep
PM-872	In His Time
PM-873	Loving You Dear Valentine
PM-874	Loving You Dear Valentine
PM-881	God Bless You For Touching My Life
PM-882	You Just Cannot Chuck A Good Friendship
PM-890	Beatitude Ornament Series (Set of 7)
PM-891	You Will Always Be My Choice
PM-892	Mow Power To Ya
PM-901	Ten Years And Still Going Strong
PM-902	You Are A Blessing To Me
PM-911	One Step At A Time
PM-912	Lord Keep Me In Teepee Top Shape
PM-921	Only Love Can Make A Home

SHARING SEASON ORNAMENTS

PM-864	1986	Birds Of A Feather Collect Together
PM-009	1987	Sharing Season Ornament
520349	1988	A Growing Love
522961	1989	Always Room For One More
PM-904	1990	My Happiness
PM-037	1991	Sharing The Good News Together

Individually, the seven Beatitude Ornaments are:

PM-190	Blessed are the Poor in Spirit, for Theirs is The Kingdom of Heaven
PM-290	Blessed are They that Mourn, for They Shall be Comforted
PM-390	Blessed are the Meek, for They Shall Inherit the Earth
PM-490	Blessed are They that Hunger and Thirst for Righteousness, for They Shall be Filled
PM-590	Blessed are the Merciful, for They Shall Obtain Mercy
PM-690	Blessed are the Pure in Heart, for They Shall See God
PM-790	Blessed are the Peacemakers, for they will be Called Sons of God

QUICK REFERENCE CALENDAR

	1981	1982
R E T I R E D	E-1378 God Loveth A Cheerful Giver E-2011 Come Let Us Adore Him	E-1374B Praise The Lord Anyhow
S U S P E N D E D		
A N N U A L S	E-5622 Let The Heavens Rejoice E-5629 Let The Heavens Rejoice	E-2357 I'll Play My Drum For Him E-2358 I'll Play My Drum For Him E-2359 I'll Play My Drum For Him

	1983		1984	

RETIRED

	1983		1984	
	E-3112	God's Speed	E-1373B	Smile, God Loves You
	E-3118	Eggs Over Easy	E-1380G	His Burden Is Light
			E-1380B	O, How I Love Jesus
			E-2368	The First Noel
			E-2806	Christmas Is A Time To Share
			E-5211	God Understands
			E-6120	We Have Seen His Star

SUSPENDED

			1984	
			E-1375B	Prayer Changes Things
			E-1377A	He Leadeth Me
			E-1377B	He Careth For You
			E-1379A	Love Is Kind
			E-1379B	God Understands
			E-1381	Jesus Is The Answer
			E-2010	We Have Seen His Star
			E-2012	Jesus Is Born
			E-2013	Unto Us A Child Is Born
			E-2345	May Your Christmas Be Cozy
			E-2350	Dropping In For Christmas
			E-2352	O Come All Ye Faithful
			E-2355	I'll Play My Drum For Him
			E-2365	The First Noel
			E-2366	The First Noel
			E-2367	The First Noel
			E-2381	Mouse with Cheese
			E-2386	Camel, Donkey, Cow Ornaments
			E-2801	Jesus Is Born
			E-2802	Christmas Is The Time To Share
			E-2803	Crown Him Lord Of All
			E-2804	Peace On Earth
			E-2807	Crown Him Lord Of All
			E-2808	Unto Us A Child Is Born
			E-3105	He Watches Over Us All
			E-3108	The Hand That Rocks The Future
			E-3119	It's What's Inside That Counts
			E-4723	Peace Amid The Storm
			E-4725	Peace On Earth
			E-4726	Peace On Earth
			E-5200	Bear Ye One Another's Burdens
			E-5201	Love Lifted Me
			E-5202	Thank You For Coming To My Ade
			E-5203	Let Not The Sun Go Down Upon Your Wrath
			E-5207	My Guardian Angel
			E-5210	Prayer Changes Things
			E-5214	Prayer Changes Things
			E-5623	Jesus Is Born
			E-5633	Come Let Us Adore Him
			E-5634	Wee Three Kings
			E-7155	Thanking Him For You
			E-7161	His Sheep Am I
			E-7162	Love Is Sharing
			E-7163	God Is Watching Over You
			E-7164	Bless This House
			E-7168	My Guardian Angel
			E-7169	My Guardian Angel
			E-9275	Jesus Loves Me
			E-9276	Jesus Loves Me
			E-9283A	Forever Friends - Dog
			E-9283B	Forever Friends - Cat

ANNUALS

	1983		1984	
	E-0505	Christmastime Is For Sharing	E-5383	Wishing You A Merry Christmas
	E-0513	Surround Us With Joy	E-5387	Wishing You A Merry Christmas
	E-0518	Blessed Are The Pure In Heart	E-5392	Baby's First Christmas
	E-0522	Surrounded With Joy	E-5393	Wishing You A Merry Christmas
			E-5396	The Wonder Of Christmas

QUICK REFERENCE CALENDAR

	1985		1986	
R E T I R E D	E-2376	Dropping Over For Christmas	E-0519	Sharing Our Season Together
	E-2805	Wishing You A Season Filled With Joy	E-0532	Let Heaven And Nature Sing
			E-2353	O Come All Ye Faithful
	E-2850	Mother Sew Dear	E-2369	Dropping In For Christmas
	E-3107	Blessed Are The Peacemakers	E-2841	Baby's First Picture
	E-3111	Be Not Weary In Well Doing	E-7157	There Is Joy In Serving Jesus
	E-7185	Love Is Sharing	E-9274	Taste And See That The Lord Is Good
S U S P E N D E D	E-0526	He Upholdeth Those Who Call	E-0501	Sharing Our Season Together
	E-0537	Jesus Is The Light	E-0502	Jesus Is The Light That Shines
	E-2344	Joy To The World	E-0503	Blessings From My House To Yours
	E-2349	Tell Me The Story Of Jesus	E-0508	Prepare Ye The Way Of The Lord
	E-2356	I'll Play My Drum For Him	E-0520	Wee Three Kings
	E-2372	Baby's First Christmas	E-0531	O Come All Ye Faithful
	E-2377	Our First Christmas Together	E-0535	Love Is Patient
	E-2378	Our First Christmas Together	E-0536	Love Is Patient
	E-2809	Jesus Is Born	E-2361	Christmas Joy From Head To Toe
	E-4722	Love Cannot Break A True Friendship	E-2826	May Your Birthday Be A Blessing
	E-5205	My Guardian Angel	E-2827	I Get A Kick Out Of You
	E-5208	Jesus Loves Me	E-3120	To Thee With Love
	E-5209	Jesus Loves Me	E-5376	May Your Christmas Be Blessed
	E-5619	Come Let Us Adore Him	E-5380	A Monarch Is Born
	E-5620	We Have Seen His Star	E-5382	For God So Loved The World
	E-5627	But Love Goes On Forever	E-5385	Oh Worship The Lord
	E-5628	But Love Goes On Forever	E-5386	Oh Worship The Lord
	E-5630	Unto Us A Child Is Born	E-5389	Peace On Earth
	E-5631	Baby's First Christmas	E-5394	Wishing You A Merry Christmas
	E-5632	Baby's First Christmas	E-6901	Collection Plaque
	E-5639	Isn't He Wonderful	E-7153	God Is Love, Dear Valentine
	E-5640	Isn't He Wonderful	E-7154	God Is Love, Dear Valentine
	E-5641	They Followed The Star	E-7160	The Perfect Grandpa
	E-5642	Silent Knight	E-7186	Let The Whole World Know
	E-6214B	Mikey	E-7241	Mother Sew Dear
	E-6214G	Debbie	E-9261	Seek Ye The Lord
	E-7156	I Believe In Miracles	E-9262	Seek Ye The Lord
	E-7159	Lord Give Me Patience	E-9287	Peace On Earth
	E-7167	The Lord Bless You And Keep You	E-9288	Sending You A Rainbow
	E-7170	Jesus Loves Me	12203	Get Into The Habit Of Prayer
	E-7171	Jesus Loves Me	12343	Jesus Is Coming Soon
	E-7172	Rejoicing With You	12424	Aaron
	E-7175	The Lord Bless You And Keep You	12432	Bethany
	E-7176	The Lord Bless You And Keep You	12475	P.D.
	E-9251	Love Is Patient	12483	Trish
	E-9253	The End Is In Sight		
	E-9263	How Can Two Walk Together Except They Agree		
	E-9280	Jesus Loves Me		
	E-9281	Jesus Loves Me		
	E-9285	If God Be For Us, Who Can Be Against Us		
A N N U A L S			12084	Autumn's Praise*
			12092	Winter's Song*
			12122	Autumn's Praise*
	12068	The Voice Of Spring*	12130	Winter's Song*
	12076	Summer's Joy*	100641	Four Seasons Thimbles*
	12106	The Voice Of Spring*	102938	God Bless America*
	12114	Summer's Joy*		
			101834	I'm Sending You A White Christmas
	15237	Tell Me The Story Of Jesus	102318	Wishing You A Cozy Christmas
	15539	Baby's First Christmas	102326	Wishing You A Cozy Christmas
	15547	Baby's First Christmas	102334	Wishing You A Cozy Christmas
	15768	God Sent His Love	102342	Wishing You A Cozy Christmas
	15865	God Sent His Love	102350	Our First Christmas Together
	15873	God Sent His Love	102466	Reindeer Ornament
	15881	God Sent His Love	102504	Baby's First Christmas
	15903	Baby's First Christmas	102512	Baby's First Christmas
	15911	Baby's First Christmas		
	*Not Dated		*Not Dated	

	1987		1988

RETIRED

1987		1988	
E-0530	His Eye Is On The Sparrow	E-1373G	Jesus Is The Light
E-2351	Holy Smokes	E-2371	Unicorn
E-5377	Love Is Kind	E-2822	This Is Your Day To Shine
E-5388	Joy To The World	E-5645	Rejoice O Earth
E-9273	Let Love Reign	12467	The Lord Will Carry You Through
		100129	Lord Keep Me On My Toes

SUSPENDED

1987		1988	
E-0507	God Sent His Son	E-0515	To A Special Dad
E-0509	Bringing God's Blessing To You	E-0533	Tell Me The Story Of Jesus
E-0521	Blessed Are The Pure In Heart	E-0539	Katie Lynne
E-2823	To God Be The Glory	E-2343	Joy To The World
E-4720	The Lord Bless You And Keep You	E-2348	May Your Christmas Be Warm
E-5216	The Lord Bless You And Keep You	E-2362	Baby's First Christmas
E-5381	His Name Is Jesus	E-2840	Baby's First Step
E-6613	God Sends The Gift Of His Love	E-5206	My Guardian Angel
E-7165	Let The Whole World Know	E-6118	But Love Goes On Forever
E-7177	The Lord Bless You And Keep You	E-7181	Mother Sew Dear
E-7178	The Lord Bless You And Keep You	E-7183	The Purr-fect Grandma
E-9260	God's Promises Are Sure	E-7242	The Purr-fect Grandma
E-9289	Trust In The Lord	E-9266	I'm Falling For Somebunny
12017	Loving You	E-9266	Our Love Is Heaven Scent
12025	Loving You	12335	You Can Fly
12033	God's Precious Gift	12351	Halo, And Merry Christmas
12211	Baby's First Haircut	100021	To My Favorite Paw
12297	It Is Better To Give Than To Receive	100668	Clown Thimbles
12408	We Saw A Star	102431	Serve With A Smile
		102458	Serve With A Smile
		102490	Sharing Our Christmas Together

ANNUALS

1987		1988	
E-2838	This Is The Day Which The Lord Hath Made*	114022	The Good Lord Blessed Us Tenfold*
100536	I Picked A Very Special Mom*	115231	You Are My Main Event*
102903	We Are All Precious In His Sight*	115479	Blessed Are They That Overcome*
107999	He Walks With Me*		
		115282	Baby's First Christmas
102954	My Peace I Give Unto Thee	115304	Time To Wish You A Merry Christmas
104515	Bear The Good News Of Christmas	115312	Time To Wish You A Merry Christmas
109401	Baby's First Christmas	115320	Time To Wish You A Merry Christmas
109428	Baby's First Christmas	115339	Time To Wish You A Merry Christmas
109770	Love Is The Best Gift Of All	520233	Our First Christmas Together
109835	Love Is The Best Gift Of All	520241	Baby's First Christmas
109843	Love Is The Best Gift Of All	520276	You Are My Gift Come True
110930	Love Is The Best Gift Of All	520284	Merry Christmas, Deer
112399	Our First Christmas Together	520292	Hang On For The Holly Days
*Not Dated		*Not Dated	

QUICK REFERENCE CALENDAR

1989

RETIRED

E-0506	Surrounded With Joy
E-0525	You Can't Run Away From God
E-0534	To Thee With Love
12459	Waddle I Do Without You
15504	God Sent You Just In Time
100269	Help Lord, I'm In A Spot

SUSPENDED

E-2346	Let Heaven And Nature Sing
E-2364	Goat
E-2851	Kristy
E-5213	God Is Love
E-5378	Joy To The World
E-5390	May God Bless You With A Perfect Holiday Season
E-5391	Love Is Kind
E-9252	Forgiving Is Forgetting
12149	Part Of Me Wants To Be Good
12165	Lord, Keep My Life In Tune
15822	May Your Christmas Be Happy
15830	Happiness Is The Lord
16012	Baby's First Trip
16020	God Bless You With Rainbows
100544	Brotherly Love
100625	God Is Love, Dear Valentine
102415	It's A Perfect Boy
102962	It's The Birthday Of A King

ANNUALS

520861	Sharing Begins In The Heart*
522376	His Love Will Shine On You*
520462	Christmas Is Ruff Without You
521558	Our First Christmas Together
522546	Oh Holy Night
522554	Oh Holy Night
522821	Oh Holy Night
522848	Oh Holy Night
523003	May Your Christmas Be A Happy Home
523062	Peace On Earth
523194	Baby's First Christmas
523208	Baby's First Christmas

*Not Dated

1990

RETIRED

E-0504	Christmastime Is For Sharing
E-9268	Nobody's Perfect!
100102	Make Me A Blessing
102423	Lord, Keep Me On My Toes
520772	Many Moons In Same Canoe, Blessum You

SUSPENDED

E-0512	It's A Perfect Boy
E-0517	The Perfect Grandpa
E-9259	We're In It Together
E-9282A	To Somebunny Special
E-9282B	You're Worth Your Weight In Gold
E-9282C	Especially For Ewe
12157	This Is The Day The Lord Has Made
12173	There's A Song In My Heart
12254	Love Covers All
12378	Happiness Is The Lord
12386	Lord Give Me A Song
12394	He Is My Song
12580	Lord Keep My Life In Tune
100145	God Bless The Day We Found You
100153	God Bless The Day We Found You
100161	Serving The Lord
100293	Serving The Lord
104027	Love Is The Glue That Mends
104396	Happy Days Are Here Again
104825	Sitting Pretty
105813	To Tell The Tooth You're Special
106216	Lord Help Me Make The Grade
111120	I'm A Possibility

ANNUALS

523526	I'm A PRECIOUS MOMENTS Fan*
524522	Always In His Care*
525049	Good Friends Are Forever*
525057	Bundles Of Joy*
617334	Rejoice O Earth*
520497	Wishing You A Purr-fect Holiday
523704	May Your Christmas Be A Happy Home
523771	Baby's First Christmas
523798	Baby's First Christmas
523801	Wishing You A Yummy Christmas
523828	Once Upon A Holy Night
523836	Once Upon A Holy Night
523844	Once Upon A Holy Night
523852	Once Upon A Holy Night
525324	Our First Christmas Together

*Not Dated

	1991		1992

RETIRED

	1991	1992
E-2375	Dropping Over For Christmas	
100196	The Spirit Is Willing But The Flesh Is Weak	
100528	Scent From Above	
101842	Smile Along The Way	
113980	Rejoice O Earth	
520640	I'm So Glad You Fluttered Into My Life	

1992 Retired:
- E-7156 — I Believe In Miracles
- E-7156R — I Believe In Miracles
- 101850 — Lord, Help Us Keep Our Act Together

SUSPENDED (1991)

E-2385	Our First Christmas Together
E-2834	Sharing Our Joy Together
E-3104	Blessed Are The Pure In Heart
E-5397	Timmy
E-9267	Animal Collection
E-9267A	Teddy Bear
E-9267B	Dog
E-9267C	Bunny
E-9267D	Cat
E-9267E	Lamb
E-9267F	Pig
12009	Love Covers All
100056	Sending My Love
100633	The Lord Bless You And Keep You
102474	Rocking Horse
105635	Have I Got News For You
105643	Something's Missing When You're Not Around
106151	We're Pulling For You
109487	Believe The Impossible
111333	O Come Let Us Adore Him
113972	God Sent You Just In Time
113999	Cheers To The Leader
114006	My Love Will Never Let You Go
115290	Our First Christmas Together
520802	My Days Are Blue Without You
520810	We Need A Good Friend Through The Ruff Times
520853	I Belong To The Lord
521868	The Greatest Of These Is Love

ANNUALS

1991

524263	HE Loves Me*
527114	Sharing A Gift Of Love*
527122	You Can Always Bring A Friend*
520438	Sno-Bunny Falls For You Like I Do
522945	Our First Christmas Together
523534	I Will Cherish The Old Rugged Cross
523860	Blessings From Me To Thee
524166	May Your Christmas Be Merry
524174	May Your Christmas Be Merry
524182	May Your Christmas Be Merry
524190	May Your Christmas Be Merry
526940	May Your Christmas Be Merry
527084	Baby's First Christmas
527092	Baby's First Christmas

*Not Dated

1992

523380	Blessed Are The Ones Who Mourn*
523437	Blessed Are The Humble*
526185	You Are My Happiness*
527173	A Universal Love*
527319	An Event Worth Wading For*
527564	God Bless The USA*
527777	This Land Is Our Land*
520411	I'm Nuts About You
525960	We Are God's Workmanship
527475	Baby's First Christmas
527483	Baby's First Christmas
527688	But The Greatest Of These Is Love
527696	But The Greatest Of These Is Love
527718	But The Greatest Of These Is Love
527726	But The Greatest Of These Is Love
527734	But The Greatest Of These Is Love
527742	But The Greatest Of These Is Love
528870	Our First Christmas Together

*Not Dated

HOW TO READ A GREENBOOK LISTING

GREENBOOK Listings are in Enesco Item Number order.

Enesco PRECIOUS MOMENTS Collectors' Club and Enesco PRECIOUS MOMENTS Birthday Club pieces are in separate sections at the end of the Listings.

Enesco Item Numbers can be found on the understamp of most pieces produced from 1982 to the present.

If you don't know the Enesco Item Number, but you do know the Inspirational Title, use the ALPHA-LOG to obtain the Enesco Item Number. If you don't know the Enesco Item Number or the Inspirational Title, use the ART CHART to obtain the Enesco Item Number.

The following is a step-by-step explanation of how to read a GREENBOOK listing using the figurine E-1374B, *Praise The Lord Anyhow*, as an example:

PRAISE THE LORD ANYHOW		Figurine	One of the "Original 21"					
E-1374B	79	Boy with Dog and	UPP	$ 8.00	5.00"	NM	Retired/Sec	$115.00
(19)	81	Ice Cream Cone	UPP	8.00		TRI	Retired/Sec	90.00
	82		UPP	17.00		HRG	Retired/Sec	75.00

Variations exist in the color of the dog's nose and the flavor of ice cream.

This portion of a listing is the **INSPIRATIONAL TITLE**.

PRAISE THE LORD ANYHOW		Figurine	One of the "Original 21"					
E-1374B	79	Boy with Dog and	UPP	$ 8.00	5.00"	NM	Retired/Sec	$115.00
(19)	81	Ice Cream Cone	UPP	8.00		TRI	Retired/Sec	90.00
	82		UPP	17.00		HRG	Retired/Sec	75.00

Variations exist in the color of the dog's nose and the flavor of ice cream.

This portion of a listing is the **TYPE OF PRODUCT**.

PRAISE THE LORD ANYHOW		Figurine	One of the "Original 21"					
E-1374B	79	Boy with Dog and	UPP	$ 8.00	5.00"	NM	Retired/Sec	$115.00
(19)	81	Ice Cream Cone	UPP	8.00		TRI	Retired/Sec	90.00
	82		UPP	17.00		HRG	Retired/Sec	75.00

Variations exist in the color of the dog's nose and the flavor of ice cream.

This portion of a listing is reserved for **ADDITIONAL INFORMATION**. For example, if the piece is one of the "Original 21" that will be noted here. Other information appearing here includes series or set information, if a piece is dated, the tune if it's a musical, if it has a certificate, if it's individually numbered, or if the piece is a Nativity Addition.

PRAISE THE LORD ANYHOW   Figurine   One of the "Original 21"

E-1374B	79	Boy with Dog and	UPP	$ 8.00	5.00"	NM	Retired/Sec	$115.00
(19)	81	Ice Cream Cone	UPP	8.00		TRI	Retired/Sec	90.00
	82		UPP	17.00		HRG	Retired/Sec	75.00

Variations exist in the color of the dog's nose and the flavor of ice cream.

This portion of a listing is the **ENESCO ITEM NUMBER**. It appears in brochures, catalogs, ads, and on the understamp of most pieces produced from 1982 to the present. It is a quick and *absolute* means of identification.

PRAISE THE LORD ANYHOW   Figurine   One of the "Original 21"

E-1374B	79	Boy with Dog and	UPP	$ 8.00	5.00"	NM	Retired/Sec	$115.00
(19)	81	Ice Cream Cone	UPP	8.00		TRI	Retired/Sec	90.00
	82		UPP	17.00		HRG	Retired/Sec	75.00

Variations exist in the color of the dog's nose and the flavor of ice cream.

This portion of a listing is the **GREENBOOK ART CHART NUMBER**.

PRAISE THE LORD ANYHOW   Figurine   One of the "Original 21"

E-1374B	79	Boy with Dog and	UPP	$ 8.00	5.00"	NM	Retired/Sec	$115.00
(19)	81	Ice Cream Cone	UPP	8.00		TRI	Retired/Sec	90.00
	82		UPP	17.00		HRG	Retired/Sec	75.00

Variations exist in the color of the dog's nose and the flavor of ice cream.

This portion of a listing is the **YEAR OF ISSUE**. The GREENBOOK lists the year of issue for each change in annual symbol. A very common error made by collectors is to mistake the copyright date for the year of issue because the copyright date appears on the understamp written out as © 19XX. *In other words, in order to determine what year your piece was produced, you must refer to the annual symbol, not the © date.*

PRAISE THE LORD ANYHOW   Figurine   One of the "Original 21"

E-1374B	79	Boy with Dog and	UPP	$ 8.00	5.00"	NM	Retired/Sec	$115.00
(19)	81	Ice Cream Cone	UPP	8.00		TRI	Retired/Sec	90.00
	82		UPP	17.00		HRG	Retired/Sec	75.00

Variations exist in the color of the dog's nose and the flavor of ice cream.

This portion of a listing is the **DESCRIPTIVE TITLE**.

PRAISE THE LORD ANYHOW   Figurine   One of the "Original 21"

E-1374B	79	Boy with Dog and	UPP	$ 8.00	5.00"	NM	Retired/Sec	$115.00
(19)	81	Ice Cream Cone	UPP	8.00		TRI	Retired/Sec	90.00
	82		UPP	17.00		HRG	Retired/Sec	75.00

Variations exist in the color of the dog's nose and the flavor of ice cream.

This portion of a listing is the **EDITION SIZE**. Editions are either limited or open (unlimited). The GREENBOOK identifies editions that are limited in one of five ways. They are: 1) A Specific Number - i.e. 15,000, 2) By Year (Annual), 3) Two-Year Collectible (2yr), 4) Available to Club Members Only (MemOnly), or 5) An Unspecified Production Period (UPP).

.....continued on next page

HOW TO READ A GREENBOOK LISTING CONTINUED

PRAISE THE LORD ANYHOW   Figurine   One of the "Original 21"

E-1374B	79	Boy with Dog and	UPP	$ 8.00	5.00"	NM	Retired/Sec	$115.00
(19)	81	Ice Cream Cone	UPP	8.00		TRI	Retired/Sec	90.00
	82		UPP	17.00		HRG	Retired/Sec	75.00

Variations exist in the color of the dog's nose and the flavor of ice cream.

This portion of a listing is the **ISSUE PRICE** (Suggested Retail Price). GREENBOOK Listings include issue prices for each piece when it was first introduced and for each year the annual symbol is/was changed.

PRAISE THE LORD ANYHOW   Figurine   One of the "Original 21"

E-1374B	79	Boy with Dog and	UPP	$ 8.00	5.00"	NM	Retired/Sec	$115.00
(19)	81	Ice Cream Cone	UPP	8.00		TRI	Retired/Sec	90.00
	82		UPP	17.00		HRG	Retired/Sec	75.00

Variations exist in the color of the dog's nose and the flavor of ice cream.

This portion of a listing is the **SIZE** in inches; diameter for plates and plaques, height for figurines, bells...

PRAISE THE LORD ANYHOW   Figurine   One of the "Original 21"

E-1374B	79	Boy with Dog and	UPP	$ 8.00	5.00"	NM	Retired/Sec	$115.00
(19)	81	Ice Cream Cone	UPP	8.00		TRI	Retired/Sec	90.00
	82		UPP	17.00		HRG	Retired/Sec	75.00

Variations exist in the color of the dog's nose and the flavor of ice cream.

This portion of a listing is the **ANNUAL SYMBOL**. Since mid-1981 Enesco has indicated when PRECIOUS MOMENTS collectibles were produced by including an annual symbol as part of the understamp. Pieces crafted prior to mid-1981 have no annual symbol and have become known as "No Marks."

The GREENBOOK defines "No Mark" as prior to mid-1981.

There are also "Unmarked" PRECIOUS MOMENTS collectibles. It was not until 1984 that some product types such as plates and ornaments were marked with an annual symbol. The GREENBOOK defines 1981, 1982, and 1983 pieces that fall into this category as "Unmarked." "Unmarked " pieces are designated as "UM" in the listings. (HINT: Most "Unmarked" pieces will have the Enesco Item Number on the understamp but not an Annual Symbol.)

An "Unmarked" piece can also be a production error. Some pieces simply miss getting marked.

The facing page illustrates the different symbols and their meanings.

.....continued on next page

ANNUAL SYMBOLS

Prior to 1981	"No Mark" (NM)		
1981	Triangle (TRI)		Symbol of the Triune - God, the Father, Son and Holy Spirit
1982	Hourglass (HRG)		Represents the time we have on earth to serve the Lord
1983	Fish (FSH)		Earliest symbol used by believers of the early apostolic church
1984	Cross (CRS)		Symbol of Christianity recognized worldwide
1985	Dove (DVE)		Symbol of love and peace
1986	Olive Branch (OLB)		Symbol of peace and understanding
1987	Cedar Tree (CED)		Symbol of strength, beauty, and preservation
1988	Flower (FLW)		Represents God's love toward His children
1989	Bow & Arrow (B&A)		Represents the power of the Bible
1990	Flame (FLM)		For those who have gone through the fire of life and found comfort in believing
1991	Vessel (VSL)		A reminder of God's love which flows through the vessel of life
1992	G-Clef (G/CL)		Symbolizes the harmony of God's Love
Special Symbols:	Diamond (DIA)	Easter Seal Lily	Rosebud '91 Flag (FLG) '92 Flag (FLG/*)

PRAISE THE LORD ANYHOW		Figurine		One of the "Original 21"					
E-1374B	79	Boy with Dog and		UPP	$ 8.00	5.00"	NM	Retired/Sec	$115.00
(19)	81	Ice Cream Cone		UPP	8.00		TRI	Retired/Sec	90.00
	82			UPP	17.00		HRG	Retired/Sec	75.00

Variations exist in the color of the dog's nose and the flavor of ice cream.

This portion of a listing is the **MARKET STATUS**. Enesco periodically retires and suspends individual pieces. As a result, GREENBOOK uses nine different classifications of availability or market status. They are:

PRIMARY   Piece available from retailers at issue price.

SECONDARY   Piece *not* generally available from retailers at issue price.

RETIRED/PRIMARY   Piece with specific Enesco Item Number will never be produced again. Piece still available from retailers at issue price.

RETIRED/SECONDARY   Piece with specific Enesco Item Number will never be produced again. Piece *not* generally available from retailers at issue price.

SUSPENDED/PRIMARY   Piece with specific Enesco Item Number not currently being produced but may be re-sculpted and re-introduced in the future. Piece still available from retailers at issue price.

SUSPENDED/SECONDARY   Piece with specific Enesco Item Number not currently being produced but may be re-sculpted and re-introduced in the future. Piece *not* generally available from retailers at issue price.

SUSPENDED/RETIRED/SECONDARY   Piece with specific Enesco Item Number was suspended, re-introduced, and subsequently retired. Piece *not* generally available from retailers at issue price.

DISCONTINUED/PRIMARY   Production ceased on piece with specific Enesco Item Number. Piece still available from retailers at issue price.

DISCONTINUED/SECONDARY   Production ceased on piece with specific Enesco Item Number. Piece *not* generally available from retailers at issue price.

PRAISE THE LORD ANYHOW		Figurine		One of the "Original 21"					
E-1374B	79	Boy with Dog and		UPP	$ 8.00	5.00"	NM	Retired/Sec	$115.00
(19)	81	Ice Cream Cone		UPP	8.00		TRI	Retired/Sec	90.00
	82			UPP	17.00		HRG	Retired/Sec	75.00

Variations exist in the color of the dog's nose and the flavor of ice cream.

This portion of a listing is the **GREENBOOK MARKET PRICE**. It reflects the current primary and secondary market prices for each piece. The prices reported *are not absolute* but are a reliable guide based on extensive experience in gathering information about market prices and how they are affected by market status as well as edition limits, year of issue, and popularity of the piece.

CHEAT SHEET

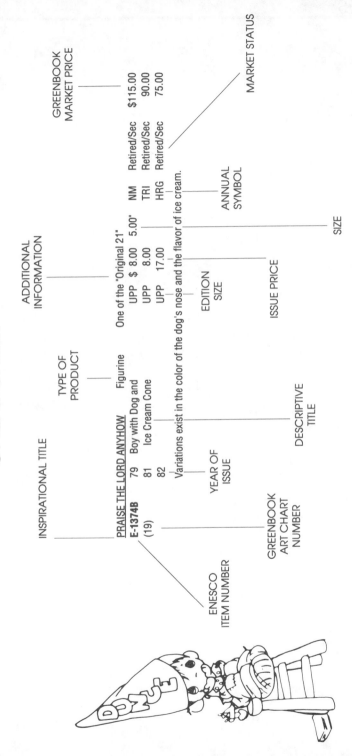

INSPIRATIONAL TITLE

TYPE OF PRODUCT

ADDITIONAL INFORMATION

GREENBOOK MARKET PRICE

MARKET STATUS

PRAISE THE LORD ANYHOW

E-1374B	79	Boy with Dog and	Figurine	One of the "Original 21"			
(19)	81	Ice Cream Cone		UPP $ 8.00	5.00"	NM	Retired/Sec	$115.00
	82			UPP 8.00		TRI	Retired/Sec	90.00
				UPP 17.00		HRG	Retired/Sec	75.00

Variations exist in the color of the dog's nose and the flavor of ice cream.

ANNUAL SYMBOL

SIZE

EDITION SIZE

ISSUE PRICE

DESCRIPTIVE TITLE

YEAR OF ISSUE

GREENBOOK ART CHART NUMBER

ENESCO ITEM NUMBER

NOTES

GREENBOOK LISTINGS

The GREENBOOK LISTINGS are where specific factual information as well as GREENBOOK Market Prices for each collectible can be found. GREENBOOK Listings are in Enesco Item Number order. The Enesco PRECIOUS MOMENTS Collectors' Club and The Enesco PRECIOUS MOMENTS Birthday Club pieces are in separate sections at the end of the Listings. Enesco Item Numbers can be found on the understamp of most pieces produced from 1982 to the present. If you don't know the Enesco Item Number, but you do know the Inspirational Title, use the ALPHA-LOG to obtain the Enesco Item Number. If you don't know the Enesco Item Number or the Inspirational Title, use the ART CHART to obtain the Enesco Item Number.

SHARING OUR SEASON TOGETHER		Figurine						
E-0501	83	Boy Pushing Girl on Sled	UPP	$50.00	4.90"	FSH	Susp/Sec	$145.00
(118)	84		UPP	50.00		CRS	Susp/Sec	130.00
	85		UPP	50.00		DVE	Susp/Sec	125.00
	86		UPP	50.00		OLB	Susp/Sec	120.00

JESUS IS THE LIGHT THAT SHINES		Figurine						
E-0502	83	Boy with Candle & Mouse	UPP	$22.50	5.25"	FSH	Susp/Sec	$60.00
(119)	84		UPP	23.00		CRS	Susp/Sec	52.00
	85		UPP	23.00		DVE	Susp/Sec	45.00
	86		UPP	23.00		OLB	Susp/Sec	45.00

BLESSINGS FROM MY HOUSE TO YOURS		Figurine						
E-0503	83	Girl in Snow Looking at	UPP	$27.00	5.80"	FSH	Susp/Sec	$75.00
(120)	84	Birdhouse	UPP	27.00		CRS	Susp/Sec	70.00
	85		UPP	27.00		DVE	Susp/Sec	65.00
	86		UPP	27.00		OLB	Susp/Sec	62.00

CHRISTMASTIME IS FOR SHARING		Figurine						
E-0504	83	Boy Giving Teddy to	UPP	$37.00	5.25"	FSH	Retired/Sec	$95.00
(121)	84	a Poor Boy	UPP	37.00		CRS	Retired/Sec	85.00
	85		UPP	37.00		DVE	Retired/Sec	85.00
	86		UPP	37.00		OLB	Retired/Sec	75.00
	87		UPP	37.00		CED	Retired/Sec	75.00
	88		UPP	40.00		FLW	Retired/Sec	70.00
	89		UPP	47.50		B&A	Retired/Sec	70.00
	90		UPP	50.00		FLM	Retired/Sec	65.00

CHRISTMASTIME IS FOR SHARING		Plate, Dated	Second Issue "Joy Of Christmas" Series					
E-0505	83	Boy Giving Teddy to	Annual	$40.00	8.50"	UM	Secondary	$90.00
(121)		a Poor Boy						

SURROUNDED WITH JOY		Figurine						
E-0506	83	Boy with Wreath	UPP	$21.00	4.15"	FSH	Retired/Sec	$80.00
(122)	84		UPP	21.00		CRS	Retired/Sec	65.00
	85		UPP	21.00		DVE	Retired/Sec	65.00
	86		UPP	21.00		OLB	Retired/Sec	60.00
	87		UPP	21.00		CED	Retired/Sec	60.00
	88		UPP	23.00		FLW	Retired/Sec	55.00
	89		UPP	27.50		B&A	Retired/Sec	55.00

GOD SENT HIS SON		Figurine						
E-0507	83	Girl Looking into Manger	UPP	$32.50	5.50"	FSH	Susp/Sec	$75.00
(123)	84		UPP	32.50		CRS	Susp/Sec	70.00
	85		UPP	32.50		DVE	Susp/Sec	70.00
	86		UPP	32.50		OLB	Susp/Sec	65.00
	87		UPP	32.50		CED	Susp/Sec	60.00

PREPARE YE THE WAY OF THE LORD		Figurine	6 Piece Set					
E-0508	83	Angels Preparing Manger	UPP	$75.00	5.75"	FSH	Susp/Sec	$120.00
(124)	84		UPP	75.00		CRS	Susp/Sec	110.00
	85		UPP	75.00		DVE	Susp/Sec	95.00
	86		UPP	75.00		OLB	Susp/Sec	95.00

BRINGING GOD'S BLESSING TO YOU		Figurine						
E-0509	83	Girl Angel Pushing Jesus	UPP	$35.00	5.50"	FSH	Susp/Sec	$75.00
(125)	84	in Buggy	UPP	35.00		CRS	Susp/Sec	70.00
	85		UPP	35.00		DVE	Susp/Sec	70.00
	86		UPP	35.00		OLB	Susp/Sec	65.00
	87		UPP	35.00		CED	Susp/Sec	60.00

TUBBY'S FIRST CHRISTMAS Figurine Nativity Addition

E-0511	83	Rooster & Bird on Pig	UPP	$12.00	3.25"	FSH	Secondary	$30.00
(126)	84		UPP	12.00		CRS	Secondary	25.00
	85		UPP	12.00		DVE	Secondary	20.00
	86		UPP	12.00		OLB	Secondary	16.50
	87		UPP	12.00		CED	Secondary	16.50
	88		UPP	13.50		FLW	Secondary	16.50
	89		UPP	15.00		B&A	Secondary	16.50
	90		UPP	16.50		FLM	Primary	16.50
	91		UPP	16.50		VSL	Primary	16.50
	92		OPEN	16.50		G/CL	Primary	16.50

IT'S A PERFECT BOY Figurine Nativity Addition

E-0512	83	Boy Angel with Red Cross	UPP	$18.50	4.75"	FSH	Susp/Sec	$55.00
(127)	84	Bag	UPP	18.50		CRS	Susp/Sec	50.00
	85		UPP	18.50		DVE	Susp/Sec	50.00
	86		UPP	18.50		OLB	Susp/Sec	45.00
	87		UPP	18.50		CED	Susp/Sec	40.00
	88		UPP	21.00		FLW	Susp/Sec	40.00
	89		UPP	25.00		B&A	Susp/Sec	40.00
	90		UPP	27.50		FLM	Susp/Sec	40.00

SURROUND US WITH JOY Ornament, Dated

E-0513	83	Boy with Wreath	Annual	$ 9.00	3.00"	FSH	Secondary	$60.00
(122)								

MOTHER SEW DEAR Ornament

E-0514	83	Mother Needlepointing	UPP	$ 9.00	3.00"	FSH	Secondary	$28.00
(30)	84		UPP	10.00		CRS	Secondary	22.00
	85		UPP	10.00		DVE	Secondary	18.00
	86		UPP	10.00		OLB	Secondary	15.00
	87		UPP	10.00		CED	Secondary	15.00
	88		UPP	11.00		FLW	Secondary	15.00
	89		UPP	13.50		B&A	Secondary	15.00
	90		UPP	15.00		FLM	Primary	15.00
	91		UPP	15.00		VSL	Primary	15.00
	92		OPEN	15.00		G/CL	Primary	15.00

TO A SPECIAL DAD Ornament

E-0515	83	Boy in Dad's Duds	UPP	$ 9.00	3.00"	FSH	Susp/Sec	$45.00
(59)	84		UPP	10.00		CRS	Susp/Sec	40.00
	85		UPP	10.00		DVE	Susp/Sec	38.00
	86		UPP	10.00		OLB	Susp/Sec	35.00
	87		UPP	10.00		CED	Susp/Sec	35.00
	88		UPP	11.00		FLW	Susp/Sec	35.00

THE PURR-FECT GRANDMA Ornament

E-0516	83	Grandma in Rocker	UPP	$ 9.00	3.00"	FSH	Secondary	$32.00
(33)	84		UPP	10.00		CRS	Secondary	25.00
	85		UPP	10.00		DVE	Secondary	18.00
	86		UPP	10.00		OLB	Secondary	15.00
	87		UPP	10.00		CED	Secondary	15.00
	88		UPP	11.00		FLW	Secondary	15.00
	89		UPP	13.50		B&A	Secondary	15.00
	90		UPP	15.00		FLM	Primary	15.00
	91		UPP	15.00		VSL	Primary	15.00
	92		OPEN	15.00		G/CL	Primary	15.00

THE PERFECT GRANDPA   Ornament

E-0517	83	Grandpa in Rocking Chair	UPP	$ 9.00	3.00"	FSH	Susp/Sec	$38.00
(109)	84		UPP	10.00		CRS	Susp/Sec	35.00
	85		UPP	10.00		DVE	Susp/Sec	32.00
	86		UPP	10.00		OLB	Susp/Sec	30.00
	87		UPP	10.00		CED	Susp/Sec	30.00
	88		UPP	11.00		FLW	Susp/Sec	25.00
	89		UPP	13.50		B&A	Susp/Sec	25.00
	90		UPP	15.00		FLM	Susp/Sec	25.00

BLESSED ARE THE PURE IN HEART   Ornament, Dated

E-0518	83	Baby in Cradle	Annual	$ 9.00	2.00"	FSH	Secondary	$40.00
(28)								

SHARING OUR SEASON TOGETHER   Musical   TUNE: Winter Wonderland

E-0519	83	Boy Pushing Girl on Sled	UPP	$70.00	6.00"	FSH	Retired/Sec	$150.00
(118)	84		UPP	70.00		CRS	Retired/Sec	135.00
	85		UPP	70.00		DVE	Retired/Sec	125.00
	86		UPP	70.00		OLB	Retired/Sec	115.00

WEE THREE KINGS   Musical   TUNE: We Three Kings

E-0520	83	Three Kings	UPP	$60.00	7.00"	FSH	Susp/Sec	$110.00
(66)	84		UPP	60.00		CRS	Susp/Sec	100.00
	85		UPP	60.00		DVE	Susp/Sec	95.00
	86		UPP	60.00		OLB	Susp/Sec	90.00

BLESSED ARE THE PURE IN HEART   Frame

E-0521	83	Baby in Cradle	UPP	$18.00	4.50"	FSH	Susp/Sec	$40.00
(28)	84		UPP	19.00		CRS	Susp/Sec	35.00
	85		UPP	19.00		DVE	Susp/Sec	30.00
	86		UPP	19.00		OLB	Susp/Sec	30.00
	87		UPP	19.00		CED	Susp/Sec	30.00

SURROUNDED WITH JOY   Bell, Dated

E-0522	83	Boy with Wreath	Annual	$18.00	5.15"	UM	Secondary	$65.00
(122)								

ONWARD CHRISTIAN SOLDIERS   Figurine

E-0523	*	Knight in Armor	UPP	$24.00	6.25"	UM	Secondary	$90.00
(128)	83		UPP	24.00		FSH	Secondary	55.00
	84		UPP	24.00		CRS	Secondary	42.00
	85		UPP	24.00		DVE	Secondary	40.00
	86		UPP	24.00		OLB	Secondary	35.00
	87		UPP	24.00		CED	Secondary	35.00
	88		UPP	30.00		FLW	Secondary	35.00
	89		UPP	33.00		B&A	Secondary	35.00
	90		UPP	35.00		FLM	Primary	35.00
	91		UPP	35.00		VSL	Primary	35.00
	92		OPEN	35.00		G/CL	Primary	35.00

* UNMARKED (UM) pieces could have been produced in any of the years of production.
Also exists with a DECAL FISH Annual Symbol.

YOU CAN'T RUN AWAY FROM GOD   Figurine

E-0525	83	Boy and Dog Running Away	UPP	$28.50	5.15"	HRG	Retired/Sec	$135.00
(129)	83		UPP	28.50		FSH	Retired/Sec	95.00
	84		UPP	28.50		CRS	Retired/Sec	80.00
	85		UPP	28.50		DVE	Retired/Sec	80.00
	86		UPP	28.50		OLB	Retired/Sec	75.00
	87		UPP	28.50		CED	Retired/Sec	70.00
	88		UPP	35.00		FLW	Retired/Sec	70.00
	89		UPP	38.50		B&A	Retired/Sec	70.00

Also exists with a DECAL FISH Annual Symbol.

HE UPHOLDETH THOSE WHO CALL — Figurine

E-0526 (130)								
E-0526	*	Angel Catching Skater	UPP	$35.00	5.15"	UM	Susp/Sec	$105.00
(130)	83		UPP	35.00		FSH	Susp/Sec	75.00
	84		UPP	35.00		CRS	Susp/Sec	68.00
	85		UPP	35.00		DVE	Susp/Sec	65.00

* UNMARKED (UM) pieces could have been produced in any of the years of production.
Also exists with a removable INKED FISH Annual Symbol.
Fall 1986 GOODNEWSLETTER announced Sam had wanted this piece to be titled "He Upholdeth Those Who **Fall**" and went on to say if/when the piece was brought back from Suspension the title would be changed to "...Fall." From that point on, in much of their written literature, Enesco began referring to the suspended figurine as "...Fall." This has confused many collectors. Thinking the understamp should say "...Fall," they presume their "...Call" piece is an error or variation. See 6th Edition, page 220.

HIS EYE IS ON THE SPARROW — Figurine

E-0530 (131)								
E-0530	83	Girl with Bird in Hand	UPP	$28.50	5.25"	FSH	Retired/Sec	$110.00
(131)	84		UPP	28.50		CRS	Retired/Sec	100.00
	85		UPP	28.50		DVE	Retired/Sec	95.00
	86		UPP	28.50		OLB	Retired/Sec	95.00
	87		UPP	28.50		CED	Retired/Sec	90.00

O COME ALL YE FAITHFUL — Ornament

E-0531 (86)								
E-0531	83	Boy Caroller	UPP	$10.00	3.25"	FSH	Susp/Sec	$55.00
(86)	84		UPP	10.00		CRS	Susp/Sec	50.00
	85		UPP	10.00		DVE	Susp/Sec	45.00
	86		UPP	10.00		OLB	Susp/Sec	42.00

LET HEAVEN AND NATURE SING — Ornament

E-0532 (81)								
E-0532	83	Angel with Book and Songbird	UPP	$ 9.00	3.10"	FSH	Retired/Sec	$50.00
(81)	84		UPP	10.00		CRS	Retired/Sec	42.00
	85		UPP	10.00		DVE	Retired/Sec	35.00
	86		UPP	10.00		OLB	Retired/Sec	35.00

TELL ME THE STORY OF JESUS — Ornament

E-0533 (83)								
E-0533	83	Girl with Doll Reading Book	UPP	$ 9.00	3.00"	FSH	Susp/Sec	$55.00
(83)	84		UPP	10.00		CRS	Susp/Sec	48.00
	85		UPP	10.00		DVE	Susp/Sec	45.00
	86		UPP	10.00		OLB	Susp/Sec	40.00
	87		UPP	10.00		CED	Susp/Sec	40.00
	88		UPP	11.00		FLW	Susp/Sec	35.00

TO THEE WITH LOVE — Ornament

E-0534 (43)								
E-0534	83	Girl with Box of Kittens	UPP	$ 9.00	3.25"	FSH	Retired/Sec	$55.00
(43)	84		UPP	10.00		CRS	Retired/Sec	48.00
	85		UPP	10.00		DVE	Retired/Sec	48.00
	86		UPP	10.00		OLB	Retired/Sec	45.00
	87		UPP	10.00		CED	Retired/Sec	40.00
	88		UPP	11.00		FLW	Retired/Sec	32.00
	89		UPP	13.50		B&A	Retired/Sec	30.00

There are CEDAR TREE pieces with two hooks from the Retailers Wreath, #111465. For further information, see 6th Ed., pg. 209.

LOVE IS PATIENT — Ornament

E-0535 (132)								
E-0535	83	Boy with Slate	UPP	$ 9.00	2.75"	FSH	Susp/Sec	$55.00
(132)	84		UPP	10.00		CRS	Susp/Sec	50.00
	85		UPP	10.00		DVE	Susp/Sec	42.00
	86		UPP	10.00		OLB	Susp/Sec	40.00

LOVE IS PATIENT — Ornament

E-0536 (133)								
E-0536	83	Girl with Slate	UPP	$ 9.00	3.10"	FSH	Susp/Sec	$70.00
(133)	84		UPP	10.00		CRS	Susp/Sec	55.00
	85		UPP	10.00		DVE	Susp/Sec	52.00
	86		UPP	10.00		OLB	Susp/Sec	50.00

JESUS IS THE LIGHT THAT SHINES — Ornament

E-0537 (119)								
E-0537	83	Boy in Night Cap with Candle	UPP	$ 9.00	3.00"	FSH	Susp/Sec	$62.00
(119)	84		UPP	10.00		CRS	Susp/Sec	55.00
	85		UPP	10.00		DVE	Susp/Sec	55.00

138

WEE THREE KINGS Plate — Third Issue "Christmas Collection" Series — Individually Numbered

E-0538	83	Three Kings	15,000	$40.00	8.50"	UM	Secondary	$40.00
(66)								

KATIE LYNNE Doll

E-0539	83	Baby Collector's Doll	UPP	$150.00	16.00"	UM	Susp/Sec	$185.00
(134)	83		UPP	150.00		FSH	Susp/Sec	180.00
	84		UPP	165.00		CRS	Susp/Sec	175.00
	85		UPP	165.00		DVE	Susp/Sec	175.00
	86		UPP	165.00		OLB	Susp/Sec	175.00
	87		UPP	165.00		CED	Susp/Sec	175.00
	88		UPP	175.00		FLW	Susp/Sec	175.00

JESUS LOVES ME Figurine — One of the "Original 21"

E-1372B	79	Boy with Teddy	UPP	$ 7.00	4.50"	NM	Secondary	$90.00
(1)	81		UPP	10.00		TRI	Secondary	60.00
	82		UPP	15.00		HRG	Secondary	45.00
	83		UPP	15.00		FSH	Secondary	35.00
	84		UPP	17.00		CRS	Secondary	30.00
	85		UPP	17.00		DVE	Secondary	25.00
	86		UPP	17.00		OLB	Secondary	25.00
	87		UPP	17.00		CED	Secondary	25.00
	88		UPP	21.00		FLW	Secondary	25.00
	89		UPP	23.00		B&A	Secondary	25.00
	90		UPP	25.00		FLM	Primary	25.00
	91		UPP	25.00		VSL	Primary	25.00
	92		OPEN	25.00		G/CL	Primary	25.00

JESUS LOVES ME Figurine — One of the "Original 21"

E-1372G	79	Girl with Bunny	UPP	$ 7.00	4.50"	NM	Secondary	$115.00
(2)	81		UPP	10.00		TRI	Secondary	75.00
	82		UPP	15.00		HRG	Secondary	50.00
	83		UPP	15.00		FSH	Secondary	40.00
	84		UPP	17.00		CRS	Secondary	35.00
	85		UPP	17.00		DVE	Secondary	30.00
	86		UPP	17.00		OLB	Secondary	25.00
	87		UPP	17.00		CED	Secondary	25.00
	88		UPP	21.00		FLW	Secondary	25.00
	89		UPP	23.00		B&A	Secondary	25.00
	90		UPP	25.00		FLM	Primary	25.00
	91		UPP	25.00		VSL	Primary	25.00
	92		OPEN	25.00		G/CL	Primary	25.00

SMILE, GOD LOVES YOU Figurine — One of the "Original 21"

E-1373B	79	Boy with Black Eye	UPP	$ 7.00	4.50"	NM	Retired/Sec	$95.00
(3)	81		UPP	12.00		TRI	Retired/Sec	80.00
	82		UPP	15.00		HRG	Retired/Sec	65.00
	83		UPP	15.00		FSH	Retired/Sec	60.00
	84		UPP	17.00		CRS	Retired/Sec	55.00

JESUS IS THE LIGHT Figurine — One of the "Original 21"

E-1373G	79	Girl with Doll and Candle	UPP	$ 7.00	4.50"	NM	Retired/Sec	$125.00
(4)	81		UPP	10.00		TRI	Retired/Sec	85.00
	82		UPP	15.00		HRG	Retired/Sec	70.00
	83		UPP	15.00		FSH	Retired/Sec	60.00
	84		UPP	17.00		CRS	Retired/Sec	58.00
	85		UPP	17.00		DVE	Retired/Sec	55.00
	86		UPP	17.00		OLB	Retired/Sec	52.00
	87		UPP	17.00		CED	Retired/Sec	50.00
	88		UPP	21.00		FLW	Retired/Sec	45.00

PRAISE THE LORD ANYHOW Figurine — One of the "Original 21"

E-1374B	79	Boy with Dog	UPP	$ 8.00	5.00"	NM	Retired/Sec	$115.00
(19)	81	and Ice Cream Cone	UPP	8.00		TRI	Retired/Sec	90.00
	82		UPP	17.00		HRG	Retired/Sec	75.00

Variations exist in the color of the dog's nose and the flavor of ice cream.

MAKE A JOYFUL NOISE — Figurine — One of the "Original 21"

E-1374G	79	Girl with Goose	UPP	$ 8.00	4.75"	NM	Secondary	$115.00
(5)	81		UPP	13.00		TRI	Secondary	80.00
	82		UPP	17.00		HRG	Secondary	50.00
	83		UPP	17.00		FSH	Secondary	38.00
	84		UPP	19.00		CRS	Secondary	35.00
	85		UPP	19.00		DVE	Secondary	30.00
	86		UPP	19.00		OLB	Secondary	30.00
	87		UPP	19.00		CED	Secondary	27.50
	88		UPP	23.00		FLW	Secondary	27.50
	89		UPP	25.00		B&A	Secondary	27.50
	90		UPP	27.50		FLM	Primary	27.50
	91		UPP	27.50		VSL	Primary	27.50
	92		OPEN	27.50		G/CL	Primary	27.50

LOVE LIFTED ME — Figurine — One of the "Original 21"

E-1375A	79	Boy & Girl on Seesaw	UPP	$11.00	5.00"	NM	Secondary	$115.00
(6)	81		UPP	17.00		TRI	Secondary	80.00
	82		UPP	21.00		HRG	Secondary	60.00
	83		UPP	21.00		FSH	Secondary	50.00
	84		UPP	22.50		CRS	Secondary	42.00
	85		UPP	22.50		DVE	Secondary	40.00
	86		UPP	22.50		OLB	Secondary	35.00
	87		UPP	22.50		CED	Secondary	35.00
	88		UPP	30.00		FLW	Secondary	35.00
	89		UPP	33.00		B&A	Secondary	35.00
	90		UPP	35.00		FLM	Primary	35.00
	91		UPP	35.00		VSL	Primary	35.00
	92		OPEN	35.00		G/CL	Primary	35.00

PRAYER CHANGES THINGS — Figurine — One of the "Original 21"

E-1375B	79	Boy & Girl with Bluebirds	UPP	$11.00	5.00"	NM	Susp/Sec	$195.00
(7)	81	on Shovel	UPP	17.00		TRI	Susp/Sec	150.00
	82		UPP	21.00		HRG	Susp/Sec	130.00
	83		UPP	21.00		FSH	Susp/Sec	120.00
	84		UPP	22.50		CRS	Susp/Sec	115.00

LOVE ONE ANOTHER — Figurine — One of the "Original 21"

E-1376	79	Boy & Girl Sitting on Stump	UPP	$10.00	4.75"	NM	Secondary	$115.00
(8)	81		UPP	16.00		TRI	Secondary	80.00
	82		UPP	21.00		HRG	Secondary	55.00
	83		UPP	21.00		FSH	Secondary	48.00
	84		UPP	22.50		CRS	Secondary	40.00
	85		UPP	22.50		DVE	Secondary	38.00
	86		UPP	22.50		OLB	Secondary	35.00
	87		UPP	22.50		CED	Secondary	35.00
	88		UPP	30.00		FLW	Secondary	35.00
	89		UPP	33.00		B&A	Secondary	35.00
	90		UPP	35.00		FLM	Primary	35.00
	91		UPP	35.00		VSL	Primary	35.00
	92		OPEN	35.00		G/CL	Primary	35.00

HE LEADETH ME — Figurine — One of the "Original 21"

E-1377A	79	Boy Leading Lamb	UPP	$ 9.00	4.75"	NM	Susp/Sec	$115.00
(9)	81		UPP	15.00		TRI	Susp/Sec	95.00
	82		UPP	19.00		HRG	Susp/Sec	85.00
	83		UPP	19.00		FSH	Susp/Sec	80.00
	84		UPP	19.00		CRS	Susp/Sec	75.00

Classic Variation: The incorrect Inspirational Title, "He Careth For You," is on the understamp decal of some NO MARK pieces. This is one of the most difficult to find of all the classic variations. The few known sales are in the $250 range.

HE CARETH FOR YOU   Figurine   One of the "Original 21"

E-1377B	79	Boy Helping Lamb	UPP	$9.00	4.00"	NM	Susp/Sec	$115.00
(10)	81		UPP	15.00		TRI	Susp/Sec	100.00
	82		UPP	19.00		HRG	Susp/Sec	90.00
	83		UPP	19.00		FSH	Susp/Sec	85.00
	84		UPP	19.00		CRS	Susp/Sec	80.00

GOD LOVETH A CHEERFUL GIVER   Figurine   One of the "Original 21"   First Retirement - May 1981

E-1378	79	Girl with Puppies	UPP	$11.00	5.15"	NM	Retired/Sec	$845.00
(20)								

LOVE IS KIND   Figurine   One of the "Original 21"

E-1379A	79	Boy with Turtle	UPP	$8.00	4.50"	NM	Susp/Sec	$120.00
(11)	81		UPP	13.00		TRI	Susp/Sec	100.00
	82		UPP	17.00		HRG	Susp/Sec	95.00
	83		UPP	17.00		FSH	Susp/Sec	90.00
	84		UPP	19.00		CRS	Susp/Sec	80.00

GOD UNDERSTANDS   Figurine   One of the "Original 21"

E-1379B	79	Boy with Report Card	UPP	$8.00	5.00"	NM	Susp/Sec	$120.00
(12)	81		UPP	13.00		TRI	Susp/Sec	105.00
	82		UPP	17.00		HRG	Susp/Sec	90.00
	83		UPP	17.00		FSH	Susp/Sec	85.00
	84		UPP	19.00		CRS	Susp/Sec	80.00

O, HOW I LOVE JESUS   Figurine   One of the "Original 21"

E-1380B	79	Indian Boy	UPP	$8.00	4.75"	NM	Retired/Sec	$120.00
(13)	81		UPP	13.00		TRI	Retired/Sec	105.00
	82		UPP	17.00		HRG	Retired/Sec	90.00
	83		UPP	17.00		FSH	Retired/Sec	80.00
	84		UPP	19.00		CRS	Retired/Sec	75.00

HIS BURDEN IS LIGHT   Figurine   One of the "Original 21"

E-1380G	79	Indian Girl	UPP	$8.00	4.75"	NM	Retired/Sec	$135.00
(14)	81		UPP	13.00		TRI	Retired/Sec	110.00
	82		UPP	17.00		HRG	Retired/Sec	85.00
	83		UPP	17.00		FSH	Retired/Sec	80.00
	84		UPP	19.00		CRS	Retired/Sec	75.00

JESUS IS THE ANSWER   Figurine   One of the "Original 21"

E-1381	79	Boy Patching World	UPP	$11.50	4.50"	NM	Susp/Sec	$165.00
(15)	81		UPP	19.00		TRI	Susp/Sec	140.00
	82		UPP	21.00		HRG	Susp/Sec	130.00
	83		UPP	21.00		FSH	Susp/Sec	125.00
	84		UPP	22.50		CRS	Susp/Sec	120.00

E-1381 was re-sculpted and re-introduced in April 1992 as E-1381R:

JESUS IS THE ANSWER   Figurine

E-1381R	92	Boy Holding a Stethoscope	OPEN	$55.00	4.50"	G/CL	Primary	$55.00
(611)		to a Bandaged World						

    In this re-sculpted figurine the globe reflects boundary changes as well as new nations that have emerged as a result of recent political changes around the world. The figurine will benefit research at St. Jude Children's Hospital.

WE HAVE SEEN HIS STAR   Figurine   One of the "Original 21"

E-2010	79	Boy Holding Lamb	UPP	$8.00	5.50"	NM	Susp/Sec	$100.00
(16)	82		UPP	17.00		HRG	Susp/Sec	80.00
	83		UPP	17.00		FSH	Susp/Sec	75.00
	84		UPP	17.00		CRS	Susp/Sec	75.00

COME LET US ADORE HIM   Figurine   One of the "Original 21"   First Retirement - May 1981

E-2011	79	Boy with Manger Baby	UPP	$5.00	5.00"	NM	Retired/Sec	$310.00
(21)								

JESUS IS BORN — Figurine — One of the "Original 21"

E-2012	79	Boy & Girl Playing Angels	UPP	$12.00	6.25"	NM	Susp/Sec	$120.00
(17)	82		UPP	22.50		HRG	Susp/Sec	105.00
	83		UPP	22.50		FSH	Susp/Sec	90.00
	84		UPP	22.50		CRS	Susp/Sec	85.00

UNTO US A CHILD IS BORN — Figurine — One of the "Original 21"

E-2013	79	Boy & Girl Reading Book	UPP	$12.00	4.75"	NM	Susp/Sec	$120.00
(18)	82		UPP	22.50		HRG	Susp/Sec	100.00
	83		UPP	22.50		FSH	Susp/Sec	90.00
	84		UPP	22.50		CRS	Susp/Sec	85.00

JOY TO THE WORLD — Ornament

E-2343	82	Boy Angel Playing Trumpet	UPP	$ 9.00	2.00"	UM	Susp/Sec	$55.00
(79)	84		UPP	10.00		CRS	Susp/Sec	50.00
	85		UPP	10.00		DVE	Susp/Sec	45.00
	86		UPP	10.00		OLB	Susp/Sec	42.00
	87		UPP	10.00		CED	Susp/Sec	40.00
	88		UPP	11.00		FLW	Susp/Sec	40.00

JOY TO THE WORLD — Candle Climbers — Set of 2

E-2344	82	Boy Angel Playing Trumpet	UPP	$20.00	2.50"	UM	Susp/Sec	$75.00
(79)	84		UPP	20.00		CRS	Susp/Sec	65.00
	85		UPP	20.00		DVE	Susp/Sec	60.00

MAY YOUR CHRISTMAS BE COZY — Figurine

E-2345	82	Boy in Pajamas with Teddy	UPP	$23.00	4.25"	HRG	Susp/Sec	$80.00
(80)	83		UPP	23.00		FSH	Susp/Sec	70.00
	84		UPP	25.00		CRS	Susp/Sec	65.00

LET HEAVEN AND NATURE SING — Musical — TUNE: Joy To The World

E-2346	*	Angel with Friends Carolling	UPP	$50.00	6.00"	UM	Susp/Sec	$130.00
(81)	82		UPP	50.00		HRG	Susp/Sec	125.00
	83		UPP	55.00		FSH	Susp/Sec	120.00
	84		UPP	60.00		CRS	Susp/Sec	120.00
	85		UPP	60.00		DVE	Susp/Sec	115.00
	86		UPP	60.00		OLB	Susp/Sec	115.00
	87		UPP	60.00		CED	Susp/Sec	115.00
	88		UPP	65.00		FLW	Susp/Sec	110.00
	89		UPP	75.00		B&A	Susp/Sec	110.00

* UNMARKED (UM) pieces could have been produced in any of the years of production.

LET HEAVEN AND NATURE SING — Plate — Second Issue "Christmas Collection" Series — Individually Numbered

E-2347	82	Angel with Friends Carolling	15,000	$40.00	8.50"	UM	Secondary	$45.00
(81)						OLB	Secondary	45.00

MAY YOUR CHRISTMAS BE WARM — Figurine

E-2348	82	Boy Next to a Potbellied Stove	UPP	$30.00	4.75"	HRG	Susp/Sec	$100.00
(82)	83		UPP	30.00		FSH	Susp/Sec	90.00
	84		UPP	33.00		CRS	Susp/Sec	90.00
	85		UPP	33.00		DVE	Susp/Sec	85.00
	86		UPP	33.00		OLB	Susp/Sec	80.00
	87		UPP	33.00		CED	Susp/Sec	80.00
	88		UPP	37.00		FLW	Susp/Sec	75.00

TELL ME THE STORY OF JESUS — Figurine

E-2349	82	Girl Reading Book to Doll	UPP	$30.00	5.00"	HRG	Susp/Sec	$100.00
(83)	83		UPP	30.00		FSH	Susp/Sec	95.00
	84		UPP	33.00		CRS	Susp/Sec	90.00
	85		UPP	33.00		DVE	Susp/Sec	85.00

DROPPING IN FOR CHRISTMAS — Figurine

E-2350	82	Boy Ice Skater in Santa Cap	UPP	$18.00	5.15"	HRG	Susp/Sec	$75.00
(84)	83		UPP	18.00		FSH	Susp/Sec	70.00
	84		UPP	18.00		CRS	Susp/Sec	65.00

HOLY SMOKES   Figurine

E-2351	82	Two Angels with Candles	UPP	$27.00	5.75"	HRG	Retired/Sec	$120.00
(85)	83		UPP	27.00		FSH	Retired/Sec	105.00
	84		UPP	30.00		CRS	Retired/Sec	100.00
	85		UPP	30.00		DVE	Retired/Sec	95.00
	86		UPP	30.00		OLB	Retired/Sec	90.00
	87		UPP	30.00		CED	Retired/Sec	90.00

O COME ALL YE FAITHFUL   Musical   TUNE: O Come All Ye Faithful

E-2352	*	Boy Carolling by Lamp Post	UPP	$45.00	7.25"	UM	Susp/Sec	$120.00
(86)	82		UPP	45.00		HRG	Susp/Sec	120.00
	83		UPP	45.00		FSH	Susp/Sec	115.00
	84		UPP	50.00		CRS	Susp/Sec	110.00

* UNMARKED (UM) pieces could have been produced in any of the years of production.

O COME ALL YE FAITHFUL   Figurine

E-2353	82	Boy Carolling by Lamp Post	UPP	$27.50	6.25"	HRG	Retired/Sec	$85.00
(86)	83		UPP	27.50		FSH	Retired/Sec	75.00
	84		UPP	30.00		CRS	Retired/Sec	70.00
	85		UPP	30.00		DVE	Retired/Sec	70.00
	86		UPP	30.00		OLB	Retired/Sec	70.00

I'LL PLAY MY DRUM FOR HIM   Musical   TUNE: Little Drummer Boy

E-2355	82	Drummer Boy at Manger	UPP	$45.00	6.75"	HRG	Susp/Sec	$140.00
(87)	83		UPP	45.00		FSH	Susp/Sec	130.00
	84		UPP	50.00		CRS	Susp/Sec	125.00

I'LL PLAY MY DRUM FOR HIM   Figurine

E-2356	82	Drummer Boy at Manger	UPP	$30.00	5.50"	HRG	Susp/Sec	$105.00
(87)	83		UPP	30.00		FSH	Susp/Sec	75.00
	84		UPP	33.00		CRS	Susp/Sec	70.00
	85		UPP	33.00		DVE	Susp/Sec	65.00

I'LL PLAY MY DRUM FOR HIM   Plate, Dated   First Issue "Joy of Christmas" Series

E-2357	82	Drummer Boy at Manger	Annual	$40.00	8.50"	UM	Secondary	$90.00
(87)								

I'LL PLAY MY DRUM FOR HIM   Bell, Dated?*

E-2358	82	Drummer Boy	Annual	$17.00	5.75"	UM	Secondary	$65.00
(87)		* Prototypes were dated, it appears actual production wasn't.						

I'LL PLAY MY DRUM FOR HIM   Ornament, Dated

E-2359	82	Drummer Boy	Annual	$9.00	3.25"	HRG	Secondary	$100.00
(87)								

I'LL PLAY MY DRUM FOR HIM   Figurine   Nativity Addition

E-2360	82	Drummer Boy	UPP	$16.00	5.00"	HRG	Secondary	$45.00
(87)	83		UPP	16.00		FSH	Secondary	35.00
	84		UPP	17.00		CRS	Secondary	32.00
	85		UPP	17.00		DVE	Secondary	30.00
	86		UPP	17.00		OLB	Secondary	25.00
	87		UPP	17.00		CED	Secondary	25.00
	88		UPP	19.00		FLW	Secondary	25.00
	89		UPP	23.00		B&A	Secondary	25.00
	90		UPP	25.00		FLM	Primary	25.00
	91		UPP	25.00		VSL	Primary	25.00
	92		OPEN	25.00		G/CL	Primary	25.00

CHRISTMAS JOY FROM HEAD TO TOE   Figurine

E-2361	82	Girl with Stocking	UPP	$25.00	5.50"	HRG	Susp/Sec	$75.00
(88)	83		UPP	25.00		FSH	Susp/Sec	65.00
	84		UPP	27.50		CRS	Susp/Sec	65.00
	85		UPP	27.50		DVE	Susp/Sec	60.00
	86		UPP	27.50		OLB	Susp/Sec	55.00

BABY'S FIRST CHRISTMAS   Ornament

E-2362	82	Baby Girl in Christmas	UPP	$ 9.00	3.50"	UM	Susp/Sec	$55.00
(89)	84	Stocking	UPP	10.00		CRS	Susp/Sec	35.00
	85		UPP	10.00		DVE	Susp/Sec	35.00
	86		UPP	10.00		OLB	Susp/Sec	30.00
	87		UPP	10.00		CED	Susp/Sec	30.00
	88		UPP	11.00		FLW	Susp/Sec	28.00

Classic Variation: "Straight Hair." UNMARKED pieces exist in four variations: 1) Straight hair and no caption, 2) Curly hair and no caption, 3) Straight hair with the caption, "Baby's First Christmas," and, 4) Curly hair with the caption, "Baby's First Christmas." Subsequent pieces (CROSS through FLOWER) were curly hair with the caption. The straight hair, with or without the caption, is considered the variation. The GREENBOOK Market Price for an UNMARKED "Straight Hair" ornament is $70.00.
Full color photo: 4th Ed., pg. 194 or 5th Ed., pg. 200. One color photo: 6th Ed., pg. 223.

CAMEL   Figurine   Nativity Addition

E-2363	82	Camel	UPP	$20.00	4.00"	HRG	Secondary	$45.00
(90)	83		UPP	20.00		FSH	Secondary	40.00
	84		UPP	22.50		CRS	Secondary	35.00
	85		UPP	22.50		DVE	Secondary	32.50
	86		UPP	22.50		OLB	Secondary	32.50
	87		UPP	22.50		CED	Secondary	32.50
	88		UPP	25.00		FLW	Secondary	32.50
	89		UPP	30.00		B&A	Secondary	32.50
	90		UPP	32.50		FLM	Primary	32.50
	91		UPP	32.50		VSL	Primary	32.50
	92		OPEN	32.50		G/CL	Primary	32.50

GOAT   Figurine   Nativity Addition

E-2364	82	Goat	UPP	$10.00	3.00"	UM	Susp/Sec	$35.00
(91)	83		UPP	10.00		FSH	Susp/Sec	32.00
	84		UPP	11.00		CRS	Susp/Sec	30.00
	85		UPP	11.00		DVE	Susp/Sec	28.00
	86		UPP	11.00		OLB	Susp/Sec	25.00
	87		UPP	11.00		CED	Susp/Sec	25.00
	88		UPP	12.00		FLW	Susp/Sec	25.00
	89		UPP	15.00		B&A	Susp/Sec	25.00

THE FIRST NOEL   Figurine   Nativity Addition

E-2365	*	Boy Angel with Candle	UPP	$16.00	4.50"	UM	Susp/Sec	$55.00
(92)	82		UPP	16.00		HRG	Susp/Sec	45.00
	83		UPP	16.00		FSH	Susp/Sec	42.00
	84		UPP	16.00		CRS	Susp/Sec	40.00

* UNMARKED (UM) pieces could have been produced in any of the years of production.

THE FIRST NOEL   Figurine   Nativity Addition

E-2366	*	Girl Angel Praying	UPP	$16.00	4.50"	UM	Susp/Sec	$55.00
(93)	82		UPP	16.00		HRG	Susp/Sec	55.00
	83		UPP	16.00		FSH	Susp/Sec	52.00
	84		UPP	16.00		CRS	Susp/Sec	50.00

* UNMARKED (UM) pieces could have been produced in any of the years of production.

THE FIRST NOEL   Ornament

E-2367	82	Boy Angel with Candle	UPP	$ 9.00	3.10"	HRG	Susp/Sec	$65.00
(92)	83		UPP	9.00		FSH	Susp/Sec	60.00
	84		UPP	10.00		CRS	Susp/Sec	55.00

THE FIRST NOEL   Ornament

E-2368	82	Girl Angel Praying	UPP	$ 9.00	3.00"	HRG	Retired/Sec	$60.00
(93)	83		UPP	9.00		FSH	Retired/Sec	48.00
	84		UPP	10.00		CRS	Retired/Sec	40.00

DROPPING IN FOR CHRISTMAS — Ornament

E-2369	*	Boy Ice Skater in Santa Cap	UPP	$ 9.00	3.50"	UM	Retired/Sec	$55.00
(84)	82		UPP	9.00		HRG	Retired/Sec	45.00
	83		UPP	9.00		FSH	Retired/Sec	45.00
	84		UPP	10.00		CRS	Retired/Sec	40.00
	85		UPP	10.00		DVE	Retired/Sec	40.00
	86		UPP	10.00		OLB	Retired/Sec	35.00

* UNMARKED (UM) pieces could have been produced in any of the years of production.

UNICORN — Ornament

E-2371	82	Unicorn	UPP	$10.00	3.00"	UM	Retired/Sec	$60.00
(94)	84		UPP	10.00		CRS	Retired/Sec	48.00
	85		UPP	11.00		DVE	Retired/Sec	40.00
	86		UPP	11.00		OLB	Retired/Sec	40.00
	87		UPP	11.00		CED	Retired/Sec	40.00
	88		UPP	12.00		FLW	Retired/Sec	40.00

BABY'S FIRST CHRISTMAS — Ornament

E-2372	82	Boy Holding Block	UPP	$ 9.00	2.75"	UM	Susp/Sec	$45.00
(95)	84		UPP	10.00		CRS	Susp/Sec	40.00
	85		UPP	10.00		DVE	Susp/Sec	35.00

Exists with and without caption, "Baby's First Christmas," in UNMARKED version.

BUNDLES OF JOY — Figurine

E-2374	82	Girl with Presents	UPP	$27.50	6.75"	HRG	Secondary	$80.00
(96)	83		UPP	27.50		FSH	Secondary	60.00
	84		UPP	30.00		CRS	Secondary	52.00
	85		UPP	30.00		DVE	Secondary	45.00
	86		UPP	30.00		OLB	Secondary	45.00
	87		UPP	30.00		CED	Secondary	45.00
	88		UPP	33.50		FLW	Secondary	45.00
	89		UPP	40.00		B&A	Secondary	45.00
	90		UPP	45.00		FLM	Primary	45.00
	91		UPP	45.00		VSL	Primary	45.00
	92		OPEN	45.00		G/CL	Primary	45.00

DROPPING OVER FOR CHRISTMAS — Figurine

E-2375	82	Girl with Pie	UPP	$30.00	5.15"	HRG	Retired/Sec	$95.00
(97)	83		UPP	30.00		FSH	Retired/Sec	85.00
	84		UPP	33.00		CRS	Retired/Sec	85.00
	85		UPP	33.00		DVE	Retired/Sec	80.00
	86		UPP	33.00		OLB	Retired/Sec	80.00
	87		UPP	33.00		CED	Retired/Sec	75.00
	88		UPP	37.00		FLW	Retired/Sec	75.00
	89		UPP	42.50		B&A	Retired/Sec	70.00
	90		UPP	45.00		FLM	Retired/Sec	70.00
	91		UPP	45.00		VSL	Retired/Sec	70.00

DROPPING OVER FOR CHRISTMAS — Ornament

E-2376	82	Girl with Pie	UPP	$ 9.00	3.00"	HRG	Retired/Sec	$55.00
(97)	83		UPP	9.00		FSH	Retired/Sec	45.00
	84		UPP	10.00		CRS	Retired/Sec	40.00
	85		UPP	10.00		DVE	Retired/Sec	38.00

OUR FIRST CHRISTMAS TOGETHER — Figurine

E-2377	82	Girl Knitting Tie for Boy	UPP	$35.00	5.15"	HRG	Susp/Sec	$85.00
(98)	83		UPP	35.00		FSH	Susp/Sec	75.00
	84		UPP	37.50		CRS	Susp/Sec	70.00
	85		UPP	37.50		DVE	Susp/Sec	68.00

OUR FIRST CHRISTMAS TOGETHER — Plate

E-2378	82	Girl Knitting Tie for Boy	UPP	$30.00	7.00"	UM	Susp/Sec	$55.00
(98)	84		UPP	30.00		CRS	Susp/Sec	45.00
	85		UPP	30.00		DVE	Susp/Sec	45.00

MOUSE WITH CHEESE — Ornament

E-2381	82	Mouse with Cheese	UPP	$ 9.00	2.50"	HRG	Susp/Sec	$130.00
(99)	83		UPP	9.00		FSH	Susp/Sec	115.00
	84		UPP	10.00		CRS	Susp/Sec	110.00

OUR FIRST CHRISTMAS TOGETHER — Ornament

E-2385	82	Bride and Groom	UPP	$10.00	4.00"	HRG	Susp/Sec	$40.00
(38)	83		UPP	10.00		FSH	Susp/Sec	35.00
	84		UPP	10.00		CRS	Susp/Sec	30.00
	85		UPP	11.00		DVE	Susp/Sec	28.00
	86		UPP	11.00		OLB	Susp/Sec	25.00
	87		UPP	11.00		CED	Susp/Sec	25.00
	88		UPP	12.00		FLW	Susp/Sec	20.00
	89		UPP	15.00		B&A	Susp/Sec	20.00
	90		UPP	15.00		FLM	Susp/Prim	15.00
	91		UPP	15.00		VSL	Susp/Prim	15.00

CAMEL, DONKEY, AND COW — Ornaments — Set of 3

E-2386	*	Camel, Donkey, Cow	UPP	$25.00	2.25"	UM	Susp/Sec	$85.00
(100)	82		UPP	25.00		HRG	Susp/Sec	75.00
	83	Mixed sets UM/HRG are common.	UPP	25.00		FSH	Susp/Sec	70.00
	84	Use lower value.	UPP	27.50		CRS	Susp/Sec	70.00

* UNMARKED (UM) pieces could have been produced in any of the years of production.

HOUSE SET AND PALM TREE — Figurines — Set of 3 — Mini Nativity Addition

E-2387	82	Mini Houses and Palm Tree	UPP	$45.00	3.00"	HRG	Secondary	$95.00
(101)	83		UPP	45.00		FSH	Secondary	85.00
	84		UPP	50.00		CRS	Secondary	80.00
	85		UPP	50.00		DVE	Secondary	75.00
	86		UPP	50.00		OLB	Secondary	75.00
	87		UPP	50.00		CED	Secondary	70.00
	88		UPP	55.00		FLW	Secondary	70.00
	89		UPP	65.00		B&A	Secondary	70.00
	90		UPP	70.00		FLM	Primary	70.00
	91		UPP	70.00		VSL	Primary	70.00
	92		OPEN	70.00		G/CL	Primary	70.00

COME LET US ADORE HIM — Figurines — Set of 11

E-2395	82	Mini Nativity Set	UPP	$80.00	3.50"	HRG*	Secondary	$155.00
(22)	83		UPP	80.00		FSH	Secondary	140.00
	84		UPP	90.00		CRS	Secondary	130.00
	85		UPP	90.00		DVE	Secondary	125.00
	86		UPP	90.00		OLB	Secondary	120.00
	87		UPP	90.00		CED	Secondary	120.00
	88		UPP	95.00		FLW	Secondary	120.00
	89		UPP	110.00		B&A	Secondary	120.00
	90		UPP	120.00		FLM	Secondary	120.00
	91		UPP	120.00		VSL	Primary	120.00
	92		OPEN	120.00		G/CL	Primary	120.00

Classic Variation: "Turban Nativity." Known as the "Turban Nativity," the shepherd holding a lamb was replaced in some HOURGLASS sets with a shepherd wearing a turban. "Turban Boy" shepherds were also shipped individually to retailers as replacement pieces, so collectors were sometimes able to add the "Turban Boy" as a twelfth piece to this eleven piece mini Nativity Set. The GREENBOOK Market Price for the "Turban Nativity" is $195.00. The GREENBOOK Market Price for the individual "Turban Boy" piece is $75.00.
Full color photo: 4th Ed., pg. 194 or 5th Ed., pg. 199. One color photo 6th Ed., pg. 221.

COME LET US ADORE HIM — Figurines — Set of 9

E-2800	80	Nativity Set	UPP	$70.00	4.75"	NM	Disc/Sec	$200.00
(22)	81		UPP	70.00		TRI	Disc/Sec	170.00
	82	Mixed sets TRI/HRG and HRG/FSH	UPP	80.00		HRG	Disc/Sec	160.00
	83	are common. Take lower value.	UPP	80.00		FSH	Disc/Sec	150.00
	84		UPP	90.00		CRS	Disc/Sec	145.00
	85		UPP	90.00		DVE	Disc/Sec	145.00

Re-sculpted - See #104000, page 192.

JESUS IS BORN — Figurine

E-2801	Year	Description		Price	Size	Symbol	Status	Value
E-2801	80	Angels in Chariot	UPP	$37.00	5.75"	NM	Susp/Sec	$350.00
(23)	81		UPP	45.00		TRI	Susp/Sec	325.00
	82		UPP	50.00		HRG	Susp/Sec	300.00
	83		UPP	50.00		FSH	Susp/Sec	275.00
	84		UPP	50.00		CRS	Susp/Sec	250.00

CHRISTMAS IS A TIME TO SHARE — Figurine

	Year	Description		Price	Size	Symbol	Status	Value
E-2802	80	Boy Giving Toy Lamb	UPP	$20.00	5.00"	NM	Susp/Sec	$85.00
(24)	81		UPP	22.50		TRI	Susp/Sec	75.00
	82		UPP	25.00		HRG	Susp/Sec	65.00
	83		UPP	25.00		FSH	Susp/Sec	65.00
	84		UPP	27.50		CRS	Susp/Sec	60.00
	*		UPP	27.50		DVE	Susp/Sec	55.00

*Piece was suspended in 1984 yet exists in a DOVE Annual Symbol.

CROWN HIM LORD OF ALL — Figurine

	Year	Description		Price	Size	Symbol	Status	Value
E-2803	80	Boy Holding Crown at Manger	UPP	$20.00	4.50"	NM	Susp/Sec	$90.00
(25)	81		UPP	22.50		TRI	Susp/Sec	75.00
	82		UPP	25.00		HRG	Susp/Sec	65.00
	83		UPP	25.00		FSH	Susp/Sec	65.00
	84		UPP	27.50		CRS	Susp/Sec	60.00

PEACE ON EARTH — Figurine

	Year	Description		Price	Size	Symbol	Status	Value
E-2804	80	Boy Angel on Globe	UPP	$20.00	6.00"	NM	Susp/Sec	$145.00
(26)	81	with Teddy	UPP	22.50		TRI	Susp/Sec	135.00
	82		UPP	25.00		HRG	Susp/Sec	130.00
	83		UPP	25.00		FSH	Susp/Sec	120.00
	84		UPP	27.50		CRS	Susp/Sec	115.00

WISHING YOU A SEASON FILLED WITH JOY — Figurine

	Year	Description		Price	Size	Symbol	Status	Value
E-2805	80	Boy in Santa Cap with Dog	UPP	$20.00	4.25"	NM	Retired/Sec	$120.00
(27)	81		UPP	22.50		TRI	Retired/Sec	110.00
	82		UPP	25.00		HRG	Retired/Sec	100.00
	83		UPP	25.00		FSH	Retired/Sec	85.00
	84		UPP	27.50		CRS	Retired/Sec	80.00
	85		UPP	27.50		DVE	Retired/Sec	75.00

NM thru CRS have only one dog's eye painted. DVE exists w/both one and two eyes painted.

CHRISTMAS IS A TIME TO SHARE — Musical — TUNE: Away in a Manger

	Year	Description		Price	Size	Symbol	Status	Value
E-2806	80	Boy Giving Toy Lamb	UPP	$35.00	6.00"	NM	Retired/Sec	$170.00
(24)	81	to Baby Jesus	UPP	35.00		TRI	Retired/Sec	160.00
	82		UPP	40.00		HRG	Retired/Sec	155.00
	83		UPP	45.00		FSH	Retired/Sec	145.00
	84		UPP	50.00		CRS	Retired/Sec	140.00

CROWN HIM LORD OF ALL — Musical — TUNE: O Come All Ye Faithful

	Year	Description		Price	Size	Symbol	Status	Value
E-2807	80	Boy Kneeling at Manger	UPP	$35.00	5.50"	NM	Susp/Sec	$110.00
(25)	81	with Crown	UPP	40.00		TRI	Susp/Sec	95.00
	82		UPP	45.00		HRG	Susp/Sec	95.00
	83		UPP	45.00		FSH	Susp/Sec	90.00
	84		UPP	45.00		CRS	Susp/Sec	85.00

UNTO US A CHILD IS BORN — Musical — TUNE: Jesus Loves Me

	Year	Description		Price	Size	Symbol	Status	Value
E-2808	80	Boy and Girl Reading Book	UPP	$35.00	5.75"	NM	Susp/Sec	$115.00
(18)	81		UPP	40.00		TRI	Susp/Sec	105.00
	82		UPP	45.00		HRG	Susp/Sec	95.00
	83		UPP	45.00		FSH	Susp/Sec	90.00
	84		UPP	50.00		CRS	Susp/Sec	85.00

JESUS IS BORN — Musical — TUNE: Hark! The Herald Angels Sing

	Year	Description		Price	Size	Symbol	Status	Value
E-2809	80	Boy and Girl Playing Angels	UPP	$35.00	7.00"	NM	Susp/Sec	$125.00
(17)	81		UPP	45.00		TRI	Susp/Sec	115.00
	82		UPP	45.00		HRG	Susp/Sec	110.00
	83		UPP	45.00		FSH	Susp/Sec	95.00
	84		UPP	50.00		CRS	Susp/Sec	90.00
	85		UPP	50.00		DVE	Susp/Sec	90.00

COME LET US ADORE HIM — Musical — TUNE: Joy To The World

E-2810	80	Nativity Scene	UPP	$45.00	6.50"	NM	Secondary	$125.00
(22)	81		UPP	45.00		TRI	Secondary	115.00
	82		UPP	60.00		HRG	Secondary	110.00
	83		UPP	60.00		FSH	Secondary	105.00
	84		UPP	65.00		CRS	Secondary	90.00
	85		UPP	65.00		DVE	Secondary	85.00
	86		UPP	65.00		OLB	Secondary	85.00
	87		UPP	65.00		CED	Secondary	85.00
	88		UPP	70.00		FLW	Secondary	85.00
	89		UPP	80.00		B&A	Secondary	85.00
	90		UPP	85.00		FLM	Primary	85.00
	91		UPP	85.00		VSL	Primary	85.00
	92		OPEN	85.00		G/CL	Primary	85.00

YOU HAVE TOUCHED SO MANY HEARTS — Figurine

E-2821	84	Girl with Hearts	UPP	$25.00	5.50"	FSH	Secondary	$50.00
(161)	84		UPP	25.00		CRS	Secondary	42.00
	85		UPP	25.00		DVE	Secondary	40.00
	86		UPP	25.00		OLB	Secondary	38.00
	87		UPP	25.00		CED	Secondary	35.00
	88		UPP	30.00		FLW	Secondary	35.00
	89		UPP	33.00		B&A	Secondary	35.00
	90		UPP	35.00		FLM	Primary	35.00
	91		UPP	35.00		VSL	Primary	35.00
	92		OPEN	35.00		G/CL	Primary	35.00

THIS IS YOUR DAY TO SHINE — Figurine

E-2822	84	Girl Polishing Table	UPP	$37.50	6.00"	FSH	Retired/Sec	$135.00
(162)	84		UPP	37.50		CRS	Retired/Sec	90.00
	85		UPP	37.50		DVE	Retired/Sec	85.00
	86		UPP	37.50		OLB	Retired/Sec	80.00
	87		UPP	37.50		CED	Retired/Sec	80.00
	88		UPP	40.00		FLW	Retired/Sec	75.00

TO GOD BE THE GLORY — Figurine

E-2823	84	Boy Holding Picture Frame	UPP	$40.00	5.50"	FSH	Susp/Sec	$80.00
(163)	84		UPP	40.00		CRS	Susp/Sec	70.00
	85		UPP	40.00		DVE	Susp/Sec	65.00
	86		UPP	40.00		OLB	Susp/Sec	65.00
	87		UPP	40.00		CED	Susp/Sec	60.00

TO A VERY SPECIAL MOM — Figurine

E-2824	84	Girl with Floppy Hat	UPP	$27.50	5.75"	CRS	Secondary	$50.00
(164)	85		UPP	27.50		DVE	Secondary	45.00
	86		UPP	27.50		OLB	Secondary	40.00
	87		UPP	27.50		CED	Secondary	37.50
	88		UPP	32.50		FLW	Secondary	37.50
	89		UPP	35.00		B&A	Secondary	37.50
	90		UPP	37.50		FLM	Primary	37.50
	91		UPP	37.50		VSL	Primary	37.50
	92		OPEN	37.50		G/CL	Primary	37.50

TO A VERY SPECIAL SISTER — Figurine

E-2825	84	Girl Putting Bows in	UPP	$37.50	5.50"	CRS	Secondary	$65.00
(165)	85	Sister's Hair	UPP	37.50		DVE	Secondary	55.00
	86		UPP	37.50		OLB	Secondary	50.00
	87		UPP	37.50		CED	Secondary	50.00
	88		UPP	40.00		FLW	Secondary	50.00
	89		UPP	45.00		B&A	Secondary	50.00
	90		UPP	50.00		FLM	Primary	50.00
	91		UPP	50.00		VSL	Primary	50.00
	92		OPEN	50.00		G/CL	Primary	50.00

MAY YOUR BIRTHDAY BE A BLESSING — Figurine

E-2826	84	Girl at Table with Dolls	UPP	$37.50	5.25"	FSH	Susp/Sec	$95.00
(166)	84		UPP	37.50		CRS	Susp/Sec	80.00
	85		UPP	37.50		DVE	Susp/Sec	75.00
	86		UPP	37.50		OLB	Susp/Sec	70.00

I GET A KICK OUT OF YOU — Figurine

E-2827	84	Girl with Bucket on Head	UPP	$50.00	4.75"	FSH	Susp/Sec	$130.00
(167)	84		UPP	50.00		CRS	Susp/Sec	110.00
	85		UPP	50.00		DVE	Susp/Sec	105.00
	86		UPP	50.00		OLB	Susp/Sec	100.00

PRECIOUS MEMORIES — Figurine

E-2828	84	Girl at Trunk with	UPP	$45.00	5.50"	CRS	Secondary	$75.00
(168)	85	Wedding Gown	UPP	45.00		DVE	Secondary	70.00
	86		UPP	45.00		OLB	Secondary	65.00
	87		UPP	45.00		CED	Secondary	60.00
	88		UPP	50.00		FLW	Secondary	60.00
	89		UPP	55.00		B&A	Secondary	60.00
	90		UPP	60.00		FLM	Primary	60.00
	91		UPP	60.00		VSL	Primary	60.00
	92		OPEN	60.00		G/CL	Primary	60.00

I'M SENDING YOU A WHITE CHRISTMAS — Figurine

E-2829	84	Girl Mailing Snowball	UPP	$37.50	5.00"	CRS	Secondary	$65.00
(169)	85		UPP	37.50		DVE	Secondary	55.00
	86		UPP	37.50		OLB	Secondary	50.00
	87		UPP	37.50		CED	Secondary	50.00
	88		UPP	40.00		FLW	Secondary	50.00
	89		UPP	47.50		B&A	Secondary	50.00
	90		UPP	50.00		FLM	Primary	50.00
	91		UPP	50.00		VSL	Primary	50.00
	92		OPEN	50.00		G/CL	Primary	50.00

BRIDESMAID — Figurine — First Issue "Bridal" Series

E-2831	84	Bridesmaid	UPP	$13.50	4.25"	CRS	Secondary	$30.00
(170)	85		UPP	13.50		DVE	Secondary	25.00
	86		UPP	13.50		OLB	Secondary	22.00
	87		UPP	13.50		CED	Secondary	20.00
	88		UPP	16.00		FLW	Secondary	20.00
	89		UPP	17.50		B&A	Secondary	20.00
	90		UPP	19.50		FLM	Primary	19.50
	91		UPP	19.50		VSL	Primary	19.50
	92		OPEN	19.50		G/CL	Primary	19.50

GOD BLESS THE BRIDE — Figurine

E-2832	84	Bride with Flower Girl	UPP	$35.00	5.50"	CRS	Secondary	$58.00
(171)	85		UPP	35.00		DVE	Secondary	55.00
	86		UPP	35.00		OLB	Secondary	52.00
	87		UPP	35.00		CED	Secondary	50.00
	88		UPP	40.00		FLW	Secondary	50.00
	89		UPP	45.00		B&A	Secondary	50.00
	90		UPP	50.00		FLM	Primary	50.00
	91		UPP	50.00		VSL	Primary	50.00
	92		OPEN	50.00		G/CL	Primary	50.00

RINGBEARER — Figurine — Fourth Issue "Bridal" Series

E-2833	85	Ringbearer	UPP	$11.00	3.00"	DVE	Secondary	$25.00
(208)	86		UPP	11.00		OLB	Secondary	20.00
	87		UPP	11.00		CED	Secondary	18.00
	88		UPP	13.00		FLW	Secondary	17.00
	89		UPP	15.00		B&A	Secondary	17.00
	90		UPP	16.50		FLM	Primary	16.50
	91		UPP	16.50		VSL	Primary	16.50
	92		OPEN	16.50		G/CL	Primary	16.50

SHARING OUR JOY TOGETHER — Figurine

E-2834	Year	Bridesmaid with Kitten	Status	Price	Size	Mark	Market	Value
E-2834	86	Bridesmaid with Kitten	UPP	$31.00	5.50"	OLB	Susp/Sec	$55.00
(268)	87		UPP	31.00		CED	Susp/Sec	50.00
	88		UPP	36.00		FLW	Susp/Sec	50.00
	89		UPP	38.50		B&A	Susp/Sec	50.00
	90		UPP	40.00		FLM	Susp/Prim	40.00
	91		UPP	40.00		VSL	Susp/Prim	40.00

FLOWER GIRL — Figurine — Third Issue "Bridal" Series

E-2835	Year	Flower Girl	Status	Price	Size	Mark	Market	Value
E-2835	85	Flower Girl	UPP	$11.00	3.00"	DVE	Secondary	$28.00
(209)	86		UPP	11.00		OLB	Secondary	25.00
	87		UPP	11.00		CED	Secondary	20.00
	88		UPP	13.00		FLW	Secondary	18.00
	89		UPP	15.00		B&A	Secondary	18.00
	90		UPP	16.50		FLM	Primary	16.50
	91		UPP	16.50		VSL	Primary	16.50
	92		OPEN	16.50		G/CL	Primary	16.50

GROOMSMAN — Figurine — Second Issue "Bridal" Series

E-2836	Year	Groomsman with Frog	Status	Price	Size	Mark	Market	Value
E-2836	84	Groomsman with Frog	UPP	$13.50	4.25"	CRS	Secondary	$30.00
(172)	85		UPP	13.50		DVE	Secondary	25.00
	86		UPP	13.50		OLB	Secondary	22.00
	87		UPP	13.50		CED	Secondary	20.00
	88		UPP	16.00		FLW	Secondary	20.00
	89		UPP	17.50		B&A	Secondary	20.00
	90		UPP	19.50		FLM	Primary	19.50
	91		UPP	19.50		VSL	Primary	19.50
	92		OPEN	19.50		G/CL	Primary	19.50

GROOM — Figurine — Sixth Issue "Bridal" Series

E-2837	Year	Groom	Status	Price	Size	Mark	Market	Value
E-2837	86	Groom	UPP	$15.00	4.50"	OLB*	Secondary	$40.00
(269)	87		UPP	15.00		CED	Secondary	30.00
	88		UPP	18.00		FLW	Secondary	25.00
	89		UPP	20.00		B&A	Secondary	23.00
	90		UPP	22.50		FLM	Primary	22.50
	91		UPP	22.50		VSL	Primary	22.50
	92		OPEN	22.50		G/CL	Primary	22.50

*Termed the "No Hands Groom," during the first year of production (OLIVE BRANCH Annual Symbol) this piece was produced with no hands. The mold was changed for the subsequent years (CEDAR TREE to present) to show the boy's hands.
Full color photograph: 5th Ed., pg. 198. One color photo: 6th Ed., pg. 222.

THIS IS THE DAY WHICH THE LORD HATH MADE — Figurine — Eighth & Final Issue "Bridal" Series

E-2838	Year	Complete Wedding Party	Status	Price	Size	Mark	Market	Value
E-2838	87	Complete Wedding Party	Annual	$175.00	5.25"	CED	Secondary	$190.00
(312)								

BABY'S FIRST STEP — Figurine — First Issue "Baby's First" Series

E-2840	Year	Angel Carrying Baby	Status	Price	Size	Mark	Market	Value
E-2840	84	Angel Carrying Baby	UPP	$35.00	5.25"	CRS	Susp/Sec	$75.00
(173)	85		UPP	35.00		DVE	Susp/Sec	70.00
	86		UPP	35.00		OLB	Susp/Sec	65.00
	87		UPP	35.00		CED	Susp/Sec	65.00
	88		UPP	40.00		FLW	Susp/Sec	60.00

BABY'S FIRST PICTURE — Figurine — Second Issue "Baby's First" Series

E-2841	Year	Angel Taking Baby's Picture	Status	Price	Size	Mark	Market	Value
E-2841	84	Angel Taking Baby's Picture	UPP	$45.00	5.00"	CRS	Retired/Sec	$125.00
(174)	85		UPP	45.00		DVE	Retired/Sec	115.00
	86		UPP	45.00		OLB	Retired/Sec	105.00

JUNIOR BRIDESMAID — Figurine — Fifth Issue "Bridal" Series

E-2845	Year	Junior Bridesmaid	Status	Price	Size	Mark	Market	Value
E-2845	86	Junior Bridesmaid	UPP	$12.50	3.75"	OLB	Secondary	$30.00
(210)	87		UPP	12.50		CED	Secondary	22.00
	88		UPP	15.00		FLW	Secondary	20.00
	89		UPP	17.00		B&A	Secondary	19.00
	90		UPP	18.50		FLM	Primary	18.50
	91		UPP	18.50		VSL	Primary	18.50
	92		OPEN	18.50		G/CL	Primary	18.50

BRIDE — Figurine — Seventh Issue "Bridal" Series

E-2846	87	Bride	UPP	$18.00	4.75"	CED	Secondary	$32.00
(313)	88		UPP	22.50		FLW	Secondary	28.00
	89		UPP	25.00		B&A	Secondary	25.00
	90		UPP	25.00		FLM	Primary	25.00
	91		UPP	25.00		VSL	Primary	25.00
	92		OPEN	25.00		G/CL	Primary	25.00

LOVE IS KIND — Plate — Fourth Issue "Inspired Thoughts" Series — Individually Numbered

E-2847	84	Boy Pushing Girl on Swing	15,000	$40.00	8.50"	UM	Secondary	$45.00
(175)						CRS	Secondary	40.00

LOVING THY NEIGHBOR — Plate — Fourth Issue "Mother's Love" Series — Individually Numbered

E-2848	84	Mother Wrapping Bread	15,000	$40.00	8.50"	CRS	Secondary	$40.00
(176)								

MOTHER SEW DEAR — Doll

E-2850	*	Mother Needlepointing	UPP	$350.00	16.00"	UM	Retired/Sec	$350.00
(30)	84		UPP	350.00		CRS	Retired/Sec	350.00
	85		UPP	350.00		DVE	Retired/Sec	350.00

* UNMARKED (UM) pieces could have been produced in any of the years of production.

KRISTY — Doll

E-2851	84	Baby Collector Doll	UPP	$150.00	12.00"	CRS	Susp/Sec	$185.00
(177)	85		UPP	150.00		DVE	Susp/Sec	170.00
	86		UPP	150.00		OLB	Susp/Sec	170.00
	87		UPP	150.00		CED	Susp/Sec	170.00
	88		UPP	160.00		FLW	Susp/Sec	170.00
	89		UPP	170.00		B&A	Susp/Sec	170.00

BABY FIGURINES — Figurines — Set of 6 — (Divide by 6 for an "each" value)

E-2852	84	Baby Figurines	UPP	$72.00	3.50"	CRS	Secondary	$150.00
(178)	85		UPP	72.00		DVE	Secondary	120.00
	86		UPP	72.00		OLB	Secondary	99.00
	87		UPP	72.00		CED	Secondary	99.00

In 1987 individual Enesco Item #s were assigned for each figurine in the above set of 6:

BABY FIGURINE — Figurine

E-2852/A	87	Baby Boy Standing	UPP	$12.00	3.75"	CED	Secondary	$16.50
(401)	88		UPP	14.00		FLW	Secondary	16.50
	89		UPP	15.00		B&A	Secondary	16.50
	90		UPP	16.50		FLM	Primary	16.50
	91		UPP	16.50		VSL	Primary	16.50
	92		OPEN	16.50		G/CL	Primary	16.50

BABY FIGURINE — Figurine

E-2852/B	87	Baby Girl with Bow in Hair	UPP	$12.00	3.75"	CED	Secondary	$16.50
(402)	88		UPP	14.00		FLW	Secondary	16.50
	89		UPP	15.00		B&A	Secondary	16.50
	90		UPP	16.50		FLM	Primary	16.50
	91		UPP	16.50		VSL	Primary	16.50
	92		OPEN	16.50		G/CL	Primary	16.50

BABY FIGURINE — Figurine

E-2852/C	87	Baby Boy Sitting	UPP	$12.00	3.00"	CED	Secondary	$16.50
(403)	88		UPP	14.00		FLW	Secondary	16.50
	89		UPP	15.00		B&A	Secondary	16.50
	90		UPP	16.50		FLM	Primary	16.50
	91		UPP	16.50		VSL	Primary	16.50
	92		OPEN	16.50		G/CL	Primary	16.50

<u>BABY FIGURINE</u>		Figurine						
E-2852/D	87	Baby Girl Clapping Hands	UPP	$12.00	3.25"	CED	Secondary	$16.50
(404)	88		UPP	14.00		FLW	Secondary	16.50
	89		UPP	15.00		B&A	Secondary	16.50
	90		UPP	16.50		FLM	Primary	16.50
	91		UPP	16.50		VSL	Primary	16.50
	92		OPEN	16.50		G/CL	Primary	16.50
<u>BABY FIGURINE</u>		Figurine						
E-2852/E	87	Baby Boy Crawling	UPP	$12.00	2.75"	CED	Secondary	$16.50
(405)	88		UPP	14.00		FLW	Secondary	16.50
	89		UPP	15.00		B&A	Secondary	16.50
	90		UPP	16.50		FLM	Primary	16.50
	91		UPP	16.50		VSL	Primary	16.50
	92		OPEN	16.50		G/CL	Primary	16.50
<u>BABY FIGURINE</u>		Figurine						
E-2852/F	87	Baby Girl Lying Down	UPP	$12.00	2.50"	CED	Secondary	$16.50
(406)	88		UPP	14.00		FLW	Secondary	16.50
	89		UPP	15.00		B&A	Secondary	16.50
	90		UPP	16.50		FLM	Primary	16.50
	91		UPP	16.50		VSL	Primary	16.50
	92		OPEN	16.50		G/CL	Primary	16.50
<u>GOD BLESSED OUR YEARS TOGETHER WITH SO MUCH LOVE & HAPPINESS</u>						Figurine		
E-2853	84	Happy Anniversary	UPP	$35.00	5.50"	CRS	Secondary	$62.00
(179)	85		UPP	35.00		DVE	Secondary	50.00
	86		UPP	35.00		OLB	Secondary	50.00
	87		UPP	35.00		CED	Secondary	50.00
	88		UPP	40.00		FLW	Secondary	50.00
	89		UPP	45.00		B&A	Secondary	50.00
	90		UPP	50.00		FLM	Primary	50.00
	91		UPP	50.00		VSL	Primary	50.00
	92		OPEN	50.00		G/CL	Primary	50.00
<u>GOD BLESSED OUR YEAR TOGETHER WITH SO MUCH LOVE & HAPPINESS</u>						Figurine		
E-2854	84	First Anniversary	UPP	$35.00	5.50"	CRS	Secondary	$60.00
(180)	85		UPP	35.00		DVE	Secondary	50.00
	86		UPP	35.00		OLB	Secondary	50.00
	87		UPP	35.00		CED	Secondary	50.00
	88		UPP	40.00		FLW	Secondary	50.00
	89		UPP	45.00		B&A	Secondary	50.00
	90		UPP	50.00		FLM	Primary	50.00
	91		UPP	50.00		VSL	Primary	50.00
	92		OPEN	50.00		G/CL	Primary	50.00
<u>GOD BLESSED OUR YEARS TOGETHER WITH SO MUCH LOVE & HAPPINESS</u>						Figurine		
E-2855	84	5th Anniversary	UPP	$35.00	5.50"	CRS	Secondary	$55.00
(181)	85		UPP	35.00		DVE	Secondary	50.00
	86		UPP	35.00		OLB	Secondary	50.00
	87		UPP	35.00		CED	Secondary	50.00
	88		UPP	40.00		FLW	Secondary	50.00
	89		UPP	45.00		B&A	Secondary	50.00
	90		UPP	50.00		FLM	Primary	50.00
	91		UPP	50.00		VSL	Primary	50.00
	92		OPEN	50.00		G/CL	Primary	50.00
<u>GOD BLESSED OUR YEARS TOGETHER WITH SO MUCH LOVE & HAPPINESS</u>						Figurine		
E-2856	84	10th Anniversary	UPP	$35.00	5.50"	CRS	Secondary	$55.00
(182)	85		UPP	35.00		DVE	Secondary	50.00
	86		UPP	35.00		OLB	Secondary	50.00
	87		UPP	35.00		CED	Secondary	50.00
	88		UPP	40.00		FLW	Secondary	50.00
	89		UPP	45.00		B&A	Secondary	50.00
	90		UPP	50.00		FLM	Primary	50.00
	91		UPP	50.00		VSL	Primary	50.00
	92		OPEN	50.00		G/CL	Primary	50.00

GOD BLESSED OUR YEARS TOGETHER WITH SO MUCH LOVE & HAPPINESS — Figurine

E-2857	84	25th Anniversary	UPP	$35.00	5.50"	CRS	Secondary	$65.00
(183)	85		UPP	35.00		DVE	Secondary	50.00
	86		UPP	35.00		OLB	Secondary	50.00
	87		UPP	35.00		CED	Secondary	50.00
	88		UPP	40.00		FLW	Secondary	50.00
	89		UPP	45.00		B&A	Secondary	50.00
	90		UPP	50.00		FLM	Primary	50.00
	91		UPP	50.00		VSL	Primary	50.00
	92		OPEN	50.00		G/CL	Primary	50.00

GOD BLESSED OUR YEARS TOGETHER WITH SO MUCH LOVE & HAPPINESS — Figurine

E-2859	84	40th Anniversary	UPP	$35.00	5.50"	CRS	Secondary	$65.00
(184)	85		UPP	35.00		DVE	Secondary	50.00
	86		UPP	35.00		OLB	Secondary	50.00
	87		UPP	35.00		CED	Secondary	50.00
	88		UPP	40.00		FLW	Secondary	50.00
	89		UPP	45.00		B&A	Secondary	50.00
	90		UPP	50.00		FLM	Primary	50.00
	91		UPP	50.00		VSL	Primary	50.00
	92		OPEN	50.00		G/CL	Primary	50.00

GOD BLESSED OUR YEARS TOGETHER WITH SO MUCH LOVE & HAPPINESS — Figurine

E-2860	84	50th Anniversary	UPP	$35.00	5.50"	CRS	Secondary	$65.00
(185)	85		UPP	35.00		DVE	Secondary	55.00
	86		UPP	35.00		OLB	Secondary	55.00
	87		UPP	35.00		CED	Secondary	52.00
	88		UPP	40.00		FLW	Secondary	50.00
	89		UPP	45.00		B&A	Secondary	50.00
	90		UPP	50.00		FLM	Primary	50.00
	91		UPP	50.00		VSL	Primary	50.00
	92		OPEN	50.00		G/CL	Primary	50.00

BLESSED ARE THE PURE IN HEART — Figurine

E-3104	80	Rocking Cradle	UPP	$ 9.00	2.75"	NM	Susp/Sec	$50.00
(28)	81		UPP	10.50		TRI	Susp/Sec	45.00
	82		UPP	12.00		HRG	Susp/Sec	42.00
	83		UPP	12.00		FSH	Susp/Sec	40.00
	84		UPP	13.50		CRS	Susp/Sec	38.00
	85		UPP	13.50		DVE	Susp/Sec	35.00
	86		UPP	13.50		OLB	Susp/Sec	35.00
	87		UPP	13.50		CED	Susp/Sec	32.00
	88		UPP	16.00		FLW	Susp/Sec	30.00
	89		UPP	17.50		B&A	Susp/Sec	28.00
	90		UPP	19.00		FLM	Susp/Sec	28.00
	91		UPP	19.00		VSL	Susp/Sec	25.00

HE WATCHES OVER US ALL — Figurine

E-3105	80	Boy on Crutches with Bible	UPP	$11.00	5.25"	NM	Susp/Sec	$85.00
(29)	81		UPP	11.00		TRI	Susp/Sec	80.00
	82		UPP	15.00		HRG	Susp/Sec	70.00
	83		UPP	15.00		FSH	Susp/Sec	65.00
	84		UPP	17.00		CRS	Susp/Sec	60.00

MOTHER SEW DEAR — Figurine

E-3106	80	Mother Needlepointing	UPP	$11.00	5.00"	NM	Secondary	$75.00
(30)	81		UPP	13.00		TRI	Secondary	60.00
	82		UPP	16.00		HRG	Secondary	48.00
	83		UPP	16.00		FSH	Secondary	40.00
	84		UPP	17.00		CRS	Secondary	30.00
	85		UPP	17.00		DVE	Secondary	28.00
	86		UPP	17.00		OLB	Secondary	28.00
	87		UPP	17.00		CED	Secondary	28.00
	88		UPP	22.50		FLW	Secondary	28.00
	89		UPP	25.00		B&A	Secondary	28.00
	90		UPP	27.50		FLM	Primary	27.50
	91		UPP	27.50		VSL	Primary	27.50
	92		OPEN	27.50		G/CL	Primary	27.50

BLESSED ARE THE PEACEMAKERS — Figurine

E-3107	80	Boy Holding Cat & Dog	UPP	$13.00	5.25"	NM	Retired/Sec	$110.00
(31)	81		UPP	15.00		TRI	Retired/Sec	90.00
	82		UPP	17.00		HRG	Retired/Sec	80.00
	83		UPP	17.00		FSH	Retired/Sec	75.00
	84		UPP	19.00		CRS	Retired/Sec	70.00
	85		UPP	19.00		DVE	Retired/Sec	65.00

THE HAND THAT ROCKS THE FUTURE — Figurine

E-3108	80	Girl Rocking Cradle	UPP	$13.00	4.50"	NM	Susp/Sec	$90.00
(32)	81		UPP	15.00		TRI	Susp/Sec	80.00
	82		UPP	17.00		HRG	Susp/Sec	70.00
	83		UPP	17.00		FSH	Susp/Sec	65.00
	84		UPP	17.00		CRS	Susp/Sec	65.00

THE PURR-FECT GRANDMA — Figurine

E-3109	80	Grandma in Rocker	UPP	$13.00	4.75"	NM	Secondary	$70.00
(33)	81		UPP	15.00		TRI	Secondary	65.00
	82		UPP	17.00		HRG	Secondary	45.00
	83		UPP	17.00		FSH	Secondary	40.00
	84		UPP	19.00		CRS	Secondary	38.00
	85		UPP	19.00		DVE	Secondary	30.00
	86		UPP	19.00		OLB	Secondary	28.00
	87		UPP	19.00		CED	Secondary	28.00
	88		UPP	23.00		FLW	Secondary	28.00
	89		UPP	25.00		B&A	Secondary	28.00
	90		UPP	27.50		FLM	Primary	27.50
	91		UPP	27.50		VSL	Primary	27.50
	92		OPEN	27.50		G/CL	Primary	27.50

LOVING IS SHARING — Figurine

E-3110B	80	Boy Sharing with Puppy	UPP	$13.00	4.50"	NM	Secondary	$80.00
(34)	81		UPP	15.00		TRI	Secondary	60.00
	82		UPP	17.00		HRG	Secondary	45.00
	83		UPP	17.00		FSH	Secondary	40.00
	84		UPP	19.00		CRS	Secondary	38.00
	85		UPP	19.00		DVE	Secondary	35.00
	86		UPP	19.00		OLB	Secondary	32.00
	87		UPP	19.00		CED	Secondary	30.00
	88		UPP	24.00		FLW	Secondary	30.00
	89		UPP	27.50		B&A	Secondary	30.00
	90		UPP	30.00		FLM	Primary	30.00
	91		UPP	30.00		VSL	Primary	30.00
	92		OPEN	30.00		G/CL	Primary	30.00

LOVING IS SHARING — Figurine

E-3110G	80	Girl Sharing with Puppy	UPP	$13.00	4.50"	NM	Secondary	$90.00
(35)	81		UPP	15.00		TRI	Secondary	60.00
	82		UPP	17.00		HRG	Secondary	50.00
	83		UPP	17.00		FSH	Secondary	40.00
	84		UPP	19.00		CRS	Secondary	35.00
	85		UPP	19.00		DVE	Secondary	32.00
	86		UPP	19.00		OLB	Secondary	30.00
	87		UPP	19.00		CED	Secondary	30.00
	88		UPP	24.00		FLW	Secondary	30.00
	89		UPP	27.50		B&A	Secondary	30.00
	90		UPP	30.00		FLM	Primary	30.00
	91		UPP	30.00		VSL	Primary	30.00
	92		OPEN	30.00		G/CL	Primary	30.00

BE NOT WEARY IN WELL DOING — Figurine

E-3111	80	Girl Helper	UPP	$14.00	4.00"	NM	Retired/Sec	$125.00
(36)	81		UPP	16.00		TRI	Retired/Sec	110.00
	82		UPP	18.00		HRG	Retired/Sec	90.00
	83		UPP	18.00		FSH	Retired/Sec	85.00
	84		UPP	19.00		CRS	Retired/Sec	80.00
	85		UPP	19.00		DVE	Retired/Sec	75.00

Classic Variation. Figurines exist in NO MARK versions with an error in the Inspirational Title on the understamp decal. Instead of "Be Not Weary In Well Doing," they read "Be Not Weary And Well Doing." The black and white boxes which the pieces were shipped in also have the incorrect title on the label. The GREENBOOK Market Price for "...And Well Doing" is $160.00. Full color photograph: 5th Ed., pg. 204.

GOD'S SPEED — Figurine

E-3112	80	Boy Jogging with Dog	UPP	$14.00	4.75"	NM	Retired/Sec	$105.00
(44)	81		UPP	16.00		TRI	Retired/Sec	90.00
	82		UPP	18.00		HRG	Retired/Sec	75.00
	83		UPP	18.00		FSH	Retired/Sec	70.00

Exists in a double mark TRIANGLE/HOURGLASS.

THOU ART MINE — Figurine

E-3113	80	Boy with Girl Writing	UPP	$16.00	5.00"	NM	Secondary	$85.00
(37)	81	in Sand	UPP	19.00		TRI	Secondary	75.00
	82		UPP	22.50		HRG	Secondary	60.00
	83		UPP	22.50		FSH	Secondary	45.00
	84		UPP	25.00		CRS	Secondary	40.00
	85		UPP	25.00		DVE	Secondary	35.00
	86		UPP	25.00		OLB	Secondary	35.00
	87		UPP	25.00		CED	Secondary	35.00
	88		UPP	30.00		FLW	Secondary	35.00
	89		UPP	33.00		B&A	Secondary	35.00
	90		UPP	35.00		FLM	Primary	35.00
	91		UPP	35.00		VSL	Primary	35.00
	92		OPEN	35.00		G/CL	Primary	35.00

THE LORD BLESS YOU AND KEEP YOU — Figurine

E-3114	80	Bride and Groom	UPP	$16.00	5.00"	NM	Secondary	$85.00
(38)	81		UPP	19.00		TRI	Secondary	65.00
	82		UPP	22.50		HRG	Secondary	60.00
	83		UPP	22.50		FSH	Secondary	50.00
	84		UPP	25.00		CRS	Secondary	45.00
	85		UPP	25.00		DVE	Secondary	40.00
	86		UPP	25.00		OLB	Secondary	38.00
	87		UPP	25.00		CED	Secondary	38.00
	88		UPP	32.50		FLW	Secondary	38.00
	89		UPP	37.50		B&A	Secondary	38.00
	90		UPP	37.50		FLM	Primary	37.50
	91		UPP	37.50		VSL	Primary	37.50
	92		OPEN	37.50		G/CL	Primary	37.50

BUT LOVE GOES ON FOREVER — Figurine

E-3115	Year		Boy and Girl Angels on Cloud		Price	Size	Mark	Status	Value
E-3115	80		Boy and Girl Angels on Cloud	UPP	$16.50	5.25"	NM	Secondary	$90.00
(39)	81			UPP	19.00		TRI	Secondary	70.00
	82			UPP	22.50		HRG	Secondary	55.00
	83			UPP	22.50		FSH	Secondary	50.00
	84			UPP	25.00		CRS	Secondary	45.00
	85			UPP	25.00		DVE	Secondary	40.00
	86			UPP	25.00		OLB	Secondary	38.00
	87			UPP	25.00		CED	Secondary	35.00
	88			UPP	30.00		FLW	Secondary	35.00
	89			UPP	33.00		B&A	Secondary	35.00
	90			UPP	35.00		FLM	Primary	35.00
	91			UPP	35.00		VSL	Primary	35.00
	92			OPEN	35.00		G/CL	Primary	35.00

THEE I LOVE — Figurine

E-3116	Year		Boy Carving Tree for Girl		Price	Size	Mark	Status	Value
E-3116	80		Boy Carving Tree for Girl	UPP	$16.50	6.00"	NM	Secondary	$100.00
(40)	81			UPP	19.00		TRI	Secondary	80.00
	82			UPP	22.50		HRG	Secondary	55.00
	83			UPP	22.50		FSH	Secondary	50.00
	84			UPP	25.00		CRS	Secondary	45.00
	85			UPP	25.00		DVE	Secondary	40.00
	86			UPP	25.00		OLB	Secondary	38.00
	87			UPP	25.00		CED	Secondary	38.00
	88			UPP	32.50		FLW	Secondary	38.00
	89			UPP	36.00		B&A	Secondary	38.00
	90			UPP	37.50		FLM	Primary	37.50
	91			UPP	37.50		VSL	Primary	37.50
	92			OPEN	37.50		G/CL	Primary	37.50

WALKING BY FAITH — Figurine

E-3117	Year		Boy Pulling Wagon with Girl		Price	Size	Mark	Status	Value
E-3117	80		Boy Pulling Wagon with Girl	UPP	$35.00	7.25"	NM	Secondary	$115.00
(41)	81			UPP	40.00		TRI	Secondary	100.00
	82			UPP	45.00		HRG	Secondary	90.00
	83			UPP	45.00		FSH	Secondary	85.00
	84			UPP	50.00		CRS	Secondary	80.00
	85			UPP	50.00		DVE	Secondary	80.00
	86			UPP	50.00		OLB	Secondary	75.00
	87			UPP	50.00		CED	Secondary	70.00
	88			UPP	60.00		FLW	Secondary	70.00
	89			UPP	67.50		B&A	Secondary	70.00
	90			UPP	70.00		FLM	Primary	70.00
	91			UPP	70.00		VSL	Primary	70.00
	92			OPEN	70.00		G/CL	Primary	70.00

EGGS OVER EASY — Figurine

E-3118	Year		Girl with Frypan		Price	Size	Mark	Status	Value
E-3118	80		Girl with Frypan	UPP	$12.00	5.00"	NM	Retired/Sec	$110.00
(45)	81			UPP	14.00		TRI	Retired/Sec	90.00
	82			UPP	15.00		HRG	Retired/Sec	80.00
	83			UPP	15.00		FSH	Retired/Sec	75.00

IT'S WHAT'S INSIDE THAT COUNTS — Figurine

E-3119	Year		Boy with Books		Price	Size	Mark	Status	Value
E-3119	80		Boy with Books	UPP	$13.00	5.25"	NM	Susp/Sec	$125.00
(42)	81			UPP	15.00		TRI	Susp/Sec	115.00
	82			UPP	17.00		HRG	Susp/Sec	100.00
	83			UPP	17.00		FSH	Susp/Sec	95.00
	84			UPP	17.00		CRS	Susp/Sec	90.00

TO THEE WITH LOVE — Figurine

E-3120	Year		Girl with Box of Kittens		Price	Size	Mark	Status	Value
E-3120	80		Girl with Box of Kittens	UPP	$13.00	5.75"	NM	Susp/Sec	$90.00
(43)	81			UPP	15.00		TRI	Susp/Sec	70.00
	82			UPP	17.00		HRG	Susp/Sec	65.00
	83			UPP	17.00		FSH	Susp/Sec	62.00
	84			UPP	19.00		CRS	Susp/Sec	62.00
	85			UPP	19.00		DVE	Susp/Sec	60.00
	86			UPP	19.00		OLB	Susp/Sec	55.00

THE LORD BLESS YOU AND KEEP YOU — Figurine

E-4720	81	Boy Graduate	UPP	$14.00	5.25"	NM	Susp/Sec	$40.00
(46)	81		UPP	14.00		TRI	Susp/Sec	35.00
	82		UPP	17.00		HRG	Susp/Sec	32.00
	83		UPP	17.00		FSH	Susp/Sec	30.00
	84		UPP	19.00		CRS	Susp/Sec	30.00
	85		UPP	19.00		DVE	Susp/Sec	30.00
	86		UPP	19.00		OLB	Susp/Sec	30.00
	87		UPP	19.00		CED	Susp/Sec	30.00

THE LORD BLESS YOU AND KEEP YOU — Figurine

E-4721	81	Girl Graduate	UPP	$14.00	5.25"	NM	Secondary	$70.00
(47)	81		UPP	14.00		TRI	Secondary	55.00
	82		UPP	17.00		HRG	Secondary	45.00
	83		UPP	17.00		FSH	Secondary	40.00
	84		UPP	19.00		CRS	Secondary	35.00
	85		UPP	19.00		DVE	Secondary	30.00
	86		UPP	19.00		OLB	Secondary	30.00
	87		UPP	19.00		CED	Secondary	30.00
	88		UPP	24.00		FLW	Secondary	30.00
	89		UPP	27.00		B&A	Secondary	30.00
	90		UPP	30.00		FLM	Secondary	30.00
	91		UPP	30.00		VSL	Secondary	30.00
	92		OPEN	30.00		G/CL	Primary	30.00

LOVE CANNOT BREAK A TRUE FRIENDSHIP — Figurine

E-4722	81	Girl with Piggy Bank	UPP	$22.50	5.00"	NM	Susp/Sec	$140.00
(48)	81		UPP	22.50		TRI	Susp/Sec	120.00
	82		UPP	25.00		HRG	Susp/Sec	115.00
	83		UPP	25.00		FSH	Susp/Sec	110.00
	84		UPP	27.50		CRS	Susp/Sec	105.00
	85		UPP	27.50		DVE	Susp/Sec	95.00

PEACE AMID THE STORM — Figurine

E-4723	81	Boy Reading Holy Bible	UPP	$22.50	4.75"	NM	Susp/Sec	$85.00
(49)	81		UPP	22.50		TRI	Susp/Sec	75.00
	82		UPP	25.00		HRG	Susp/Sec	70.00
	83		UPP	25.00		FSH	Susp/Sec	65.00
	84		UPP	27.50		CRS	Susp/Sec	60.00

REJOICING WITH YOU — Figurine

E-4724	81	Christening	UPP	$25.00	5.25"	NM	Secondary	$95.00
(50)	81		UPP	25.00		TRI	Secondary	75.00
	82		UPP	27.50		HRG	Secondary	65.00
	83		UPP	27.50		FSH	Secondary	55.00
	84		UPP	30.00		CRS	Secondary	55.00
	85		UPP	30.00		DVE	Secondary	52.00
	86		UPP	30.00		OLB	Secondary	50.00
	87		UPP	30.00		CED	Secondary	45.00
	88		UPP	37.50		FLW	Secondary	45.00
	89		UPP	40.00		B&A	Secondary	45.00
	90		UPP	45.00		FLM	Secondary	45.00
	91		UPP	45.00		VSL	Primary	45.00
	92		OPEN	45.00		G/CL	Primary	45.00

Classic Variation: "No E" or "Bibl Error." During the first years of production the "e" was missing from the word Bible. It appears as though all NO MARK, TRIANGLE, and HOURGLASS pieces as well as some FISH pieces have this variation.
Full color photograph: 4th Ed., pg. 195 or 5th Ed., pg. 203.

PEACE ON EARTH — Figurine

E-4725	81	Choir Boys with Bandages	UPP	$25.00	5.25"	NM	Susp/Sec	$90.00
(51)	81		UPP	25.00		TRI	Susp/Sec	75.00
	82		UPP	27.50		HRG	Susp/Sec	70.00
	83		UPP	27.50		FSH	Susp/Sec	65.00
	84		UPP	27.50		CRS	Susp/Sec	60.00

PEACE ON EARTH — Musical — TUNE: Jesus Loves Me

E-4726	81	Choir Boys with Bandages	UPP	$45.00	6.25"	NM	Susp/Sec	$120.00
(51)	81		UPP	45.00		TRI	Susp/Sec	110.00
	82		UPP	45.00		HRG	Susp/Sec	105.00
	83		UPP	45.00		FSH	Susp/Sec	100.00
	84		UPP	45.00		CRS	Susp/Sec	95.00

BEAR YE ONE ANOTHER'S BURDENS — Figurine

E-5200	81	Sad Boy with Teddy	UPP	$20.00	4.74"	NM	Susp/Sec	$100.00
(52)	81		UPP	20.00		TRI	Susp/Sec	85.00
	82		UPP	22.50		HRG	Susp/Sec	80.00
	83		UPP	22.50		FSH	Susp/Sec	75.00
	84		UPP	25.00		CRS	Susp/Sec	70.00

LOVE LIFTED ME — Figurine

E-5201	81	Boy Helping Friend	UPP	$25.00	5.50"	NM	Susp/Sec	$100.00
(53)	81		UPP	25.00		TRI	Susp/Sec	85.00
	82		UPP	30.00		HRG	Susp/Sec	75.00
	83		UPP	30.00		FSH	Susp/Sec	70.00
	84		UPP	33.00		CRS	Susp/Sec	65.00

THANK YOU FOR COMING TO MY ADE — Figurine

E-5202	81	Lemonade Stand	UPP	$22.50	5.50"	NM	Susp/Sec	$125.00
(54)	81		UPP	22.50		TRI	Susp/Sec	110.00
	82		UPP	27.50		HRG	Susp/Sec	105.00
	83		UPP	27.50		FSH	Susp/Sec	100.00
	84		UPP	30.00		CRS	Susp/Sec	95.00

LET NOT THE SUN GO DOWN UPON YOUR WRATH — Figurine

E-5203	81	Boy with Dog on Stairs	UPP	$22.50	6.75"	NM	Susp/Sec	$160.00
(55)	81		UPP	22.50		TRI	Susp/Sec	135.00
	82		UPP	27.50		HRG	Susp/Sec	130.00
	83		UPP	30.00		FSH	Susp/Sec	120.00
	84		UPP	30.00		CRS	Susp/Sec	115.00

THE HAND THAT ROCKS THE FUTURE — Musical — TUNE: Mozart's Lullaby

E-5204	81	Girl Rocking Cradle	UPP	$30.00	5.50"	NM	Secondary	$90.00
(32)	81		UPP	30.00		TRI	Secondary	80.00
	82		UPP	35.00		HRG	Secondary	75.00
	83		UPP	35.00		FSH	Secondary	70.00
	84		UPP	37.50		CRS	Secondary	65.00
	85		UPP	37.50		DVE	Secondary	60.00
	86		UPP	37.50		OLB	Secondary	55.00
	87		UPP	37.50		CED	Secondary	55.00
	88		UPP	45.00		FLW	Secondary	55.00
	89		UPP	50.00		B&A	Secondary	55.00
	90		UPP	55.00		FLM	Primary	55.00
	91		UPP	55.00		VSL	Primary	55.00
	92		OPEN	55.00		G/CL	Primary	55.00

MY GUARDIAN ANGEL — Musical — TUNE: Brahm's Lullaby

E-5205	81	Boy Angel on Cloud	UPP	$22.50	5.50"	NM	Susp/Sec	$85.00
(56)	84		UPP	27.50		CRS	Susp/Sec	75.00
	85		UPP	27.50		DVE	Susp/Sec	65.00

MY GUARDIAN ANGEL — Musical — TUNE: Brahm's Lullaby

E-5206	81	Girl Angel on Cloud	UPP	$22.50	5.50"	NM	Susp/Sec	$85.00
(57)	84		UPP	27.50		CRS	Susp/Sec	75.00
	85		UPP	27.50		DVE	Susp/Sec	70.00
	86		UPP	27.50		OLB	Susp/Sec	65.00
	87		UPP	27.50		CED	Susp/Sec	60.00
	88		UPP	33.00		FLW	Susp/Sec	60.00

MY GUARDIAN ANGELS — Night Light

E-5207	81	Boy & Girl Angels on Cloud	UPP	$30.00	3.50"	NM	Susp/Sec	$180.00
(39)	84		UPP	35.00		CRS	Susp/Sec	150.00

JESUS LOVES ME — Bell

E-5208	81	Boy with Teddy	UPP	$15.00	5.75"	NM	Susp/Sec	$50.00
(1)	84		UPP	19.00		CRS	Susp/Sec	40.00
	85		UPP	19.00		DVE	Susp/Sec	37.00

JESUS LOVES ME — Bell

E-5209	81	Girl with Bunny	UPP	$15.00	5.75"	NM	Susp/Sec	$50.00
(2)	84		UPP	19.00		CRS	Susp/Sec	45.00
	85		UPP	19.00		DVE	Susp/Sec	40.00

PRAYER CHANGES THINGS — Bell

E-5210	81	Girl Praying	UPP	$15.00	5.75"	NM	Susp/Sec	$50.00
(58)	84		UPP	19.00		CRS	Susp/Sec	40.00

GOD UNDERSTANDS — Bell

E-5211	81	Boy with Report Card	UPP	$15.00	5.75"	UM	Retired/Sec	$50.00
(12)	84		UPP	19.00		CRS	Retired/Sec	40.00

TO A SPECIAL DAD — Figurine

E-5212	81	Boy in Dad's Duds	UPP	$20.00	5.50"	NM	Secondary	$75.00
(59)	81	with Dog	UPP	20.00		TRI	Secondary	65.00
	82		UPP	22.50		HRG	Secondary	55.00
	83		UPP	22.50		FSH	Secondary	42.00
	84		UPP	25.00		CRS	Secondary	40.00
	85		UPP	25.00		DVE	Secondary	35.00
	86		UPP	25.00		OLB	Secondary	35.00
	87		UPP	25.00		CED	Secondary	35.00
	88		UPP	30.00		FLW	Secondary	35.00
	89		UPP	33.00		B&A	Secondary	35.00
	90		UPP	35.00		FLM	Primary	35.00
	91		UPP	35.00		VSL	Primary	35.00
	92		OPEN	35.00		G/CL	Primary	35.00

GOD IS LOVE — Figurine

E-5213	81	Girl with Goose in Lap	UPP	$17.00	5.00"	NM	Susp/Sec	$100.00
(60)	81		UPP	17.00		TRI	Susp/Sec	75.00
	82		UPP	20.00		HRG	Susp/Sec	65.00
	83		UPP	20.00		FSH	Susp/Sec	62.00
	84		UPP	22.50		CRS	Susp/Sec	60.00
	85		UPP	22.50		DVE	Susp/Sec	50.00
	86		UPP	22.50		OLB	Susp/Sec	50.00
	87		UPP	22.50		CED	Susp/Sec	50.00
	88		UPP	27.00		FLW	Susp/Sec	50.00
	89		UPP	30.00		B&A	Susp/Sec	50.00

This piece was re-sculpted in 1985. On the original mold the girl had no chin.

PRAYER CHANGES THINGS — Figurine

E-5214	81	Boy & Girl Praying at Table	UPP	$35.00	5.15"	NM	Susp/Sec	*
(61)	81	with Bible	UPP	35.00		TRI	Susp/Sec	*
	82		UPP	35.00		HRG	Susp/Sec	*
	83		UPP	35.00		FSH	Susp/Sec	$95.00
	84		UPP	37.50		CRS	Susp/Sec	90.00
						DVE	Susp/Sec	85.00

Piece was suspended in 1984 yet exists in a DOVE.

Classic Variation: "Backwards Bible." The first production of this figurine had the words "Holy Bible" inscribed on the back cover. Pieces with this error exist in NO MARK and TRIANGLE versions. Reportedly, NO MARK and TRIANGLE pieces also exist where the title is correctly placed, but these may be considered extremely rare. The majority of HOURGLASS pieces have the correctly placed title. GREENBOOK Market Prices are as follows: Backwards NO MARK $165.00, Backwards TRIANGLE $155.00, Backwards HOURGLASS $135.00, and correct HOURGLASS $120.00.

Full color photo: 4th Ed., pg. 195 or 5th Ed., pg. 202. One color photograph: 6th Ed., pg. 224.

LOVE ONE ANOTHER — Plate — First Issue "Inspired Thoughts" Series — Individually Numbered

E-5215	81	Boy and Girl on Stump	15,000	$40.00	8.50"	UM	Secondary	$65.00
(8)								

THE LORD BLESS YOU AND KEEP YOU — Plate

E-5216	81	Bride and Groom	UPP	$30.00	7.00"	UM	Susp/Sec	$45.00
(38)	84		UPP	30.00		CRS	Susp/Sec	40.00
	85		UPP	30.00		DVE	Susp/Sec	40.00
	86		UPP	30.00		OLB	Susp/Sec	40.00
	87		UPP	35.00		CED	Susp/Sec	40.00

MOTHER SEW DEAR — Plate — First Issue "Mother's Love" Series — Individually Numbered

E-5217	81	Mother Needlepointing	15,000	$40.00	8.50"	UM	Secondary	$70.00
(30)								

MAY YOUR CHRISTMAS BE BLESSED — Figurine

E-5376	84	Girl with Long Hair & Bible	UPP	$37.50	5.75"	CRS	Susp/Sec	$65.00
(186)	85		UPP	37.50		DVE	Susp/Sec	62.00
	86		UPP	37.50		OLB	Susp/Sec	60.00

LOVE IS KIND — Figurine

E-5377	84	Girl with Mouse	UPP	$27.50	4.00"	CRS	Retired/Sec	$90.00
(187)	85		UPP	27.50		DVE	Retired/Sec	85.00
	86		UPP	27.50		OLB	Retired/Sec	80.00
	87		UPP	27.50		CED	Retired/Sec	75.00

JOY TO THE WORLD — Figurine — Nativity Addition

E-5378	84	Boy Playing Harp	UPP	$18.00	4.00"	CRS	Susp/Sec	$45.00
(188)	85		UPP	18.00		DVE	Susp/Sec	40.00
	86		UPP	18.00		OLB	Susp/Sec	38.00
	87		UPP	18.00		CED	Susp/Sec	35.00
	88		UPP	20.00		FLW	Susp/Sec	35.00
	89		UPP	25.00		B&A	Susp/Sec	35.00

ISN'T HE PRECIOUS — Figurine — Nativity Addition

E-5379	84	Girl with Broom	UPP	$20.00	5.00"	CRS	Secondary	$42.00
(189)	85		UPP	20.00		DVE	Secondary	38.00
	86		UPP	20.00		OLB	Secondary	35.00
	87		UPP	20.00		CED	Secondary	32.00
	88		UPP	22.50		FLW	Secondary	30.00
	89		UPP	27.50		B&A	Secondary	30.00
	90		UPP	30.00		FLM	Primary	30.00
	91		UPP	30.00		VSL	Primary	30.00
	92		OPEN	30.00		G/CL	Primary	30.00

With the opening of a new production facility in Indonesia, numerous pieces of whiteware (unpainted figurines) were inadvertently shipped to retailers. The few known sales of this piece range from $250.00 to $400.00. Full color photograph: 5th Ed., pg. 204.

A MONARCH IS BORN — Figurine

E-5380	84	Boy with Butterfly at Manger	UPP	$33.00	5.00"	CRS	Susp/Sec	$65.00
(190)	85		UPP	33.00		DVE	Susp/Sec	62.00
	86		UPP	33.00		OLB	Susp/Sec	60.00

HIS NAME IS JESUS — Figurine

E-5381	84	Boys at Manger	UPP	$45.00	5.00"	CRS	Susp/Sec	$90.00
(191)	85		UPP	45.00		DVE	Susp/Sec	85.00
	86		UPP	45.00		OLB	Susp/Sec	80.00
	87		UPP	45.00		CED	Susp/Sec	75.00

FOR GOD SO LOVED THE WORLD — Figurines — Set of 4

E-5382	84	Deluxe 4 Piece Nativity	UPP	$70.00	5.00"	CRS	Susp/Sec	$125.00
(192)	85		UPP	70.00		DVE	Susp/Sec	105.00
	86		UPP	70.00		OLB	Susp/Sec	100.00

WISHING YOU A MERRY CHRISTMAS — Figurine, Dated

E-5383	84	Girl with Songbook	Annual	$17.00	4.75"	CRS	Secondary	$45.00
(193)								

I'LL PLAY MY DRUM FOR HIM   Figurine   Mini Nativity Addition

E-5384	84	Drummer Boy	UPP	$10.00	3.50"	CRS	Secondary	$27.00
(87)	85		UPP	10.00		DVE	Secondary	22.00
	86		UPP	10.00		OLB	Secondary	20.00
	87		UPP	10.00		CED	Secondary	18.00
	88		UPP	11.00		FLW	Secondary	18.00
	89		UPP	13.50		B&A	Secondary	15.00
	90		UPP	15.00		FLM	Primary	15.00
	91		UPP	15.00		VSL	Primary	15.00
	92		OPEN	15.00		G/CL	Primary	15.00

OH WORSHIP THE LORD   Figurine   Mini Nativity Addition

E-5385	84	Boy Angel with Candle	UPP	$10.00	3.25"	CRS	Susp/Sec	$35.00
(194)	85		UPP	10.00		DVE	Susp/Sec	30.00
	86		UPP	10.00		OLB	Susp/Sec	30.00

OH WORSHIP THE LORD   Figurine   Mini Nativity Addition

E-5386	84	Girl Angel Praying	UPP	$10.00	3.25"	CRS	Susp/Sec	$45.00
(195)	85		UPP	10.00		DVE	Susp/Sec	40.00
	86		UPP	10.00		OLB	Susp/Sec	40.00

WISHING YOU A MERRY CHRISTMAS   Ornament, Dated

E-5387	84	Girl with Songbook	Annual	$10.00	3.00"	CRS	Secondary	$35.00
(193)								

JOY TO THE WORLD   Ornament

E-5388	84	Boy Playing Harp	UPP	$10.00	2.50"	CRS	Retired/Sec	$45.00
(188)	85		UPP	10.00		DVE	Retired/Sec	40.00
	86		UPP	10.00		OLB	Retired/Sec	38.00
	87		UPP	10.00		CED	Retired/Sec	35.00

PEACE ON EARTH   Ornament

E-5389	84	Boy in Choir	UPP	$10.00	3.00"	CRS	Susp/Sec	$45.00
(196)	85		UPP	10.00		DVE	Susp/Sec	30.00
	86		UPP	10.00		OLB	Susp/Sec	30.00

MAY GOD BLESS YOU WITH A PERFECT SEASON   Ornament

E-5390	84	Girl in Scarf and Hat	UPP	$10.00	3.00"	CRS	Susp/Sec	$35.00
(197)	85		UPP	10.00		DVE	Susp/Sec	32.00
	86		UPP	10.00		OLB	Susp/Sec	28.00
	87		UPP	10.00		CED	Susp/Sec	25.00
	88		UPP	11.00		FLW	Susp/Sec	25.00
	89		UPP	13.50		B&A	Susp/Sec	25.00

LOVE IS KIND   Ornament

E-5391	84	Girl with Gift	UPP	$10.00	2.50"	CRS	Susp/Sec	$38.00
(198)	85		UPP	10.00		DVE	Susp/Sec	32.00
	86		UPP	10.00		OLB	Susp/Sec	30.00
	87		UPP	10.00		CED	Susp/Sec	30.00
	88		UPP	11.00		FLW	Susp/Sec	28.00
	89		UPP	13.50		B&A	Susp/Sec	28.00

BLESSED ARE THE PURE IN HEART   Ornament, Dated

E-5392	84	Baby in Cradle	Annual	$10.00	2.00"	CRS	Secondary	$35.00
(28)								

WISHING YOU A MERRY CHRISTMAS   Bell, Dated

E-5393	84	Girl with Songbook	Annual	$19.00	5.75"	CRS	Secondary	$42.00
(193)								

WISHING YOU A MERRY CHRISTMAS   Musical   TUNE: We Wish You A Merry Christmas

E-5394	84	Carollers with Puppy	UPP	$55.00	6.50"	CRS	Susp/Sec	$100.00
(200)	85		UPP	55.00		DVE	Susp/Sec	90.00
	86		UPP	55.00		OLB	Susp/Sec	85.00

UNTO US A CHILD IS BORN   Plate   Fourth Issue "Christmas Collection" Series
Individually Numbered

E-5395	84	Shepherds and Lambs	15,000	$40.00	8.50"	UM	Secondary	$45.00
(201)		on Hillside				CRS	Secondary	40.00

THE WONDER OF CHRISTMAS   Plate, Dated   Third Issue "Joy of Christmas" Series

E-5396	84	Boy Pulling Girl and Tree	Annual	$40.00	8.50"	CRS	Secondary	$70.00
(202)		on Sled						

TIMMY   Doll

E-5397	84	Boy Jogger	UPP	$125.00	10.00"	CRS	Susp/Sec	$170.00
(203)	85		UPP	125.00		DVE	Susp/Sec	155.00
	86		UPP	125.00		OLB	Susp/Sec	155.00
	87		UPP	125.00		CED	Susp/Prim	150.00
	88		UPP	135.00		FLW	Susp/Prim	150.00
	89		UPP	145.00		B&A	Susp/Prim	150.00
	90		UPP	150.00		FLM	Susp/Prim	150.00
	91		UPP	150.00		VSL	Susp/Prim	150.00

COME LET US ADORE HIM   Figurine

E-5619	*	Manger Child	UPP	$10.00	2.00"	UM	Susp/Sec	$45.00
(62)	81		UPP	10.00		TRI	Susp/Sec	40.00
	82		UPP	10.50		HRG	Susp/Sec	32.00
	83		UPP	10.50		FSH	Susp/Sec	30.00
	84		UPP	11.00		CRS	Susp/Sec	30.00
	85		UPP	11.00		DVE	Susp/Sec	30.00

* UNMARKED pieces could have been produced in any of the years of production.

WE HAVE SEEN HIS STAR   Bell

E-5620	81	Boy Holding Lamb	UPP	$15.00	5.50"	UM	Susp/Sec	$50.00
(16)	84		UPP	15.00		CRS	Susp/Sec	45.00
	85		UPP	15.00		DVE	Susp/Sec	40.00

DONKEY   Figurine   Nativity Addition

E-5621	81	Donkey	UPP	$ 6.00	2.75"	UM	Secondary	$32.00
(63)	84		UPP	9.00		CRS	Secondary	20.00
	85		UPP	9.00		DVE	Secondary	18.00
	86		UPP	9.00		OLB	Secondary	15.00
	87		UPP	10.00		CED	Secondary	15.00
	88		UPP	11.00		FLW	Secondary	14.00
	89		UPP	12.00		B&A	Secondary	14.00
	90		UPP	13.50		FLM	Primary	13.50
	91		UPP	13.50		VSL	Primary	13.50
	92		OPEN	13.50		G/CL	Primary	13.50

LET THE HEAVENS REJOICE   Bell, Dated

E-5622	81	Praying Angel Boy	Annual	$15.00	5.75"	UM	Secondary	$180.00
(77)								

JESUS IS BORN   Bell

E-5623	81	Shepherd	UPP	$15.00	5.75"	UM	Susp/Sec	$50.00
(64)	84		UPP	15.00		CRS	Susp/Sec	45.00

THEY FOLLOWED THE STAR Figurines Set of 3

E-5624	*	3 Kings on Camels	UPP	$130.00	8.75"	UM	Secondary	$295.00
(65)	81		UPP	130.00		TRI	Secondary	270.00
	82		UPP	150.00		HRG	Secondary	240.00
	83		UPP	150.00		FSH	Secondary	230.00
	84		UPP	165.00		CRS	Secondary	220.00
	85		UPP	165.00		DVE	Secondary	215.00
	86		UPP	165.00		OLB	Secondary	205.00
	87		UPP	165.00		CED	Secondary	200.00
	88		UPP	175.00		FLW	Secondary	200.00
	89		UPP	190.00		B&A	Secondary	200.00
	90		UPP	200.00		FLM	Primary	200.00
	91		UPP	200.00		VSL	Primary	200.00
	92		OPEN	200.00		G/CL	Primary	200.00

* UNMARKED (UM) pieces could have been produced in any of the years of production.

BUT LOVE GOES ON FOREVER Ornament

E-5627	*	Boy Angel on Cloud	UPP	$ 6.00	3.00"	UM	Susp/Sec	$125.00
(56)	81		UPP	6.00		TRI	Susp/Sec	125.00
	82		UPP	6.00		HRG	Susp/Sec	120.00
	83		UPP	9.00		FSH	Susp/Sec	95.00
	84		UPP	10.00		CRS	Susp/Sec	90.00
	85		UPP	10.00		DVE	Susp/Sec	80.00

* UNMARKED (UM) pieces could have been produced in any of the years of production.

BUT LOVE GOES ON FOREVER Ornament

E-5628	*	Girl Angel on Cloud	UPP	$ 6.00	3.00"	UM	Susp/Sec	$ 120.00
(57)	81		UPP	6.00		TRI	Susp/Sec	150.00
	82		UPP	6.00		HRG	Susp/Sec	130.00
	83		UPP	9.00		FSH	Susp/Sec	110.00
	84		UPP	10.00		CRS	Susp/Sec	105.00
	85		UPP	10.00		DVE	Susp/Sec	105.00

* UNMARKED (UM) pieces could have been produced in any of the years of production.

LET THE HEAVENS REJOICE Ornament, Dated

E-5629	81	Praying Angel Boy	Annual	$6.00	3.10"	TRI	Secondary	$225.00
(77)								

Some ornaments are without the patch on the angel. The GREENBOOK Market Price is $250.00.

UNTO US A CHILD IS BORN Ornament

E-5630	*	Shepherd	UPP	$ 6.00	3.25"	UM	Susp/Sec	$65.00
(64)	81		UPP	6.00		TRI	Susp/Sec	60.00
	82		UPP	6.00		HRG	Susp/Sec	55.00
	83		UPP	9.00		FSH	Susp/Sec	50.00
	84		UPP	10.00		CRS	Susp/Sec	45.00
	85		UPP	10.00		DVE	Susp/Sec	45.00

* UNMARKED (UM) pieces could have been produced in any of the years of production.

BABY'S FIRST CHRISTMAS Ornament

E-5631	*	Boy with Teddy	UPP	$ 6.00	3.00"	UM	Susp/Sec	$65.00
(1)	81		UPP	6.00		TRI	Susp/Sec	60.00
	82		UPP	6.50		HRG	Susp/Sec	55.00
	83		UPP	9.00		FSH	Susp/Sec	50.00
	84		UPP	10.00		CRS	Susp/Sec	45.00
	85		UPP	10.00		DVE	Susp/Sec	45.00

* UNMARKED (UM) pieces could have been produced in any of the years of production.

BABY'S FIRST CHRISTMAS Ornament

E-5632	*	Girl with Bunny	UPP	$ 6.00	3.00"	UM	Susp/Sec	$75.00
(2)	81		UPP	6.00		TRI	Susp/Sec	70.00
	82		UPP	6.50		HRG	Susp/Sec	60.00
	83		UPP	9.00		FSH	Susp/Sec	55.00
	84		UPP	10.00		CRS	Susp/Sec	50.00
	85		UPP	10.00		DVE	Susp/Sec	45.00

* UNMARKED (UM) pieces could have been produced in any of the years of production.

COME LET US ADORE HIM — Ornaments — Set of 4

E-5633	*	Jesus, Mary, Joseph & Lamb	UPP	$22.00	2.50"	UM	Susp/Sec	$130.00
(22)	81	Mixed sets TRI/HRG and HRG/FSH are common. Take lower value.	UPP	22.00		TRI	Susp/Sec	135.00
	82		UPP	25.00		HRG	Susp/Sec	125.00
	83		UPP	31.50		FSH	Susp/Sec	105.00
	84		UPP	31.50		CRS	Susp/Sec	95.00

* UNMARKED (UM) pieces could have been produced in any of the years of production.

WEE THREE KINGS — Ornaments — Set of 3

E-5634	*	Three Kings	UPP	$19.00	3.50"	UM	Susp/Sec	$125.00
(66)	81	Mixed sets TRI/HRG and HRG/FSH are common. Take lower value.	UPP	19.00		TRI	Susp/Sec	125.00
	82		UPP	19.00		HRG	Susp/Sec	120.00
	83		UPP	25.00		FSH	Susp/Sec	110.00
	84		UPP	27.50		CRS	Susp/Sec	100.00

* UNMARKED (UM) pieces could have been produced in any of the years of production.

WEE THREE KINGS — Figurines — Set of 3 — Nativity Addition

E-5635	*	Three Kings	UPP	$40.00	5.50"	UM	Secondary	$125.00
(66)	81	Mixed sets TRI/HRG and HRG/FSH are common. Take lower value.	UPP	40.00		TRI	Secondary	110.00
	82		UPP	50.00		HRG	Secondary	100.00
	83		UPP	50.00		FSH	Secondary	90.00
	84		UPP	55.00		CRS	Secondary	85.00
	85		UPP	55.00		DVE	Secondary	80.00
	86		UPP	55.00		OLB	Secondary	75.00
	87		UPP	55.00		CED	Secondary	75.00
	88		UPP	60.00		FLW	Secondary	75.00
	89		UPP	70.00		B&A	Secondary	75.00
	90		UPP	75.00		FLM	Primary	75.00
	91		UPP	75.00		VSL	Primary	75.00
	92		OPEN	75.00		G/CL	Primary	75.00

* UNMARKED (UM) pieces could have been produced in any of the years of production.

REJOICE O EARTH — Figurine — Nativity Addition

E-5636	*	Angel with Trumpet	UPP	$15.00	5.00"	UM	Secondary	$65.00
(67)	81		UPP	15.00		TRI	Secondary	60.00
	82		UPP	19.00		HRG	Secondary	45.00
	83		UPP	19.00		FSH	Secondary	40.00
	84		UPP	20.00		CRS	Secondary	35.00
	85		UPP	20.00		DVE	Secondary	32.00
	86		UPP	20.00		OLB	Secondary	30.00
	87		UPP	20.00		CED	Secondary	30.00
	88		UPP	22.50		FLW	Secondary	30.00
	89		UPP	27.50		B&A	Secondary	30.00
	90		UPP	30.00		FLM	Primary	30.00
	91		UPP	30.00		VSL	Primary	30.00
	92		OPEN	30.00		G/CL	Primary	30.00

* UNMARKED (UM) pieces could have been produced in any of the years of production.

THE HEAVENLY LIGHT — Figurine — Nativity Addition

E-5637	*	Angel with Flashlight	UPP	$15.00	4.85"	UM	Secondary	$60.00
(68)	81		UPP	15.00		TRI	Secondary	60.00
	82		UPP	17.00		HRG	Secondary	50.00
	83		UPP	17.00		FSH	Secondary	40.00
	84		UPP	19.00		CRS	Secondary	35.00
	85		UPP	19.00		DVE	Secondary	30.00
	86		UPP	19.00		OLB	Secondary	28.00
	87		UPP	19.00		CED	Secondary	28.00
	88		UPP	21.00		FLW	Secondary	28.00
	89		UPP	25.00		B&A	Secondary	28.00
	90		UPP	27.50		FLM	Secondary	28.00
	91		UPP	27.50		VSL	Primary	27.50
	92		OPEN	27.50		G/CL	Primary	27.50

* UNMARKED (UM) pieces could have been produced in any of the years of production.

COW — Figurine — Nativity Addition

E-5638	*	Cow with Bell	UPP	$16.00	3.50"	UM	Secondary	$50.00
(69)	84		UPP	21.00		CRS	Secondary	35.00
	85		UPP	21.00		DVE	Secondary	32.50
	86		UPP	22.50		OLB	Secondary	32.50
	87		UPP	22.50		CED	Secondary	32.50
	88		UPP	27.50		FLW	Secondary	32.50
	89		UPP	30.00		B&A	Secondary	32.50
	90		UPP	32.50		FLM	Secondary	32.50
	91		UPP	32.50		VSL	Primary	32.50
	92		OPEN	32.50		G/CL	Primary	32.50

* UNMARKED (UM) pieces could have been produced in any of the years of production.

ISN'T HE WONDERFUL — Figurine — Nativity Addition

E-5639	*	Boy Angel Praying with Harp	UPP	$12.00	4.75"	UM	Susp/Sec	$60.00
(70)	81		UPP	12.00		TRI	Susp/Sec	65.00
	82		UPP	15.00		HRG	Susp/Sec	55.00
	83		UPP	15.00		FSH	Susp/Sec	55.00
	84		UPP	17.00		CRS	Susp/Sec	50.00
	85		UPP	17.00		DVE	Susp/Sec	45.00

* UNMARKED (UM) pieces could have been produced in any of the years of production.

ISN'T HE WONDERFUL — Figurine — Nativity Addition

E-5640	*	Girl Angel Praying with Harp	UPP	$12.00	4.75"	UM	Susp/Sec	$60.00
(71)	81		UPP	12.00		TRI	Susp/Sec	65.00
	82		UPP	15.00		HRG	Susp/Sec	60.00
	83		UPP	15.00		FSH	Susp/Sec	55.00
	84		UPP	17.00		CRS	Susp/Sec	50.00
	85		UPP	17.00		DVE	Susp/Sec	45.00

* UNMARKED (UM) pieces could have been produced in any of the years of production.

THEY FOLLOWED THE STAR — Figurine

E-5641	*	"Follow Me" Angel with	UPP	$75.00	6.00"	UM	Susp/Sec	$180.00
(72)	81	Three Kings	UPP	75.00		TRI	Susp/Sec	185.00
	82		UPP	90.00		HRG	Susp/Sec	175.00
	83		UPP	90.00		FSH	Susp/Sec	170.00
	84		UPP	100.00		CRS	Susp/Sec	165.00
	85		UPP	100.00		DVE	Susp/Sec	160.00

* UNMARKED (UM) pieces could have been produced in any of the years of production.

SILENT KNIGHT — Musical — TUNE: Silent Night

E-5642	*	Boy Angel & Knight	UPP	$45.00	6.25"	UM	Susp/Sec	$155.00
(73)	81		UPP	45.00		TRI	Susp/Sec	160.00
	82		UPP	55.00		HRG	Susp/Sec	145.00
	83		UPP	55.00		FSH	Susp/Sec	140.00
	84		UPP	60.00		CRS	Susp/Sec	135.00
	85		UPP	60.00		DVE	Susp/Sec	125.00

* UNMARKED (UM) pieces could have been produced in any of the years of production.
Exists in a double mark TRIANGLE/HOURGLASS.

TWO SECTION WALL — Figurines — Set of 2 — Nativity Addition

E-5644	*	Two Section Wall	UPP	$60.00	6.00"	UM	Secondary	$150.00
(74)	81		UPP	60.00		TRI	Secondary	155.00
	82		UPP	80.00		HRG	Secondary	140.00
	83		UPP	80.00		FSH	Secondary	135.00
	84		UPP	90.00		CRS	Secondary	135.00
	85		UPP	90.00		DVE	Secondary	130.00
	86		UPP	90.00		OLB	Secondary	130.00
	87		UPP	90.00		CED	Secondary	125.00
	88		UPP	100.00		FLW	Secondary	120.00
	89		UPP	110.00		B&A	Secondary	120.00
	90		UPP	120.00		FLM	Primary	120.00
	91		UPP	120.00		VSL	Primary	120.00
	92		OPEN	120.00		G/CL	Primary	120.00

* UNMARKED (UM) pieces could have been produced in any of the years of production.

REJOICE O EARTH   Musical   TUNE: Joy To The World

E-5645	*	Angel with Trumpet	UPP	$35.00	6.25"	UM	Retired/Sec	$105.00
(67)	81		UPP	35.00		TRI	Retired/Sec	125.00
	82		UPP	40.00		HRG	Retired/Sec	95.00
	83		UPP	40.00		FSH	Retired/Sec	90.00
	84		UPP	45.00		CRS	Retired/Sec	90.00
	85		UPP	45.00		DVE	Retired/Sec	85.00
	86		UPP	45.00		OLB	Retired/Sec	85.00
	87		UPP	45.00		CED	Retired/Sec	80.00
	88		UPP	50.00		FLW	Retired/Sec	80.00

* UNMARKED (UM) pieces could have been produced in any of the years of production.

COME LET US ADORE HIM   Plate   First Issue "Christmas Collection" Series
Individually Numbered

E-5646	81	Nativity Scene	15,000	$40.00	8.50"	UM	Secondary	$60.00
(22)								

BUT LOVE GOES ON FOREVER   Candle Climbers   Set of 2

E-6118	81	Angels on Clouds	UPP	$14.00	2.50"	UM	Susp/Sec	$65.00
(56 & 57)	84		UPP	20.00		CRS	Susp/Sec	60.00
	85		UPP	20.00		DVE	Susp/Sec	55.00
	86		UPP	20.00		OLB	Susp/Sec	55.00
	87		UPP	22.50		CED	Susp/Sec	50.00
	88		UPP	25.00		FLW	Susp/Sec	50.00

WE HAVE SEEN HIS STAR   Ornament

E-6120	*	Boy Holding Lamb	UPP	$ 6.00	3.00"	UM	Retired/Sec	$60.00
(16)	81		UPP	6.00		TRI	Retired/Sec	65.00
	82		UPP	6.00		HRG	Retired/Sec	60.00
	83		UPP	9.00		FSH	Retired/Sec	55.00
	84		UPP	10.00		CRS	Retired/Sec	50.00

* UNMARKED (UM) pieces could have been produced in any of the years of production.

MIKEY   Doll

E-6214B	81	Mikey	UPP	$150.00	16.50"	UM	Susp/Sec	$225.00
(75)	83		UPP	175.00		FSH	Susp/Sec	220.00
	84		UPP	200.00		CRS	Susp/Sec	220.00
	85		UPP	200.00		DVE	Susp/Sec	220.00

DEBBIE   Doll

E-6214G	81	Debbie	UPP	$150.00	16.50"	UM	Susp/Sec	$235.00
(76)	83		UPP	175.00		FSH	Susp/Sec	230.00
	84		UPP	200.00		CRS	Susp/Sec	230.00
	85		UPP	200.00		DVE	Susp/Sec	230.00

GOD SENDS THE GIFT OF HIS LOVE   Figurine

E-6613	84	Girl with Present and Kitten	UPP	$22.50	5.75"	FSH	Susp/Sec	$90.00
(204)	84		UPP	22.50		CRS	Susp/Sec	65.00
	85		UPP	22.50		DVE	Susp/Sec	60.00
	86		UPP	22.50		OLB	Susp/Sec	55.00
	87		UPP	22.50		CED	Susp/Sec	55.00

COLLECTION PLAQUE   Plaque

E-6901	82	Boy Angel on Cloud	UPP	$19.00	3.50"	HRG	Susp/Sec	$110.00
(56)	83		UPP	19.00		FSH	Susp/Sec	50.00
	84		UPP	20.00		CRS	Susp/Sec	48.00
	85		UPP	20.00		DVE	Susp/Sec	40.00
	86		UPP	20.00		OLB	Susp/Sec	40.00

Exists in a double mark HOURGLASS/FISH.

GOD IS LOVE, DEAR VALENTINE   Figurine

E-7153	82	Boy Holding Heart	UPP	$16.00	5.50"	TRI	Susp/Sec	$55.00
(102)	82		UPP	16.00		HRG	Susp/Sec	45.00
	83		UPP	16.00		FSH	Susp/Sec	40.00
	84		UPP	17.00		CRS	Susp/Sec	35.00
	85		UPP	17.00		DVE	Susp/Sec	35.00
	86		UPP	17.00		OLB	Susp/Sec	30.00

GOD IS LOVE, DEAR VALENTINE Figurine

E-7154	82	Girl Holding Heart		UPP	$16.00	5.50"	TRI	Susp/Sec	$60.00
(103)	82			UPP	16.00		HRG	Susp/Sec	45.00
	83			UPP	16.00		FSH	Susp/Sec	40.00
	84			UPP	17.00		CRS	Susp/Sec	35.00
	85			UPP	17.00		DVE	Susp/Sec	35.00
	86			UPP	17.00		OLB	Susp/Sec	35.00

THANKING HIM FOR YOU Figurine

E-7155	82	Girl Praying in Field		UPP	$16.00	5.50"	HRG	Susp/Sec	$65.00
(58)	83			UPP	16.00		FSH	Susp/Sec	60.00
	84			UPP	17.00		CRS	Susp/Sec	55.00

I BELIEVE IN MIRACLES Figurine

E-7156	82	Boy Holding Chick		UPP	$17.00	4.25"	HRG	Susp/Ret/Sec	$110.00
(105)	83			UPP	17.00		FSH	Susp/Ret/Sec	95.00
	84			UPP	19.00		CRS	Susp/Ret/Sec	90.00
	85			UPP	19.00		DVE	Susp/Ret/Sec	85.00

The above piece, E-7156, was re-introduced in July 1987 as E-7156R below. Both pieces were subsequently retired in January 1992.

I BELIEVE IN MIRACLES Figurine

E-7156R	87	Boy Holding Bluebird		UPP	$22.50	4.50"	CED	Retired/Sec	$65.00
(374)	88			UPP	22.50		FLW	Retired/Sec	55.00
	89			UPP	25.00		B&A	Retired/Sec	50.00
	90			UPP	27.50		FLM	Retired/Sec	50.00
	91			UPP	27.50		VSL	Retired/Sec	45.00

First introduced in 1982 as E-7156, the original version of this figurine had the boy holding a yellow chick. E-7156 was suspended in 1985, and in 1987 was re-sculpted and returned to production as E-7156R. Among the changes made was the addition of the incised "Sam B" on the base of the figurine, and a change in the color of the chick - from yellow to blue. The re-sculpted piece is also considerably larger than the original version. During the early part of production in 1987, the molds from the suspended piece, E-7156, were pulled and used along with the molds for the new re-introduced piece, E-7156R. Shipments of figurines crafted from the old suspended mold but with the new blue painting of the chick were made before the error was discovered. These pieces are the rare version. All rare versions have the CEDAR TREE Annual Symbol. The GREENBOOK Market Price for the rare version is $250.00.
Full color photographs: 4th Ed., pg. 197 or 5th Ed., pg. 206. One color photo: 6th Ed., pg. 226.

THERE IS JOY IN SERVING JESUS Figurine

E-7157	82	Waitress Carrying Food		UPP	$17.00	5.50"	HRG	Retired/Sec	$70.00
(106)	83			UPP	17.00		FSH	Retired/Sec	55.00
	84			UPP	19.00		CRS	Retired/Sec	50.00
	85			UPP	19.00		DVE	Retired/Sec	50.00
	86			UPP	19.00		OLB	Retired/Sec	45.00

LOVE BEARETH ALL THINGS Figurine

E-7158	82	Nurse Giving Shot to Bear		UPP	$25.00	5.15"	HRG	Secondary	$65.00
(107)	83			UPP	25.00		FSH	Secondary	55.00
	84			UPP	27.50		CRS	Secondary	45.00
	85			UPP	27.50		DVE	Secondary	37.50
	86			UPP	27.50		OLB	Secondary	37.50
	87			UPP	27.50		CED	Secondary	37.50
	88			UPP	32.50		FLW	Secondary	37.50
	89			UPP	36.00		B&A	Secondary	37.50
	90			UPP	37.50		FLM	Primary	37.50
	91			UPP	37.50		VSL	Primary	37.50
	92			OPEN	37.50		G/CL	Primary	37.50

LORD GIVE ME PATIENCE Figurine

E-7159	82	Bandaged Boy by Sign		UPP	$25.00	5.50"	HRG	Susp/Sec	$60.00
(108)	83			UPP	25.00		FSH	Susp/Sec	50.00
	84			UPP	27.50		CRS	Susp/Sec	45.00
	85			UPP	27.50		DVE	Susp/Sec	45.00

THE PERFECT GRANDPA   Figurine

E-7160	82	Grandpa in Rocking Chair	UPP	$25.00	5.00"	HRG	Susp/Sec	$60.00
(109)	83		UPP	25.00		FSH	Susp/Sec	55.00
	84		UPP	27.50		CRS	Susp/Sec	50.00
	85		UPP	27.50		DVE	Susp/Sec	50.00
	86		UPP	27.50		OLB	Susp/Sec	50.00

HIS SHEEP AM I   Figurine

E-7161	*	Shepherd Painting Lamb	UPP	$25.00	5.25"	UM	Susp/Sec	$60.00
(110)	82		UPP	25.00		HRG	Susp/Sec	60.00
	83		UPP	25.00		FSH	Susp/Sec	55.00
	84		UPP	27.50		CRS	Susp/Sec	50.00

*UNMARKED (UM) pieces could have been produced in any of the years of production.

LOVE IS SHARING   Figurine

E-7162	82	Girl at School Desk	UPP	$25.00	4.75"	HRG	Susp/Sec	$160.00
(111)	83		UPP	25.00		FSH	Susp/Sec	150.00
	84		UPP	27.50		CRS	Susp/Sec	140.00

GOD IS WATCHING OVER YOU   Figurine

E-7163	82	Boy with Ice Bag on Head	UPP	$27.50	5.25"	HRG	Susp/Sec	$85.00
(112)	83		UPP	27.50		FSH	Susp/Sec	75.00
	84		UPP	30.00		CRS	Susp/Sec	72.00

BLESS THIS HOUSE   Figurine

E-7164	82	Boy & Girl Painting Dog House	UPP	$45.00	5.50"	HRG	Susp/Sec	$175.00
(113)	83		UPP	45.00		FSH	Susp/Sec	150.00
	84		UPP	50.00		CRS	Susp/Sec	140.00

LET THE WHOLE WORLD KNOW   Figurine

E-7165	82	Boy & Girl in Baptism Bucket	UPP	$45.00	6.00"	HRG	Susp/Sec	$95.00
(114)	83		UPP	45.00		FSH	Susp/Sec	80.00
	84		UPP	50.00		CRS	Susp/Sec	80.00
	85		UPP	50.00		DVE	Susp/Sec	75.00
	86		UPP	50.00		OLB	Susp/Sec	70.00
	87		UPP	50.00		CED	Susp/Sec	70.00

THE LORD BLESS YOU AND KEEP YOU   Frame

E-7166	82	Bride and Groom	UPP	$22.50	5.50"	HRG	Secondary	$50.00
(38)	83		UPP	22.50		FSH	Secondary	45.00
	84		UPP	25.00		CRS	Secondary	40.00
	85		UPP	25.00		DVE	Secondary	35.00
	86		UPP	25.00		OLB	Secondary	32.50
	87		UPP	25.00		CED	Secondary	32.50
	88		UPP	27.50		FLW	Secondary	32.50
	89		UPP	30.00		B&A	Secondary	32.50
	90		UPP	32.50		FLM	Primary	32.50
	91		UPP	32.50		VSL	Primary	32.50
	92		OPEN	32.50		G/CL	Primary	32.50

THE LORD BLESS YOU AND KEEP YOU   Covered Box

E-7167	82	Bride and Groom	UPP	$22.50	5.00"	HRG	Susp/Sec	$50.00
(38)	83		UPP	22.50		FSH	Susp/Sec	48.00
	84		UPP	25.00		CRS	Susp/Sec	45.00
	85		UPP	25.00		DVE	Susp/Sec	45.00

MY GUARDIAN ANGEL   Frame

E-7168	82	Boy Angel	UPP	$18.00	5.50"	HRG	Susp/Sec	$45.00
(265)	83		UPP	18.00		FSH	Susp/Sec	40.00
	84		UPP	19.00		CRS	Susp/Sec	35.00

MY GUARDIAN ANGEL   Frame

E-7169	82	Girl Angel	UPP	$18.00	5.50"	HRG	Susp/Sec	$50.00
(266)	83		UPP	18.00		FSH	Susp/Sec	45.00
	84		UPP	19.00		CRS	Susp/Sec	40.00

JESUS LOVES ME		Frame						
E-7170	82	Boy with Teddy	UPP	$17.00	4.25"	HRG	Susp/Sec	$45.00
(1)	83		UPP	17.00		FSH	Susp/Sec	40.00
	84		UPP	19.00		CRS	Susp/Sec	35.00
	85		UPP	19.00		DVE	Susp/Sec	35.00

JESUS LOVES ME		Frame						
E-7171	82	Girl with Bunny	UPP	$17.00	4.25"	HRG	Susp/Sec	$50.00
(2)	83		UPP	17.00		FSH	Susp/Sec	45.00
	84		UPP	19.00		CRS	Susp/Sec	40.00
	85		UPP	19.00		DVE	Susp/Sec	40.00

REJOICING WITH YOU		Plate						
E-7172	82	Christening	UPP	$30.00	7.25"	UM	Susp/Sec	$40.00
(50)	84		UPP			CRS	Susp/Sec	40.00
	85		UPP			DVE	Susp/Sec	40.00

THE PURR-FECT GRANDMA		Plate	Second Issue "Mother's Love" Series Individually Numbered					
E-7173	82	Grandma in Rocker	15,000	$40.00	8.50"	UM	Secondary	$40.00
(33)								

MAKE A JOYFUL NOISE		Plate	Second Issue "Inspired Thoughts" Series Individually Numbered					
E-7174	82	Girl with Goose	15,000	$40.00	8.50"	UM	Secondary	$40.00
(5)								

THE LORD BLESS YOU AND KEEP YOU		Bell						
E-7175	82	Boy Graduate	UPP	$17.00	5.75"	UM	Susp/Sec	$38.00
(46)	84		UPP			CRS	Susp/Sec	35.00
	85		UPP			DVE	Susp/Sec	35.00

THE LORD BLESS YOU AND KEEP YOU		Bell						
E-7176	82	Girl Graduate	UPP	$17.00	5.75"	UM	Susp/Sec	$45.00
(47)	84		UPP			CRS	Susp/Sec	40.00
	85		UPP			DVE	Susp/Sec	40.00

THE LORD BLESS YOU AND KEEP YOU		Frame						
E-7177	82	Boy Graduate	UPP	$18.00	5.50"	HRG	Susp/Sec	$45.00
(46)	83		UPP	18.00		FSH	Susp/Sec	40.00
	84		UPP	19.00		CRS	Susp/Sec	38.00
	85		UPP	19.00		DVE	Susp/Sec	35.00
	86		UPP	19.00		OLB	Susp/Sec	33.00
	87		UPP	19.00		CED	Susp/Sec	33.00

THE LORD BLESS YOU AND KEEP YOU		Frame						
E-7178	82	Girl Graduate	UPP	$18.00	5.25"	HRG	Susp/Sec	$48.00
(47)	83		UPP	18.00		FSH	Susp/Sec	45.00
	84		UPP	19.00		CRS	Susp/Sec	40.00
	85		UPP	19.00		DVE	Susp/Sec	38.00
	86		UPP	19.00		OLB	Susp/Sec	35.00
	87		UPP	19.00		CED	Susp/Sec	35.00

THE LORD BLESS YOU AND KEEP YOU		Bell						
E-7179	82	Bride and Groom	UPP	$22.50	5.50"	UM	Secondary	$45.00
(38)	84		UPP	25.00		CRS	Secondary	40.00
	85		UPP	25.00		DVE	Secondary	38.00
	86		UPP	25.00		OLB	Secondary	35.00
	87		UPP	25.00		CED	Secondary	35.00
	88		UPP	30.00		FLW	Secondary	35.00
	89		UPP	33.00		B&A	Secondary	35.00
	90		UPP	35.00		FLM	Primary	35.00
	91		UPP	35.00		VSL	Primary	35.00
	92		OPEN	35.00		G/CL	Primary	35.00

THE LORD BLESS YOU AND KEEP YOU — Musical — TUNE: Wedding March

THE LORD BLESS YOU AND KEEP YOU			Musical		TUNE: Wedding March			
E-7180	82	Bride and Groom	UPP	$55.00	6.00"	UM	Secondary	$100.00
(38)	84	on Cake	UPP	55.00		CRS	Secondary	90.00
	85		UPP	60.00		DVE	Secondary	80.00
	86		UPP	60.00		OLB	Secondary	80.00
	87		UPP	60.00		CED	Secondary	80.00
	88		UPP	70.00		FLW	Secondary	80.00
	89		UPP	75.00		B&A	Secondary	80.00
	90		UPP	80.00		FLM	Primary	80.00
	91		UPP	80.00		VSL	Primary	80.00
	92		OPEN	80.00		G/CL	Primary	80.00

MOTHER SEW DEAR		Bell						
E-7181	82	Mother Needlepointing	UPP	$17.00	5.50"	UM	Susp/Sec	$45.00
(30)	84		UPP	19.00		CRS	Susp/Sec	42.00
	85		UPP	19.00		DVE	Susp/Sec	40.00
	86		UPP	19.00		OLB	Susp/Sec	38.00
	87		UPP	19.00		CED	Susp/Sec	35.00
	88		UPP	22.50		FLW	Susp/Sec	35.00

MOTHER SEW DEAR		Musical		TUNE: You Light Up My Life				
E-7182	82	Mother Needlepointing	UPP	$35.00	6.25"	UM	Secondary	$75.00
(30)	84		UPP	37.50		CRS	Secondary	60.00
	85		UPP	37.50		DVE	Secondary	55.00
	86		UPP	37.50		OLB	Secondary	55.00
	87		UPP	37.50		CED	Secondary	55.00
	88		UPP	45.00		FLW	Secondary	55.00
	89		UPP	50.00		B&A	Primary	55.00
	90		UPP	55.00		FLM	Primary	55.00
	91		UPP	55.00		VSL	Primary	55.00
	92		OPEN	55.00		G/CL	Primary	55.00

THE PURR-FECT GRANDMA		Bell						
E-7183	82	Grandma in Rocker	UPP	$17.00	5.50"	UM	Susp/Sec	$50.00
(33)	84		UPP	19.00		CRS	Susp/Sec	45.00
	85		UPP	19.00		DVE	Susp/Sec	40.00
	86		UPP	19.00		OLB	Susp/Sec	40.00
	87		UPP	19.00		CED	Susp/Sec	35.00
	88		UPP	22.50		FLW	Susp/Sec	35.00

THE PURR-FECT GRANDMA		Musical		TUNE: Always In My Heart				
E-7184	82	Grandma in Rocker	UPP	$35.00	6.00"	UM	Secondary	$85.00
(33)	84		UPP	37.50		CRS	Secondary	65.00
	85		UPP	37.50		DVE	Secondary	60.00
	86		UPP	37.50		OLB	Secondary	55.00
	87		UPP	37.50		CED	Secondary	55.00
	88		UPP	45.00		FLW	Secondary	55.00
	89		UPP	50.00		B&A	Primary	55.00
	90		UPP	55.00		FLM	Primary	55.00
	91		UPP	55.00		VSL	Primary	55.00
	92		OPEN	55.00		G/CL	Primary	55.00

LOVE IS SHARING		Musical		TUNE: School Days				
E-7185	82	Girl at School Desk	UPP	$40.00	5.75"	HRG	Retired/Sec	$165.00
(111)	83		UPP	40.00		FSH	Retired/Sec	150.00
	84		UPP	45.00		CRS	Retired/Sec	140.00
	85		UPP	45.00		DVE	Retired/Sec	135.00

LET THE WHOLE WORLD KNOW		Musical		TUNE: What A Friend We Have In Jesus				
E-7186	*	Boy & Girl in Baptism Bucket	UPP	$60.00	6.25"	UM	Susp/Sec	$135.00
(114)	82		UPP	60.00		HRG	Susp/Sec	120.00
	83		UPP	60.00		FSH	Susp/Sec	115.00
	84		UPP	65.00		CRS	Susp/Sec	115.00
	85		UPP	65.00		DVE	Susp/Sec	110.00
	86		UPP	65.00		OLB	Susp/Sec	110.00

* UNMARKED (UM) pieces could have been produced in any of the years of production.

MOTHER SEW DEAR		Frame						
E-7241	82	Mother Needlepointing	UPP	$18.00	5.50"	HRG	Susp/Sec	$45.00
(30)	83		UPP	18.00		FSH	Susp/Sec	40.00
	84		UPP	19.00		CRS	Susp/Sec	40.00
	85		UPP	19.00		DVE	Susp/Sec	38.00
	86		UPP	19.00		OLB	Susp/Sec	35.00

THE PURR-FECT GRANDMA		Frame						
E-7242	82	Grandma in Rocker	UPP	$18.00	5.50"	HRG	Susp/Sec	$45.00
(33)	83		UPP	18.00		FSH	Susp/Sec	40.00
	84		UPP	19.00		CRS	Susp/Sec	40.00
	85		UPP	19.00		DVE	Susp/Sec	35.00
	86		UPP	19.00		OLB	Susp/Sec	35.00
	87		UPP	19.00		CED	Susp/Sec	35.00
	88		UPP	22.50		FLW	Susp/Sec	35.00

CUBBY		Doll	Individually Numbered on Bottom of Foot					
E-7267B	82	Groom Doll	5,000	$200.00	18.00"	UM	Secondary	$450.00
(115)								

TAMMY		Doll	Individually Numbered on Bottom of Foot					
E-7267G	82	Bride Doll	5,000	$300.00	18.00"	UM	Secondary	$675.00
(116)								

RETAILER'S DOME		Figurine under Dome		Gift to Centers				
E-7350	84	Kids on Cloud under Dome	UPP	GIFT	9.00"	CRS	Secondary	$800.00
(411)							w/o dome	625.00

Full color photograph: 5th Ed., pg. 194.

LOVE IS PATIENT		Figurine						
E-9251	83	Boy Holding Blackboard	UPP	$35.00	5.00"	FSH	Susp/Sec	$75.00
(135)	84	with Teacher	UPP	35.00		CRS	Susp/Sec	70.00
	85		UPP	35.00		DVE	Susp/Sec	65.00

FORGIVING IS FORGETTING		Figurine						
E-9252	83	Boy & Girl with Bandage	UPP	$37.50	5.75"	FSH	Susp/Sec	$75.00
(136)	84		UPP	37.50		CRS	Susp/Sec	70.00
	85		UPP	37.50		DVE	Susp/Sec	65.00
	86		UPP	37.50		OLB	Susp/Sec	62.00
	87		UPP	37.50		CED	Susp/Sec	60.00
	88		UPP	42.50		FLW	Susp/Sec	60.00
	89		UPP	47.50		B&A	Susp/Sec	60.00

THE END IS IN SIGHT		Figurine						
E-9253	83	Boy with Dog Ripping Pants	UPP	$25.00	5.25"	HRG	Susp/Sec	$70.00
(137)	83		UPP	25.00		FSH	Susp/Sec	60.00
	84		UPP	25.00		CRS	Susp/Sec	55.00
	85		UPP	25.00		DVE	Susp/Sec	55.00

PRAISE THE LORD ANYHOW		Figurine						
E-9254	83	Girl at Typewriter	UPP	$35.00	4.75"	HRG	Secondary	$75.00
(138)	83		UPP	35.00		FSH	Secondary	65.00
	84		UPP	35.00		CRS	Secondary	60.00
	85		UPP	35.00		DVE	Secondary	58.00
	86		UPP	35.00		OLB	Secondary	58.00
	87		UPP	35.00		CED	Secondary	55.00
	88		UPP	40.00		FLW	Secondary	55.00
	89		UPP	47.50		B&A	Secondary	50.00
	90		UPP	50.00		FLM	Primary	50.00
	91		UPP	50.00		VSL	Primary	50.00
	92		OPEN	50.00		G/CL	Primary	50.00

Classic Variation: "Inked Fish." During 1983, the FISH appeared as part of the understamp decal on many pieces. Pieces were also produced that did not have a FISH at all - incised or decal. When this occurred we can only theorize an attempt was made to correct it by actually drawing the FISH on the bottom of the piece. This inked symbol can be washed off, creating an unmarked piece. The GREENBOOKMarket Price for the "Erasable Inked Fish is $125.00.
Full color photo: 4th Ed., pg. 200 or 5th Ed., pg. 203. One color photo: 6th Ed., pg. 225.

BLESS YOU TWO   Figurine

E-9255	83	Groom Carrying Bride	UPP	$21.00	5.25"	FSH	Secondary	$45.00
(139)	84		UPP	21.00		CRS	Secondary	40.00
	85		UPP	21.00		DVE	Secondary	38.00
	86		UPP	21.00		OLB	Secondary	33.00
	87		UPP	21.00		CED	Secondary	33.00
	88		UPP	25.00		FLW	Secondary	33.00
	89		UPP	30.00		B&A	Secondary	32.50
	90		UPP	32.50		FLM	Primary	32.50
	91		UPP	32.50		VSL	Primary	32.50
	92		OPEN	32.50		G/CL	Primary	32.50

THE HAND THAT ROCKS THE FUTURE   Plate   Third Issue "Mother's Love" Series
Individually Numbered

E-9256	83	Girl Rocking Cradle	15,000	$40.00	8.50"	UM	Secondary	$40.00
(32)								

I BELIEVE IN MIRACLES   Plate   Third Issue "Inspired Thoughts" Series   Individually Numbered

E-9257	83	Boy Holding Chick	15,000	$40.00	8.50"	UM	Secondary	$40.00
(105)	84			40.00		CRS	Secondary	40.00

WE ARE GOD'S WORKMANSHIP   Figurine

E-9258	83	Bonnet Girl with Butterfly	UPP	$19.00	5.25"	HRG	Secondary	$55.00
(140)	83		UPP	19.00		FSH	Secondary	40.00
	84		UPP	19.00		CRS	Secondary	38.00
	85		UPP	19.00		DVE	Secondary	32.00
	86		UPP	19.00		OLB	Secondary	30.00
	87		UPP	19.00		CED	Secondary	30.00
	88		UPP	22.50		FLW	Secondary	30.00
	89		UPP	25.00		B&A	Secondary	28.00
	90		UPP	27.50		FLM	Primary	27.50
	91		UPP	27.50		VSL	Primary	27.50
	92		OPEN	27.50		G/CL	Primary	27.50

WE'RE IN IT TOGETHER   Figurine

E-9259	83	Boy with Piggy	UPP	$24.00	3.75"	HRG	Susp/Sec	$70.00
(141)	83		UPP	24.00		FSH	Susp/Sec	60.00
	84		UPP	24.00		CRS	Susp/Sec	55.00
	85		UPP	24.00		DVE	Susp/Sec	50.00
	86		UPP	24.00		OLB	Susp/Sec	50.00
	87		UPP	24.00		CED	Susp/Sec	50.00
	88		UPP	30.00		FLW	Susp/Sec	45.00
	89		UPP	33.00		B&A	Susp/Sec	45.00
	90		UPP	35.00		FLM	Susp/Sec	45.00

GOD'S PROMISES ARE SURE   Figurine   "Heavenly Halos" Series

E-9260	83	Boy Angel Winding Rainbow	UPP	$30.00	5.50"	FSH	Susp/Sec	$60.00
(142)	84		UPP	30.00		CRS	Susp/Sec	55.00
	85		UPP	30.00		DVE	Susp/Sec	55.00
	86		UPP	30.00		OLB	Susp/Sec	50.00
	87		UPP	30.00		CED	Susp/Sec	50.00

SEEK YE THE LORD   Figurine

E-9261	83	Boy Graduate with Scroll	UPP	$21.00	4.75"	FSH	Susp/Sec	$50.00
(143)	84		UPP	21.00		CRS	Susp/Sec	45.00
	85		UPP	21.00		DVE	Susp/Sec	42.00
	86		UPP	21.00		OLB	Susp/Sec	40.00

All figurines with the FISH Annual Symbol do not have the "h" in the word "he" in the inscription on the graduate's scroll capitalized.
Full color photograph: 4th Ed., pg. 199 or 5th Ed., pg. 198.

SEEK YE THE LORD — Figurine

E-9262	83	Girl Graduate with Scroll	UPP	$21.00	4.75"	FSH	Susp/Sec	$60.00
(144)	84		UPP	21.00		CRS	Susp/Sec	55.00
	85		UPP	21.00		DVE	Susp/Sec	55.00
	86		UPP	21.00		OLB	Susp/Sec	50.00

All figurines with the FISH Annual Symbol do not have the "h" in the word "he" in the inscription on the graduate's scroll capitalized.
Full color photograph: 4th Ed., pg. 199 or 5th Ed., pg. 198.

HOW CAN TWO WALK TOGETHER EXCEPT THEY AGREE — Figurine

E-9263	83	Boy and Girl in Horse	UPP	$35.00	5.25"	HRG	Susp/Sec	$140.00
(145)	83	Costume	UPP	35.00		FSH	Susp/Sec	110.00
	84		UPP	35.00		CRS	Susp/Sec	95.00
	85		UPP	35.00		DVE	Susp/Sec	90.00

PRESS ON — Figurine

E-9265	83	Girl Ironing Clothes	UPP	$40.00	5.75"	HRG	Secondary	$85.00
(146)	83		UPP	40.00		FSH	Secondary	70.00
	84		UPP	40.00		CRS	Secondary	62.00
	85		UPP	40.00		DVE	Secondary	58.00
	86		UPP	40.00		OLB	Secondary	55.00
	87		UPP	40.00		CED	Secondary	55.00
	88		UPP	45.00		FLW	Secondary	55.00
	89		UPP	50.00		B&A	Secondary	55.00
	90		UPP	55.00		FLM	Primary	55.00
	91		UPP	55.00		VSL	Primary	55.00
	92		OPEN	55.00		G/CL	Primary	55.00

I'M FALLING FOR SOMEBUNNY — Box

E-9266	*	Lamb and Bunny	UPP	$13.50	3.00"	UM	Susp/Sec	$42.00
(308)	83		UPP	13.50		HRG	Susp/Sec	40.00
	83		UPP	13.50		FSH	Susp/Sec	38.00
	84		UPP	16.00		CRS	Susp/Sec	35.00
	85		UPP	16.00		DVE	Susp/Sec	32.00
	86		UPP	16.00		OLB	Susp/Sec	32.00
	87		UPP	16.00		CED	Susp/Sec	30.00
	88		UPP	18.50		FLW	Susp/Sec	30.00

* UNMARKED (UM) pieces could have been produced in any of the years of production. Some understamp decals have title "Somebunny Cares."

OUR LOVE IS HEAVEN SCENT — Box

E-9266	*	Lamb and Skunk	UPP	$13.50	3.00"	UM	Susp/Sec	$42.00
(308)	83		UPP	13.50		HRG	Susp/Sec	40.00
	83		UPP	13.50		FSH	Susp/Sec	38.00
	84		UPP	16.00		CRS	Susp/Sec	35.00
	85		UPP	16.00		DVE	Susp/Sec	32.00
	86		UPP	16.00		OLB	Susp/Sec	32.00
	87		UPP	16.00		CED	Susp/Sec	30.00
	88		UPP	18.50		FLW	Susp/Sec	30.00

* UNMARKED (UM) pieces could have been produced in any of the years of production. Some understamp decals have title "Somebunny Cares."

ANIMAL COLLECTION — Figurines — Set of 6 — (Divide by 6 for an "each" value)

E-9267	83	Animals	UPP	$39.00	2.50"	UM	Susp/Sec	$140.00
(147)	84		UPP	45.00		CRS	Susp/Sec	130.00
	85		UPP	45.00		DVE	Susp/Sec	125.00
	86		UPP	45.00		OLB	Susp/Sec	120.00
	87		UPP	45.00		CED	Susp/Sec	115.00

In 1988 individual Enesco Item #s were assigned for each figurine in the above set of 6:

E-9267/A	88	Teddy Bear	UPP	$ 8.50	2.50"	FLW	Susp/Sec	$19.00
(414)	89		UPP	10.00		B&A	Susp/Sec	18.00
	90		UPP	11.00		FLM	Susp/Sec	18.00
	91		UPP	11.00		VSL	Susp/Sec	18.00

E-9267/B	88	Dog with Slippers	UPP	$ 8.50	3.00"	FLW	Susp/Sec	$19.00
(407)	89		UPP	10.00		B&A	Susp/Sec	18.00
	90		UPP	11.00		FLM	Susp/Prim	18.00
	91		UPP	11.00		VSL	Susp/Prim	18.00
E-9267/C	88	Bunny with Carrot	UPP	$ 8.50	2.60"	FLW	Susp/Sec	$19.00
(408)	89		UPP	10.00		B&A	Susp/Sec	18.00
	90		UPP	11.00		FLM	Susp/Sec	18.00
	91		UPP	11.00		VSL	Susp/Sec	18.00
E-9267/D	88	Cat with Bow Tie	UPP	$ 8.50	2.40"	FLW	Susp/Sec	$19.00
(413)	89		UPP	10.00		B&A	Susp/Sec	18.00
	90		UPP	11.00		FLM	Susp/Sec	18.00
	91		UPP	11.00		VSL	Susp/Sec	18.00
E-9267/E	88	Lamb with Bird on Back	UPP	$ 8.50	2.60"	FLW	Susp/Sec	$19.00
(409)	89		UPP	10.00		B&A	Susp/Sec	18.00
	90		UPP	11.00		FLM	Susp/Sec	18.00
	91		UPP	11.00		VSL	Susp/Sec	18.00
E-9267/F	88	Pig with Patches	UPP	$ 8.50	2.10"	FLW	Susp/Sec	$19.00
(412)	89		UPP	10.00		B&A	Susp/Sec	18.00
	90		UPP	11.00		FLM	Susp/Sec	18.00
	91		UPP	11.00		VSL	Susp/Sec	18.00

NOBODY'S PERFECT!   Figurine

E-9268	83	Boy with Dunce Cap	UPP	$21.00	7.00"	HRG	Retired/Sec	$75.00
(148)	83		UPP	21.00		FSH	Retired/Sec	70.00
	84		UPP	21.00		CRS	Retired/Sec	70.00
	85		UPP	21.00		DVE	Retired/Sec	65.00
	86		UPP	21.00		OLB	Retired/Sec	65.00
	87		UPP	21.00		CED	Retired/Sec	60.00
	88		UPP	24.00		FLW	Retired/Sec	60.00
	89		UPP	27.00		B&A	Retired/Sec	55.00
	90		UPP	30.00		FLM	Retired/Sec	50.00

Classic Variation: "Smiling Dunce." The first HOURGLASS pieces produced are known as "Smiling Dunces" or "Smiley" and appeared with a smile. The "O" shaped mouth is the normal piece. The GREENBOOK Market Price for "Smiley" is $650.00.
Full color photo: 4th Ed., pg. 193 or 5th Ed., pg. 197. One color photo: 6th Ed., pg. 219.

LET LOVE REIGN   Figurine

E-9273	83	Girl with Chicks in Umbrella	UPP	$27.50	5.25"	HRG	Retired/Sec	*
(149)	83		UPP	27.50		FSH	Retired/Sec	$75.00
	84		UPP	27.50		CRS	Retired/Sec	72.00
	85		UPP	27.50		DVE	Retired/Sec	70.00
	86		UPP	27.50		OLB	Retired/Sec	65.00
	87		UPP	27.50		CED	Retired/Sec	65.00

* Extremely rare, consider FISH as first production symbol.

TASTE AND SEE THAT THE LORD IS GOOD   Figurine   "Heavenly Halos" Series

E-9274	83	Girl Angel Preparing Food	UPP	$22.50	6.25"	FSH	Retired/Sec	$65.00
(150)	84		UPP	22.50		CRS	Retired/Sec	60.00
	85		UPP	22.50		DVE	Retired/Sec	55.00
	86		UPP	22.50		OLB	Retired/Sec	55.00

JESUS LOVES ME   Plate

E-9275	83	Boy with Teddy	UPP	$30.00	7.25"	UM	Susp/Sec	$45.00
(1)	84		UPP	30.00		CRS	Susp/Sec	45.00

JESUS LOVES ME   Plate

E-9276	83	Girl with Bunny	UPP	$30.00	7.25"	UM	Susp/Sec	$45.00
(2)	84		UPP	30.00		CRS	Susp/Sec	45.00

JESUS LOVES ME		Figurine						
E-9278	83	Boy with Teddy	UPP	$ 9.00	3.00"	HRG	Secondary	$25.00
(1)	83		UPP	9.00		FSH	Secondary	22.00
	84		UPP	10.00		CRS	Secondary	20.00
	85		UPP	10.00		DVE	Secondary	18.00
	86		UPP	10.00		OLB	Secondary	18.00
	87		UPP	10.00		CED	Secondary	15.00
	88		UPP	12.50		FLW	Secondary	15.00
	89		UPP	13.50		B&A	Secondary	15.00
	90		UPP	15.00		FLM	Primary	15.00
	91		UPP	15.00		VSL	Primary	15.00
	92		OPEN	15.00		G/CL	Primary	15.00
JESUS LOVES ME		Figurine						
E-9279	83	Girl with Bunny	UPP	$ 9.00	3.00"	HRG	Secondary	$30.00
(2)	83		UPP	9.00		FSH	Secondary	25.00
	84		UPP	10.00		CRS	Secondary	22.00
	85		UPP	10.00		DVE	Secondary	20.00
	86		UPP	10.00		OLB	Secondary	18.00
	87		UPP	10.00		CED	Secondary	15.00
	88		UPP	12.50		FLW	Secondary	15.00
	89		UPP	13.50		B&A	Secondary	15.00
	90		UPP	15.00		FLM	Primary	15.00
	91		UPP	15.00		VSL	Primary	15.00
	92		OPEN	15.00		G/CL	Primary	15.00
JESUS LOVES ME		Box						
E-9280	83	Boy with Teddy	UPP	$17.50	5.00"	HRG	Susp/Sec	$45.00
(1)	83		UPP	17.50		FSH	Susp/Sec	40.00
	84		UPP	19.00		CRS	Susp/Sec	40.00
	85		UPP	19.00		DVE	Susp/Sec	35.00
JESUS LOVES ME		Box						
E-9281	83	Girl with Bunny	UPP	$17.50	5.00"	HRG	Susp/Sec	$45.00
(2)	83		UPP	17.50		FSH	Susp/Sec	40.00
	84		UPP	19.00		CRS	Susp/Sec	38.00
	85		UPP	19.00		DVE	Susp/Sec	35.00
TO SOMEBUNNY SPECIAL		Figurine						
E-9282	*	Bunny on Heart Base	UPP	$ 8.00	3.00"	UM	Susp/Sec	$35.00
(152)	83		UPP	8.00		HRG	Susp/Sec	30.00
	83		UPP	8.00		FSH	Susp/Sec	30.00
	84		UPP	9.00		CRS	Susp/Sec	27.00
	85		UPP	9.00		DVE	Susp/Sec	25.00
	86		UPP	9.00		OLB	Susp/Sec	25.00
	87		UPP	9.00		CED	Susp/Sec	25.00
		* UNMARKED (UM) pieces could have been produced in any of the years of production.						
E-9282A	88	Bunny on Heart Base	UPP	$10.50	3.00"	FLW	Susp/Sec	$20.00
(152)	89		UPP	12.00		B&A	Susp/Sec	20.00
	90		UPP	13.50		FLM	Susp/Sec	20.00
YOU'RE WORTH YOUR WEIGHT IN GOLD		Figurine						
E-9282	*	Pig with Patches on Base	UPP	$ 8.00	2.50"	UM	Susp/Sec	$35.00
(151)	83		UPP	8.00		HRG	Susp/Sec	30.00
	83		UPP	8.00		FSH	Susp/Sec	30.00
	84		UPP	9.00		CRS	Susp/Sec	27.00
	85		UPP	9.00		DVE	Susp/Sec	25.00
	86		UPP	9.00		OLB	Susp/Sec	25.00
	87		UPP	9.00		CED	Susp/Sec	25.00
		* UNMARKED (UM) pieces could have been produced in any of the years of production.						
E-9282B	88	Pig with Patches on Base	UPP	$10.50	2.50"	FLW	Susp/Sec	$20.00
(151)	89		UPP	12.00		B&A	Susp/Sec	20.00
	90		UPP	13.50		FLM	Susp/Sec	20.00

ESPECIALLY FOR EWE Figurine

E-9282	*	Lamb with Bird	UPP	$ 8.00	3.00"	UM	Susp/Sec	$35.00
(153)	83		UPP	8.00		HRG	Susp/Sec	30.00
	83		UPP	8.00		FSH	Susp/Sec	30.00
	84		UPP	9.00		CRS	Susp/Sec	27.00
	85		UPP	9.00		DVE	Susp/Sec	25.00
	86		UPP	9.00		OLB	Susp/Sec	25.00
	87		UPP	9.00		CED	Susp/Sec	25.00

* UNMARKED (UM) pieces could have been produced in any of the years of production. The original title for this figurine was "Loving Ewe."

E-9282C	88	Lamb with Bird	UPP	$10.50	3.00"	FLW	Susp/Sec	$20.00
(153)	89		UPP	12.00		B&A	Susp/Sec	20.00
	90		UPP	13.50		FLM	Susp/Sec	20.00

FOREVER FRIENDS Box

E-9283/A	83	Dog	UPP	$15.00	4.25"	HRG	Susp/Sec	$50.00
(309)	83		UPP	15.00		FSH	Susp/Sec	45.00
	84		UPP	17.00		CRS	Susp/Sec	40.00
						DVE		35.00

Piece was suspended in 1984 yet exists in a DOVE.

FOREVER FRIENDS Box

E-9283/B	83	Cat	UPP	$15.00	4.10"	HRG	Susp/Sec	$75.00
(309)	83		UPP	15.00		FSH	Susp/Sec	70.00
	84		UPP	17.00		CRS	Susp/Sec	65.00

IF GOD BE FOR US, WHO CAN BE AGAINST US Figurine

E-9285	83	Boy at Pulpit	UPP	$27.50	5.85"	FSH	Susp/Sec	$70.00
(154)	84		UPP	27.50		CRS	Susp/Sec	60.00
	85		UPP	27.50		DVE	Susp/Sec	55.00

PEACE ON EARTH Figurine

E-9287	83	Girl with Lion & Lamb	UPP	$37.50	5.25"	FSH	Susp/Sec	$85.00
(155)	84		UPP	37.50		CRS	Susp/Sec	75.00
	85		UPP	37.50		DVE	Susp/Sec	72.00
	86		UPP	37.50		OLB	Susp/Sec	70.00

SENDING YOU A RAINBOW Figurine "Heavenly Halos" Series

E-9288	83	Girl Angel with Sprinkler	UPP	$22.50	5.50"	FSH	Susp/Sec	$75.00
(156)	84		UPP	22.50		CRS	Susp/Sec	70.00
	85		UPP	22.50		DVE	Susp/Sec	68.00
	86		UPP	22.50		OLB	Susp/Sec	65.00

TRUST IN THE LORD Figurine "Heavenly Halos" Series

E-9289	83	Boy Angel Taking	UPP	$20.00	5.90"	FSH	Susp/Sec	$55.00
(157)	84	Flying Lessons	UPP	21.00		CRS	Susp/Sec	50.00
	85		UPP	21.00		DVE	Susp/Sec	48.00
	86		UPP	21.00		OLB	Susp/Sec	45.00
	87		UPP	21.00		CED	Susp/Sec	42.00

LOVE COVERS ALL Figurine

12009	85	Girl Making Heart Quilt	UPP	$27.50	4.50"	CRS	Susp/Sec	$60.00
(225)	85		UPP	27.50		DVE	Susp/Sec	55.00
	86		UPP	27.50		OLB	Susp/Sec	55.00
	87		UPP	27.50		CED	Susp/Sec	52.00
	88		UPP	32.50		FLW	Susp/Sec	52.00
	89		UPP	35.00		B&A	Susp/Sec	50.00
	90		UPP	37.50		FLM	Susp/Sec	50.00
	91		UPP	37.50		VSL	Susp/Sec	50.00

LOVING YOU Frame

12017	85	Boy Holding Heart	UPP	$19.00	4.50"	CRS	Susp/Sec	$40.00
(102)	85		UPP	19.00		DVE	Susp/Sec	38.00
	86		UPP	19.00		OLB	Susp/Sec	35.00
	87		UPP	19.00		CED	Susp/Sec	35.00

LOVING YOU		Frame						
12025	85	Girl Holding Heart	UPP	$19.00	4.50"	CRS	Susp/Sec	$45.00
(103)	85		UPP	19.00		DVE	Susp/Sec	40.00
	86		UPP	19.00		OLB	Susp/Sec	35.00
	87		UPP	19.00		CED	Susp/Sec	35.00
GOD'S PRECIOUS GIFT		Frame						
12033	85	Baby Boy	UPP	$19.00	4.50"	DVE	Susp/Sec	$55.00
(310)	86		UPP	19.00		OLB	Susp/Sec	50.00
	87		UPP	19.00		CED	Susp/Sec	45.00
GOD'S PRECIOUS GIFT		Frame						
12041	85	Baby Girl	UPP	$19.00	4.50"	DVE	Secondary	$45.00
(311)	86		UPP	19.00		OLB	Secondary	35.00
	87		UPP	19.00		CED	Secondary	27.50
	88		UPP	22.50		FLW	Secondary	27.50
	89		UPP	25.00		B&A	Secondary	27.50
	90		UPP	27.50		FLM	Primary	27.50
	91		UPP	27.50		VSL	Primary	27.50
	92		OPEN	27.50		G/CL	Primary	27.50
THE VOICE OF SPRING		Figurine	First Issue "The Four Seasons" Series					
12068	85	Girl with Bible	Annual	$30.00	6.40"	CRS	Secondary	$300.00
(226)	85			30.00		DVE	Secondary	275.00
SUMMER'S JOY		Figurine	Second Issue "The Four Seasons" Series					
12076	85	Girl with Ducklings	Annual	$30.00	6.40"	CRS	Secondary	$105.00
(227)	85			30.00		DVE	Secondary	95.00
AUTUMN'S PRAISE		Figurine	Third Issue "The Four Seasons" Series					
12084	86	Girl in Field of Flowers	Annual	$30.00	6.40"	DVE	Secondary	$70.00
(228)	86			30.00		OLB	Secondary	60.00
WINTER'S SONG		Figurine	Fourth Issue "The Four Seasons" Series					
12092	86	Girl in Snow with Birds	Annual	$40.00	6.40"	DVE	Secondary	$105.00
(229)	86			40.00		OLB	Secondary	100.00
THE VOICE OF SPRING		Plate	First Issue "The Four Seasons" Series					
12106	85	Girl with Bible	Annual	$40.00	8.50"	CRS	Secondary	$90.00
(226)	85			40.00		DVE	Secondary	80.00
SUMMER'S JOY		Plate	Second Issue "The Four Seasons" Series					
12114	85	Girl with Ducklings	Annual	$40.00	8.50"	CRS	Secondary	$80.00
(227)	85			40.00		DVE	Secondary	75.00
AUTUMN'S PRAISE		Plate	Third Issue "The Four Seasons" Series					
12122	86	Girl in Field of Flowers	Annual	$40.00	8.50"	OLB	Secondary	$55.00
(228)								
WINTER'S SONG		Plate	Fourth Issue "The Four Seasons" Series					
12130	86	Girl in Snow with Birds	Annual	$40.00	8.50"	DVE	Secondary	$65.00
(229)	86			40.00		OLB	Secondary	60.00
PART OF ME WANTS TO BE GOOD		Figurine						
12149	85	Angel Boy in Devil Suit	UPP	$19.00	5.10"	CRS	Susp/Sec	$50.00
(230)	85		UPP	19.00		DVE	Susp/Sec	45.00
	86		UPP	19.00		OLB	Susp/Sec	45.00
	87		UPP	19.00		CED	Susp/Sec	42.00
	88		UPP	22.50		FLW	Susp/Sec	42.00
	89		UPP	25.00		B&A	Susp/Sec	40.00
THIS IS THE DAY WHICH THE LORD HAS MADE		Figurine						
12157	87	Birthday Boy	UPP	$20.00	5.00"	OLB	Susp/Sec	$55.00
(314)	87		UPP	20.00		CED	Susp/Sec	50.00
	88		UPP	24.00		FLW	Susp/Sec	48.00
	89		UPP	27.00		B&A	Susp/Sec	45.00
	90		UPP	30.00		FLM	Susp/Sec	40.00

LORD, KEEP MY LIFE IN TUNE   Musical   "Rejoice In The Lord" Band Series   TUNE: Amazing Grace
Set of 2

12165	85	Boy Playing Piano	UPP	$37.50	4.50"	DVE	Susp/Sec	$85.00
(231)	86		UPP	37.50		OLB	Susp/Sec	82.00
	87		UPP	37.50		CED	Susp/Sec	80.00
	88		UPP	45.00		FLW	Susp/Sec	78.00
	89		UPP	50.00		B&A	Susp/Sec	75.00

THERE'S A SONG IN MY HEART   Figurine   "Rejoice In The Lord" Band Series

12173	85	Girl Playing Triangle	UPP	$11.00	3.50"	DVE	Susp/Sec	$40.00
(232)	86		UPP	11.00		OLB	Susp/Sec	35.00
	87		UPP	11.00		CED	Susp/Sec	35.00
	88		UPP	13.00		FLW	Susp/Sec	30.00
	89		UPP	15.00		B&A	Susp/Sec	30.00
	90		UPP	16.50		FLM	Susp/Sec	28.00

GET INTO THE HABIT OF PRAYER   Figurine

12203	85	Nun	UPP	$19.00	5.10"	CRS	Susp/Sec	$40.00
(233)	85		UPP	19.00		DVE	Susp/Sec	35.00
	86		UPP	19.00		OLB	Susp/Sec	32.00

BABY'S FIRST HAIRCUT   Figurine   Third Issue "Baby's First " Series

12211	85	Angel Cutting Baby's Hair	UPP	$32.50	4.50"	DVE	Susp/Sec	$75.00
(234)	86		UPP	32.50		OLB	Susp/Sec	72.00
	87		UPP	32.50		CED	Susp/Sec	70.00

CLOWN FIGURINES   Figurines   Set of 4   (Divide by 4 for an "each" value)

12238	85	Mini Clowns	UPP	$54.00	4.25"	DVE	Secondary	$105.00
(235)	86		UPP	54.00		OLB	Secondary	90.00
	87		UPP	54.00		CED	Secondary	85.00

Classic Variation. "CLOWNS" was misspelled "CROWNS" on the understamp decal of some sets. The GREENBOOK Market Price for the set of four figurines with the "CROWNS" title error is $240.00. Color photograph: 5th Ed., pg. 205.

In 1987 individual Enesco Item #s were assigned for each figurine in the above set of 4:

CLOWN FIGURINE   Figurine

12238/A	87	Boy Balancing Ball	UPP	$16.00	3.00"	CED	Secondary	$20.00
(416)	88		UPP	16.00		FLW	Secondary	19.00
	89		UPP	17.50		B&A	Secondary	19.00
	90		UPP	19.00		FLM	Primary	19.00
	91		UPP	19.00		VSL	Primary	19.00
	92		OPEN	19.00		G/CL	Primary	19.00

CLOWN FIGURINE   Figurine

12238/B	87	Girl Holding Balloon	UPP	$16.00	4.40"	CED	Secondary	$20.00
(417)	88		UPP	16.00		FLW	Secondary	19.00
	89		UPP	17.50		B&A	Secondary	19.00
	90		UPP	19.00		FLM	Primary	19.00
	91		UPP	19.00		VSL	Primary	19.00
	92		OPEN	19.00		G/CL	Primary	19.00

CLOWN FIGURINE   Figurine

12238/C	87	Boy Bending Over Ball	UPP	$16.00	3.75"	CED	Secondary	$20.00
(418)	88		UPP	16.00		FLW	Secondary	19.00
	89		UPP	17.50		B&A	Secondary	19.00
	90		UPP	19.00		FLM	Primary	19.00
	91		UPP	19.00		VSL	Primary	19.00
	92		OPEN	19.00		G/CL	Primary	19.00

CLOWN FIGURINE — Figurine

12238/D	87	Girl with Flower Pot	UPP	$16.00	3.75"	CED	Secondary	$20.00
(419)	88		UPP	16.00		FLW	Secondary	19.00
	89		UPP	17.50		B&A	Secondary	19.00
	90		UPP	19.00		FLM	Primary	19.00
	91		UPP	19.00		VSL	Primary	19.00
	92		OPEN	19.00		G/CL	Primary	19.00

PRECIOUS MOMENTS LAST FOREVER — Medallion

12246	84	Medallion	UPP	$10.00	3.25"	CRS	Secondary	$135.00
(365)								

LOVE COVERS ALL — Thimble

12254	85	Girl Making Heart Quilt	UPP	$ 5.50	2.25"	DVE	Susp/Sec	$18.00
(225)	86		UPP	5.50		OLB	Susp/Sec	15.00
	87		UPP	5.50		CED	Susp/Sec	15.00
	88		UPP	7.00		FLW	Susp/Sec	12.00
	89		UPP	8.00		B&A	Susp/Sec	12.00
	90		UPP	8.00		FLM	Susp/Sec	12.00

I GET A BANG OUT OF YOU — Figurine   First Issue "Clown" Series

12262	85	Clown Holding Balloons	UPP	$30.00	6.60"	DVE	Secondary	$55.00
(236)	86		UPP	30.00		OLB	Secondary	50.00
	87		UPP	30.00		CED	Secondary	48.00
	88		UPP	35.00		FLW	Secondary	45.00
	89		UPP	40.00		B&A	Secondary	45.00
	90		UPP	45.00		FLM	Primary	45.00
	91		UPP	45.00		VSL	Primary	45.00
	92		OPEN	45.00		G/CL	Primary	45.00

LORD KEEP ME ON THE BALL — Figurine   Fourth Issue "Clown" Series

12270	86	Clown Sitting on Ball	UPP	$30.00	7.00"	OLB	Secondary	$55.00
(270)	87		UPP	30.00		CED	Secondary	48.00
	88		UPP	35.00		FLW	Secondary	45.00
	89		UPP	40.00		B&A	Secondary	45.00
	90		UPP	45.00		FLM	Primary	45.00
	91		UPP	45.00		VSL	Primary	45.00
	92		OPEN	45.00		G/CL	Primary	45.00

IT IS BETTER TO GIVE THAN TO RECEIVE — Figurine

12297	85	Policeman Writing Ticket	UPP	$19.00	5.25"	DVE	Susp/Sec	$60.00
(237)	86		UPP	19.00		OLB	Susp/Sec	55.00
	87		UPP	19.00		CED	Susp/Sec	50.00

LOVE NEVER FAILS — Figurine

12300	85	Teacher at Desk with	UPP	$25.00	5.50"	DVE	Secondary	$50.00
(238)	86	Report Card	UPP	25.00		OLB	Secondary	40.00
	87		UPP	25.00		CED	Secondary	38.00
	88		UPP	30.00		FLW	Secondary	35.00
	89		UPP	33.00		B&A	Secondary	35.00
	90		UPP	35.00		FLM	Primary	35.00
	91		UPP	35.00		VSL	Primary	35.00
	92		OPEN	35.00		G/CL	Primary	35.00

GOD BLESS OUR HOME — Figurine

12319	85	Boy & Girl Building	UPP	$40.00	4.40"	DVE	Secondary	$68.00
(239)	86	Sandcastle	UPP	40.00		OLB	Secondary	60.00
	87		UPP	40.00		CED	Secondary	58.00
	88		UPP	45.00		FLW	Secondary	55.00
	89		UPP	50.00		B&A	Secondary	55.00
	90		UPP	55.00		FLM	Primary	55.00
	91		UPP	55.00		VSL	Primary	55.00
	92		OPEN	55.00		G/CL	Primary	55.00

YOU CAN FLY — Figurine
12335	86	Boy Angel on Cloud	UPP	$25.00	5.50"	OLB	Susp/Sec	$55.00
(271)	87		UPP	25.00		CED	Susp/Sec	50.00
	88		UPP	30.00		FLW	Susp/Sec	45.00

JESUS IS COMING SOON — Figurine
12343	85	Mary Knitting Booties	UPP	$22.50	4.75"	DVE	Susp/Sec	$40.00
(240)	86		UPP	22.50		OLB	Susp/Sec	35.00

HALO, AND MERRY CHRISTMAS — Figurine
12351	85	Angels Making Snowman	UPP	$40.00	6.10"	DVE	Susp/Sec	$125.00
(241)	86		UPP	40.00		OLB	Susp/Sec	115.00
	87		UPP	40.00		CED	Susp/Sec	110.00
	88		UPP	45.00		FLW	Susp/Sec	105.00

HAPPINESS IS THE LORD — Figurine — "Rejoice In The Lord" Band Series
12378	85	Boy Playing Banjo	UPP	$15.00	4.75"	CRS	Susp/Sec	$45.00
(242)	85		UPP	15.00		DVE	Susp/Sec	35.00
	86		UPP	15.00		OLB	Susp/Sec	35.00
	87		UPP	15.00		CED	Susp/Sec	35.00
	88		UPP	18.00		FLW	Susp/Sec	32.00
	89		UPP	20.00		B&A	Susp/Sec	30.00
	90		UPP	22.50		FLM	Susp/Sec	30.00

LORD GIVE ME A SONG — Figurine — "Rejoice In The Lord" Band Series
12386	85	Girl Playing Harmonica	UPP	$15.00	4.90"	DVE	Susp/Sec	$38.00
(243)	86		UPP	15.00		OLB	Susp/Sec	35.00
	87		UPP	15.00		CED	Susp/Sec	32.00
	88		UPP	18.00		FLW	Susp/Sec	32.00
	89		UPP	20.00		B&A	Susp/Sec	32.00
	90		UPP	22.50		FLM	Susp/Sec	32.00

HE IS MY SONG — Figurine — "Rejoice In The Lord" Band Series — Set of 2
12394	85	Boy Playing Trumpet	UPP	$17.50	4.50"	CRS	Susp/Sec	$45.00
(244)	85	with Dog	UPP	17.50		DVE	Susp/Sec	40.00
	86		UPP	17.50		OLB	Susp/Sec	38.00
	87		UPP	17.50		CED	Susp/Sec	38.00
	88		UPP	22.50		FLW	Susp/Sec	35.00
	89		UPP	25.00		B&A	Susp/Sec	35.00
	90		UPP	27.50		FLM	Susp/Sec	32.00

WE SAW A STAR — Musical — Set of 3 — TUNE: Joy To The World
12408	85	Two Angels Sawing Star	UPP	$50.00	4.75"	DVE	Susp/Sec	$85.00
(245)	86		UPP	50.00		OLB	Susp/Sec	75.00
	87		UPP	50.00		CED	Susp/Sec	70.00

HAVE A HEAVENLY CHRISTMAS — Ornament
12416	85	Boy in Airplane	UPP	$12.00	2.60"	DVE	Secondary	$28.00
(246)	86		UPP	12.00		OLB	Secondary	20.00
	87		UPP	12.00		CED	Secondary	18.00
	88		UPP	13.50		FLW	Secondary	16.00
	89		UPP	15.00		B&A	Secondary	16.00
	90		UPP	16.00		FLM	Primary	16.00
	91		UPP	16.00		VSL	Primary	16.00
	92		OPEN	16.00		G/CL	Primary	16.00

There are CEDAR TREE pieces with two hooks from the Retailers Wreath, #111465. For further information, see 6th Ed., pg. 209. There are also some ornaments, again from the Retailer's Wreath, that have the inscription "Heaven Bound" upside-down. Color photo: 5th Ed., pg. 210.

AARON — Doll
12424	85	Boy Angel	UPP	$135.00	12.00"	DVE	Susp/Sec	$140.00
(247)	86		UPP	135.00		OLB	Susp/Prim	140.00

BETHANY — Doll
12432	85	Girl Angel	UPP	$135.00	12.00"	DVE	Susp/Sec	$150.00
(248)	86		UPP	135.00		OLB	Susp/Prim	150.00

12440   GOD BLESS OUR YEARS TOGETHER
See The Enesco PRECIOUS MOMENTS Collectors' Club, Membership Pieces, page 223.

WADDLE I DO WITHOUT YOU   Figurine   Second Issue "Clown" Series

12459	85	Girl Clown with Basket	UPP	$30.00	5.50"	CRS	Retired/Sec	$95.00
(250)	85	with Goose	UPP	30.00		DVE	Retired/Sec	80.00
	86		UPP	30.00		OLB	Retired/Sec	75.00
	87		UPP	30.00		CED	Retired/Sec	70.00
	88		UPP	35.00		FLW	Retired/Sec	70.00
	89		UPP	35.00		B&A	Retired/Sec	65.00

THE LORD WILL CARRY YOU THROUGH   Figurine   Third Issue "Clown" Series

12467	86	Clown with Dog in Mud	UPP	$30.00	5.75"	DVE	Retired/Sec	$95.00
(251)	86		UPP	30.00		OLB	Retired/Sec	75.00
	87		UPP	30.00		CED	Retired/Sec	70.00
	88		UPP	35.00		FLW	Retired/Sec	65.00

P.D.   Doll

12475	85	Baby Boy	UPP	$50.00	7.00"	UM	Susp/Sec	$85.00
(252)	85		UPP	50.00		DVE	Susp/Sec	80.00
	86		UPP	50.00		OLB	Susp/Sec	75.00

TRISH   Doll

12483	85	Baby Girl	UPP	$50.00	7.00"	UM	Susp/Sec	$80.00
(253)	85		UPP	50.00		DVE	Susp/Sec	75.00
	86		UPP	50.00		OLB	Susp/Sec	75.00

ANGIE, THE ANGEL OF MERCY   Doll   Individually Numbered

12491	87	Nurse	12,500	$160.00	12.00"	CED	Secondary	$200.00
(339)								

LORD KEEP MY LIFE IN TUNE   Musical   "Rejoice In The Lord" Band Series   Set of 2
TUNE: I'd Like To Teach The World To Sing

12580	87	Girl with Piano	UPP	$37.50	4.00"	OLB	Susp/Sec	$100.00
(315)	87		UPP	37.50		CED	Susp/Sec	95.00
	88		UPP	45.00		FLW	Susp/Sec	90.00
	89		UPP	50.00		B&A	Susp/Sec	85.00
	90		UPP	55.00		FLM	Susp/Sec	85.00

MOTHER SEW DEAR   Thimble

13293	85	Mother Needlepointing	UPP	$ 5.50	2.25"	DVE	Secondary	$15.00
(30)	86		UPP	5.50		OLB	Secondary	12.00
	87		UPP	5.50		CED	Secondary	10.00
	88		UPP	7.00		FLW	Secondary	8.00
	89		UPP	8.00		B&A	Secondary	8.00
	90		UPP	8.00		FLM	Primary	8.00
	91		UPP	8.00		VSL	Primary	8.00
	92		OPEN	8.00		G/CL	Primary	8.00

THE PURR-FECT GRANDMA   Thimble

13307	85	Grandma in Rocker	UPP	$ 5.50	2.25"	DVE	Secondary	$12.00
(33)	86		UPP	5.50		OLB	Secondary	10.00
	87		UPP	5.50		CED	Secondary	10.00
	88		UPP	7.00		FLW	Secondary	8.00
	89		UPP	8.00		B&A	Secondary	8.00
	90		UPP	8.00		FLM	Primary	8.00
	91		UPP	8.00		VSL	Primary	8.00
	92		OPEN	8.00		G/CL	Primary	8.00

TELL ME THE STORY OF JESUS   Plate, Dated   Fourth Issue "Joy Of Christmas" Series

15237	85	Girl with Doll Reading Book	Annual	$40.00	8.50"	DVE	Secondary	$105.00
(83)								

MAY YOUR CHRISTMAS BE DELIGHTFUL — Figurine

No.	Yr	Description	Mark	Issue	Size	Symbol	Market	Value
15482	85	Boy Tangled in	UPP	$25.00	5.00"	DVE	Secondary	$45.00
(254)	86	Christmas Lights	UPP	25.00		OLB	Secondary	40.00
	87		UPP	25.00		CED	Secondary	38.00
	88		UPP	27.50		FLW	Secondary	35.00
	89		UPP	33.00		B&A	Secondary	35.00
	90		UPP	35.00		FLM	Primary	35.00
	91		UPP	35.00		VSL	Primary	35.00
	92		OPEN	35.00		G/CL	Primary	35.00

HONK IF YOU LOVE JESUS — Figurine — Set of 2 — Nativity Addition

No.	Yr	Description	Mark	Issue	Size	Symbol	Market	Value
15490	85	Mother Goose in Bonnet	UPP	$13.00	3.25"	DVE	Secondary	$32.00
(255)	86	with Babies	UPP	13.00		OLB	Secondary	25.00
	87		UPP	13.00		CED	Secondary	22.00
	88		UPP	15.00		FLW	Secondary	20.00
	89		UPP	17.50		B&A	Secondary	19.00
	90		UPP	19.00		FLM	Primary	19.00
	91		UPP	19.00		VSL	Primary	19.00
	92		OPEN	19.00		G/CL	Primary	19.00

GOD SENT YOU JUST IN TIME — Musical — TUNE: We Wish You A Merry Christmas

No.	Yr	Description	Mark	Issue	Size	Symbol	Market	Value
15504	85	Clown Holding a	UPP	$45.00	6.25"	DVE	Retired/Sec	$95.00
(256)	86	Jack- in- the- Box	UPP	45.00		OLB	Retired/Sec	85.00
	87		UPP	45.00		CED	Retired/Sec	80.00
	88		UPP	50.00		FLW	Retired/Sec	80.00
	89		UPP	60.00		B&A	Retired/Sec	75.00

BABY'S FIRST CHRISTMAS — Figurine, Dated

No.	Yr	Description	Mark	Issue	Size	Symbol	Market	Value
15539	85	Baby Boy with Bottle	Annual	$13.00	3.00"	DVE	Secondary	$40.00
(257)								

BABY'S FIRST CHRISTMAS — Figurine, Dated

No.	Yr	Description	Mark	Issue	Size	Symbol	Market	Value
15547	85	Baby Girl with Bottle	Annual	$13.00	3.00"	DVE	Secondary	$35.00
(258)								

GOD SENT HIS LOVE — Ornament, Dated

No.	Yr	Description	Mark	Issue	Size	Symbol	Market	Value
15768	85	Boy Holding Heart	Annual	$10.00	3.00"	DVE	Secondary	$35.00
(259)								

MAY YOU HAVE THE SWEETEST CHRISTMAS — Figurine — "Family Christmas Scene" Series

No.	Yr	Description	Mark	Issue	Size	Symbol	Market	Value
15776	85	Mother with Cookie Sheet	UPP	$17.00	4.90"	DVE	Secondary	$35.00
(260)	86		UPP	17.00		OLB	Secondary	30.00
	87		UPP	17.00		CED	Secondary	28.00
	88		UPP	19.00		FLW	Secondary	25.00
	89		UPP	23.00		B&A	Secondary	25.00
	90		UPP	25.00		FLM	Primary	25.00
	91		UPP	25.00		VSL	Primary	25.00
	92		OPEN	25.00		G/CL	Primary	25.00

THE STORY OF GOD'S LOVE — Figurine — "Family Christmas Scene" Series

No.	Yr	Description	Mark	Issue	Size	Symbol	Market	Value
15784	85	Father Reading Bible	UPP	$22.50	4.00"	DVE	Secondary	$45.00
(261)	86		UPP	22.50		OLB	Secondary	40.00
	87		UPP	22.50		CED	Secondary	38.00
	88		UPP	25.00		FLW	Secondary	35.00
	89		UPP	32.50		B&A	Secondary	35.00
	90		UPP	35.00		FLM	Primary	35.00
	91		UPP	35.00		VSL	Primary	35.00
	92		OPEN	35.00		G/CL	Primary	35.00

TELL ME A STORY — Figurine — "Family Christmas Scene" Series

15792	85	Boy Sitting Listening to	UPP	$10.00	2.00"	DVE	Secondary	$25.00
(262)	86	Story	UPP	10.00		OLB	Secondary	20.00
	87		UPP	10.00		CED	Secondary	18.00
	88		UPP	11.00		FLW	Secondary	15.00
	89		UPP	13.50		B&A	Secondary	15.00
	90		UPP	15.00		FLM	Primary	15.00
	91		UPP	15.00		VSL	Primary	15.00
	92		OPEN	15.00		G/CL	Primary	15.00

GOD GAVE HIS BEST — Figurine — "Family Christmas Scene" Series

15806	85	Girl with Ornament	UPP	$13.00	3.50"	DVE	Secondary	$28.00
(263)	86		UPP	13.00		OLB	Secondary	25.00
	87		UPP	13.00		CED	Secondary	22.00
	88		UPP	15.00		FLW	Secondary	19.00
	89		UPP	17.50		B&A	Secondary	19.00
	90		UPP	19.00		FLM	Primary	19.00
	91		UPP	19.00		VSL	Primary	19.00
	92		OPEN	19.00		G/CL	Primary	19.00

SILENT NIGHT — Musical — "Family Christmas Scene" Series — TUNE: Silent Night

15814	85	Christmas Tree	UPP	$37.50	5.60"	DVE	Secondary	$70.00
(264)	86		UPP	37.50		OLB	Secondary	65.00
	87		UPP	37.50		CED	Secondary	60.00
	88		UPP	40.00		FLW	Secondary	55.00
	89		UPP	50.00		B&A	Secondary	55.00
	90		UPP	55.00		FLM	Primary	55.00
	91		UPP	55.00		VSL	Primary	55.00
	92		OPEN	55.00		G/CL	Primary	55.00

MAY YOUR CHRISTMAS BE HAPPY — Ornament

15822	85	Girl Clown with Balloon	UPP	$10.00	3.25"	DVE	Susp/Sec	$35.00
(235)	86		UPP	10.00		OLB	Susp/Sec	30.00
	87		UPP	10.00		CED	Susp/Sec	30.00
	88		UPP	11.00		FLW	Susp/Sec	28.00
	89		UPP	13.50		B&A	Susp/Sec	25.00

HAPPINESS IS THE LORD — Ornament

15830	85	Boy Clown with Ball	UPP	$10.00	2.10"	DVE	Susp/Sec	$35.00
(235)	86		UPP	10.00		OLB	Susp/Sec	30.00
	87		UPP	10.00		CED	Susp/Sec	27.00
	88		UPP	11.00		FLW	Susp/Sec	27.00
	89		UPP	13.50		B&A	Susp/Sec	25.00

MAY YOUR CHRISTMAS BE DELIGHTFUL — Ornament

15849	85	Boy Tangled in	UPP	$10.00	3.00"	DVE	Secondary	$25.00
(254)	86	Christmas Lights	UPP	10.00		OLB	Secondary	22.00
	87		UPP	10.00		CED	Secondary	20.00
	88		UPP	11.00		FLW	Secondary	20.00
	89		UPP	13.50		B&A	Secondary	18.00
	90		UPP	15.00		FLM	Secondary	18.00
	91		UPP	15.00		VSL	Secondary	18.00
	92		OPEN	15.00		G/CL	Primary	15.00

HONK IF YOU LOVE JESUS — Ornament

15857	85	Mother Goose in Bonnet	UPP	$10.00	3.60"	DVE	Secondary	$25.00
(255)	86		UPP	10.00		OLB	Secondary	22.00
	87		UPP	10.00		CED	Secondary	20.00
	88		UPP	11.00		FLW	Secondary	18.00
	89		UPP	13.50		B&A	Secondary	15.00
	90		UPP	15.00		FLM	Primary	15.00
	91		UPP	15.00		VSL	Primary	15.00
	92		OPEN	15.00		G/CL	Primary	15.00

GOD SENT HIS LOVE — Thimble, Dated

15865	85	Boy Holding Heart	Annual	$5.50	2.20"	DVE	Secondary	$45.00
(259)								

GOD SENT HIS LOVE   Bell, Dated
15873 85 Boy Holding Heart   Annual $19.00 5.40" DVE Secondary $38.00
(259)

GOD SENT HIS LOVE   Figurine, Dated
15881 85 Boy Holding Heart   Annual $17.00 4.50" DVE Secondary $40.00
(259)

BABY'S FIRST CHRISTMAS   Ornament, Dated
15903 85 Baby Boy with Bottle   Annual $10.00 2.40" DVE Secondary $35.00
(257)

BABY'S FIRST CHRISTMAS   Ornament, Dated
15911 85 Baby Girl with Bottle   Annual $10.00 2.40" DVE Secondary $35.00
(258)

MAY YOUR BIRTHDAY BE WARM   Figurine   "Birthday Circus Train" Series
15938 86 Teddy on Caboose -   UPP $10.00 2.75" DVE Secondary $35.00
(296)   86 "For Baby"   UPP   10.00   OLB Secondary   22.00
         87   UPP   10.00   CED Secondary   15.00
         88   UPP   12.00   FLW Secondary   15.00
         89   UPP   13.50   B&A Secondary   15.00
         90   UPP   15.00   FLM Primary   15.00
         91   UPP   15.00   VSL Primary   15.00
         92   OPEN 15.00   G/CL Primary   15.00

HAPPY BIRTHDAY LITTLE LAMB   Figurine   "Birthday Circus Train" Series
15946 86 Lamb - Age 1   UPP $10.00 3.00" DVE Secondary $35.00
(297)   86   UPP   10.00   OLB Secondary   20.00
         87   UPP   10.00   CED Secondary   15.00
         88   UPP   12.00   FLW Secondary   15.00
         89   UPP   13.50   B&A Secondary   15.00
         90   UPP   15.00   FLM Primary   15.00
         91   UPP   15.00   VSL Primary   15.00
         92   OPEN 15.00   G/CL Primary   15.00

HEAVEN BLESS YOUR SPECIAL DAY   Figurine   "Birthday Circus Train" Series
15954 86 Pig - Age 3   UPP $11.00 3.50" DVE Secondary $35.00
(299)   86   UPP   11.00   OLB Secondary   16.50
         87   UPP   11.00   CED Secondary   16.50
         88   UPP   13.50   FLW Secondary   16.50
         89   UPP   15.00   B&A Secondary   16.50
         90   UPP   16.50   FLM Primary   16.50
         91   UPP   16.50   VSL Primary   16.50
         92   OPEN 16.50   G/CL Primary   16.50

GOD BLESS YOU ON YOUR BIRTHDAY   Figurine   "Birthday Circus Train" Series
15962 86 Seal - Age 2   UPP $11.00 3.75" DVE Secondary $38.00
(298)   86   UPP   11.00   OLB Secondary   25.00
         87   UPP   11.00   CED Secondary   16.50
         88   UPP   13.50   FLW Secondary   16.50
         89   UPP   15.00   B&A Secondary   16.50
         90   UPP   16.50   FLM Primary   16.50
         91   UPP   16.50   VSL Primary   16.50
         92   OPEN 16.50   G/CL Primary   16.50

MAY YOUR BIRTHDAY BE GIGANTIC   Figurine   "Birthday Circus Train" Series
15970 86 Elephant - Age 4   UPP $12.50 3.50" DVE Secondary $40.00
(300)   86   UPP   12.50   OLB Secondary   25.00
         87   UPP   12.50   CED Secondary   18.50
         88   UPP   15.00   FLW Secondary   18.50
         89   UPP   17.00   B&A Secondary   18.50
         90   UPP   18.50   FLM Primary   18.50
         91   UPP   18.50   VSL Primary   18.50
         92   OPEN 18.50   G/CL Primary   18.50

THIS DAY IS SOMETHING TO ROAR ABOUT — Figurine — "Birthday Circus Train" Series

	Year		Status	Price	Size	Mark	Market	Value
15989	86	Lion - Age 5	UPP	$13.50	4.00"	DVE	Secondary	$38.00
(301)	86		UPP	13.50		OLB	Secondary	25.00
	87		UPP	13.50		CED	Secondary	20.00
	88		UPP	17.50		FLW	Secondary	20.00
	89		UPP	20.00		B&A	Secondary	20.00
	90		UPP	20.00		FLM	Primary	20.00
	91		UPP	20.00		VSL	Primary	20.00
	92		OPEN	20.00		G/CL	Primary	20.00

KEEP LOOKING UP — Figurine — "Birthday Circus Train" Series

	Year		Status	Price	Size	Mark	Market	Value
15997	86	Giraffe - Age 6	UPP	$13.50	5.50"	DVE	Secondary	$37.00
(302)	86		UPP	13.50		OLB	Secondary	25.00
	87		UPP	13.50		CED	Secondary	20.00
	88		UPP	17.50		FLW	Secondary	20.00
	89		UPP	20.00		B&A	Secondary	20.00
	90		UPP	20.00		FLM	Primary	20.00
	91		UPP	20.00		VSL	Primary	20.00
	92		OPEN	20.00		G/CL	Primary	20.00

BLESS THE DAYS OF OUR YOUTH — Figurine — "Birthday Circus Train" Series

	Year		Status	Price	Size	Mark	Market	Value
16004	86	Clown with Pull Rope	UPP	$15.00	5.25"	DVE	Secondary	$40.00
(303)	86		UPP	15.00		OLB	Secondary	30.00
	87		UPP	15.00		CED	Secondary	22.50
	88		UPP	19.50		FLW	Secondary	22.50
	89		UPP	22.50		B&A	Secondary	22.50
	90		UPP	22.50		FLM	Primary	22.50
	91		UPP	22.50		VSL	Primary	22.50
	92		OPEN	22.50		G/CL	Primary	22.50

BABY'S FIRST TRIP — Figurine — Fourth Issue "Baby's First" Series

	Year		Status	Price	Size	Mark	Market	Value
16012	86	Angel Pushing Buggy	UPP	$32.50	5.00"	OLB	Susp/Sec	$85.00
(267)	87		UPP	32.50		CED	Susp/Sec	80.00
	88		UPP	40.00		FLW	Susp/Sec	75.00
	89		UPP	45.00		B&A	Susp/Sec	70.00

GOD BLESS YOU WITH RAINBOWS — Night Light

	Year		Status	Price	Size	Mark	Market	Value
16020	86	Angel behind Rainbow	UPP	$45.00	5.00"	DVE	Susp/Sec	$95.00
(199)	86		UPP	45.00		OLB	Susp/Sec	85.00
	87		UPP	45.00		CED	Susp/Sec	80.00
	88		UPP	52.50		FLW	Susp/Sec	80.00
	89		UPP	57.50		B&A	Susp/Sec	75.00

TO MY FAVORITE PAW — Figurine

	Year		Status	Price	Size	Mark	Market	Value
100021	86	Boy Sitting with Teddy	UPP	$22.50	3.50"	DVE	Susp/Sec	$65.00
(211)	86		UPP	22.50		OLB	Susp/Sec	55.00
	87		UPP	22.50		CED	Susp/Sec	50.00
	88		UPP	27.00		FLW	Susp/Sec	45.00

TO MY DEER FRIEND — Figurine

	Year		Status	Price	Size	Mark	Market	Value
100048	87	Girl with Flowers and Deer	UPP	$33.00	5.75"	OLB	Secondary	$95.00
(316)	87		UPP	33.00		CED	Secondary	60.00
	88		UPP	40.00		FLW	Secondary	50.00
	89		UPP	45.00		B&A	Secondary	50.00
	90		UPP	50.00		FLM	Primary	50.00
	91		UPP	50.00		VSL	Primary	50.00
	92		OPEN	50.00		G/CL	Primary	50.00

SENDING MY LOVE — Figurine

	Year		Status	Price	Size	Mark	Market	Value
100056	86	Boy with Bow & Arrow	UPP	$22.50	5.75"	DVE	Susp/Sec	$55.00
(212)	86	on Cloud	UPP	22.50		OLB	Susp/Sec	45.00
	87		UPP	22.50		CED	Susp/Sec	42.00
	88		UPP	27.00		FLW	Susp/Sec	40.00
	89		UPP	30.00		B&A	Susp/Sec	40.00
	90		UPP	32.50		FLM	Susp/Sec	40.00
	91		UPP	32.50		VSL	Susp/Prim	32.50

WORSHIP THE LORD — Figurine

100064	86	Girl Kneeling at	UPP	$24.00	5.25"	DVE	Secondary	$50.00
(213)	86	Church Window	UPP	24.00		OLB	Secondary	40.00
	87		UPP	24.00		CED	Secondary	38.00
	88		UPP	30.00		FLW	Secondary	35.00
	89		UPP	33.00		B&A	Secondary	35.00
	90		UPP	35.00		FLM	Primary	35.00
	91		UPP	35.00		VSL	Primary	35.00
	92		OPEN	35.00		G/CL	Primary	35.00

TO MY FOREVER FRIEND — Figurine

100072	86	Two Girls with Flowers	UPP	$33.00	5.50"	DVE	Secondary	$95.00
(214)	86		UPP	33.00		OLB	Secondary	65.00
	87		UPP	33.00		CED	Secondary	55.00
	88		UPP	40.00		FLW	Secondary	50.00
	89		UPP	45.00		B&A	Secondary	50.00
	90		UPP	50.00		FLM	Primary	50.00
	91		UPP	50.00		VSL	Primary	50.00
	92		OPEN	50.00		G/CL	Primary	50.00

HE'S THE HEALER OF BROKEN HEARTS — Figurine

100080	87	Girl & Boy with	UPP	$33.00	5.50"	OLB	Secondary	$60.00
(317)	87	Bandaged Heart	UPP	33.00		CED	Secondary	55.00
	88		UPP	40.00		FLW	Secondary	50.00
	89		UPP	45.00		B&A	Secondary	50.00
	90		UPP	50.00		FLM	Primary	50.00
	91		UPP	50.00		VSL	Primary	50.00
	92		OPEN	50.00		G/CL	Primary	50.00

MAKE ME A BLESSING — Figurine

100102	87	Girl with Sick Bear	UPP	$35.00	5.50"	OLB	Retired/Sec	$135.00
(323)	87		UPP	35.00		CED	Retired/Sec	90.00
	88		UPP	40.00		FLW	Retired/Sec	80.00
	89		UPP	45.00		B&A	Retired/Sec	75.00
	90		UPP	50.00		FLM	Retired/Sec	70.00

LORD I'M COMING HOME — Figurine

100110	86	Baseball Player with Bat	UPP	$22.50	5.00"	DVE	Secondary	$70.00
(215)	86		UPP	22.50		OLB	Secondary	35.00
	87		UPP	22.50		CED	Secondary	32.50
	88		UPP	27.00		FLW	Secondary	32.50
	89		UPP	30.00		B&A	Secondary	32.50
	90		UPP	32.50		FLM	Primary	32.50
	91		UPP	32.50		VSL	Primary	32.50
	92		OPEN	32.50		G/CL	Primary	32.50

LORD KEEP ME ON MY TOES — Figurine

100129	86	Ballerina	UPP	$22.50	5.75"	DVE	Retired/Sec	$85.00
(216)	86		UPP	22.50		OLB	Retired/Sec	75.00
	87		UPP	22.50		CED	Retired/Sec	72.00
	88		UPP	27.00		FLW	Retired/Sec	70.00

THE JOY OF THE LORD IS MY STRENGTH — Figurine

100137	86	Mother with Babies	UPP	$35.00	5.40"	DVE	Secondary	$85.00
(217)	86		UPP	35.00		OLB	Secondary	65.00
	87		UPP	35.00		CED	Secondary	55.00
	88		UPP	40.00		FLW	Secondary	50.00
	89		UPP	47.50		B&A	Secondary	50.00
	90		UPP	50.00		FLM	Primary	50.00
	91		UPP	50.00		VSL	Primary	50.00
	92		OPEN	50.00		G/CL	Primary	50.00

GOD BLESS THE DAY WE FOUND YOU — Figurine

100145	86	Mom & Dad with	UPP	$40.00	5.50"	OLB	Susp/Sec	$75.00
(272)	87	Adopted Daughter	UPP	40.00		CED	Susp/Sec	70.00
	88		UPP	47.50		FLW	Susp/Sec	70.00
	89		UPP	50.00		B&A	Susp/Sec	65.00
	90		UPP	55.00		FLM	Susp/Sec	65.00

GOD BLESS THE DAY WE FOUND YOU — Figurine

100153	86	Mom & Dad with	UPP	$40.00	5.50"	OLB	Susp/Sec	$75.00
(273)	87	Adopted Son	UPP	40.00		CED	Susp/Sec	70.00
	88		UPP	47.50		FLW	Susp/Sec	70.00
	89		UPP	50.00		B&A	Susp/Sec	65.00
	90		UPP	55.00		FLM	Susp/Sec	65.00

SERVING THE LORD — Figurine

100161	86	Tennis Girl	UPP	$19.00	5.00"	DVE	Susp/Sec	$50.00
(218)	86		UPP	19.00		OLB	Susp/Sec	45.00
	87		UPP	19.00		CED	Susp/Sec	40.00
	88		UPP	22.50		FLW	Susp/Sec	40.00
	89		UPP	25.00		B&A	Susp/Sec	35.00
	90		UPP	27.50		FLM	Susp/Sec	35.00

I'M A POSSIBILITY — Figurine

100188	86	Boy with Football	UPP	$22.00	5.25"	OLB	Secondary	$40.00
(274)	87		UPP	22.00		CED	Secondary	32.50
	88		UPP	27.00		FLW	Secondary	32.50
	89		UPP	30.00		B&A	Secondary	32.50
	90		UPP	32.50		FLM	Primary	32.50
	91		UPP	32.50		VSL	Primary	32.50
	92		OPEN	32.50		G/CL	Primary	32.50

THE SPIRIT IS WILLING BUT THE FLESH IS WEAK — Figurine

100196	87	Girl on Scale	UPP	$19.00	5.50"	CED	Retired/Sec	$65.00
(324)	88		UPP	24.00		FLW	Retired/Sec	60.00
	89		UPP	27.00		B&A	Retired/Sec	55.00
	90		UPP	30.00		FLM	Retired/Prim	55.00
	91		UPP	30.00		VSL	Retired/Prim	50.00

THE LORD GIVETH AND THE LORD TAKETH AWAY — Figurine

100226	87	Girl with Cat & Bird Cage	UPP	$33.50	5.25"	CED	Secondary	$50.00
(340)	88		UPP	36.00		FLW	Secondary	40.00
	89		UPP	38.50		B&A	Secondary	40.00
	90		UPP	40.00		FLM	Primary	40.00
	91		UPP	40.00		VSL	Primary	40.00
	92		OPEN	40.00		G/CL	Primary	40.00

FRIENDS NEVER DRIFT APART — Figurine

100250	86	Kids in Boat	UPP	$35.00	4.25"	DVE	Secondary	$70.00
(219)	86		UPP	35.00		OLB	Secondary	58.00
	87		UPP	35.00		CED	Secondary	50.00
	88		UPP	42.50		FLW	Secondary	50.00
	89		UPP	47.50		B&A	Secondary	50.00
	90		UPP	50.00		FLM	Primary	50.00
	91		UPP	50.00		VSL	Primary	50.00
	92		OPEN	50.00		G/CL	Primary	50.00

HELP LORD, I'M IN A SPOT — Figurine

100269	86	Boy Standing in Ink Spot	UPP	$18.50	5.25"	OLB	Retired/Sec	$65.00
(275)	87		UPP	18.50		CED	Retired/Sec	60.00
	88		UPP	22.50		FLW	Retired/Sec	60.00
	89		UPP	25.00		B&A	Retired/Sec	55.00

HE CLEANSED MY SOUL   Figurine

100277	86	Girl in Old Bath Tub	UPP	$24.00	4.90"	DVE	Secondary	$50.00
(220)	86		UPP	24.00		OLB	Secondary	42.00
	87		UPP	24.00		CED	Secondary	40.00
	88		UPP	30.00		FLW	Secondary	35.00
	89		UPP	33.00		B&A	Secondary	35.00
	90		UPP	35.00		FLM	Primary	35.00
	91		UPP	35.00		VSL	Primary	35.00
	92		OPEN	35.00		G/CL	Primary	35.00

HEAVEN BLESS YOU   Musical   TUNE: Brahm's Lullaby

100285	86	Baby with Bunny & Turtle	UPP	$45.00	5.00"	DVE	Secondary	$75.00
(221)	86		UPP	45.00		OLB	Secondary	65.00
	87		UPP	45.00		CED	Secondary	60.00
	88		UPP	52.50		FLW	Secondary	60.00
	89		UPP	57.50		B&A	Secondary	60.00
	90		UPP	60.00		FLM	Primary	60.00
	91		UPP	60.00		VSL	Primary	60.00
	92		OPEN	60.00		G/CL	Primary	60.00

SERVING THE LORD   Figurine

100293	86	Tennis Boy	UPP	$19.00	5.25"	DVE	Susp/Sec	$50.00
(222)	86		UPP	19.00		OLB	Susp/Sec	45.00
	87		UPP	19.00		CED	Susp/Sec	42.00
	88		UPP	22.50		FLW	Susp/Sec	40.00
	89		UPP	25.00		B&A	Susp/Sec	38.00
	90		UPP	27.50		FLM	Susp/Sec	35.00

BONG BONG   Doll   Individually Numbered

100455	86	Boy Clown	12,000	$150.00	13.00"	OLB	Secondary	$220.00
(289)								

CANDY   Doll   Individually Numbered

100463	86	Girl Clown	12,000	$150.00	13.00"	OLB	Secondary	$245.00
(290)								

GOD BLESS OUR FAMILY   Figurine

100498	87	Parents of the Groom	UPP	$35.00	5.50"	CED	Secondary	$55.00
(325)	88		UPP	40.00		FLW	Secondary	50.00
	89		UPP	45.00		B&A	Primary	50.00
	90		UPP	50.00		FLM	Primary	50.00
	91		UPP	50.00		VSL	Primary	50.00
	92		OPEN	50.00		G/CL	Primary	50.00

GOD BLESS OUR FAMILY   Figurine

100501	87	Parents of the Bride	UPP	$35.00	5.50"	CED	Secondary	$55.00
(326)	88		UPP	40.00		FLW	Secondary	50.00
	89		UPP	45.00		B&A	Primary	50.00
	90		UPP	50.00		FLM	Primary	50.00
	91		UPP	50.00		VSL	Primary	50.00
	92		OPEN	50.00		G/CL	Primary	50.00

SCENT FROM ABOVE   Figurine

100528	87	Girl with Skunk	UPP	$19.00	5.25"	OLB	Retired/Sec	$65.00
(327)	87		UPP	19.00		CED	Retired/Sec	60.00
	88		UPP	23.00		FLW	Retired/Sec	55.00
	89		UPP	25.00		B&A	Retired/Sec	55.00
	90		UPP	27.50		FLM	Retired/Sec	52.00
	91		UPP	27.50		VSL	Retired/Sec	50.00

I PICKED A (VERY) SPECIAL MOM   Figurine

100536	87	Boy with His	Annual	$37.50	5.50"	CED	Secondary	$60.00
(328)		Gardening Mother						

The original announced title for this figurine was "I Picked A Special Mom" and it appears as though all of these annual figurines were produced with an "I Picked A Special Mom" understamp.

BROTHERLY LOVE — Figurine

100544	86	Pilgrim & Indian with Turkey	UPP	$37.00	4.50"	OLB	Susp/Sec	$65.00
(276)	87		UPP	37.00		CED	Susp/Sec	60.00
	88		UPP	42.50		FLW	Susp/Sec	55.00
	89		UPP	47.50		B&A	Susp/Sec	55.00

GOD IS LOVE, DEAR VALENTINE — Thimble

100625	86	Girl Holding Heart	UPP	$5.50	2.25"	DVE	Susp/Sec	$18.00
(103)	86		UPP	5.50		OLB	Susp/Sec	15.00
	87		UPP	5.50		CED	Susp/Sec	12.00
	88		UPP	7.00		FLW	Susp/Sec	12.00
	89		UPP	8.00		B&A	Susp/Sec	10.00

THE LORD BLESS YOU AND KEEP YOU — Thimble

100633	86	Bride	UPP	$5.50	2.25"	DVE	Susp/Sec	$18.00
(313)	86		UPP	5.50		OLB	Susp/Sec	15.00
	87		UPP	5.50		CED	Susp/Sec	15.00
	88		UPP	7.00		FLW	Susp/Sec	12.00
	89		UPP	8.00		B&A	Susp/Sec	12.00
	90		UPP	8.00		FLM	Susp/Sec	10.00
	91		UPP	8.00		VSL	Susp/Prim	8.00

FOUR SEASONS THIMBLES — Thimbles — Set of 4

100641	86	Four Seasons Thimbles	Annual	$20.00	2.00"	OLB	Secondary	$55.00
(226-229)								

CLOWN THIMBLES — Thimbles — Set of 2

100668	86	Clowns	UPP	$11.00	2.00"	OLB	Susp/Sec	$30.00
(235)	87		UPP	11.00		CED	Susp/Sec	25.00
	88		UPP	14.00		FLW	Susp/Sec	20.00

OUR FIRST CHRISTMAS TOGETHER — Musical — TUNE: We Wish You A Merry Christmas

101702	86	Boy & Girl in Box	UPP	$50.00	5.50"	OLB	Secondary	$80.00
(277)	87		UPP	50.00		CED	Secondary	70.00
	88		UPP	55.00		FLW	Secondary	70.00
	89		UPP	67.50		B&A	Secondary	70.00
	90		UPP	70.00		FLM	Primary	70.00
	91		UPP	70.00		VSL	Primary	70.00
	92		OPEN	70.00		G/CL	Primary	70.00

NO TEARS PAST THE GATE — Figurine

101826	87	Girl at Gate to Heaven	UPP	$40.00	6.25"	CED	Secondary	$70.00
(329)	88		UPP	47.50		FLW	Secondary	60.00
	89		UPP	55.00		B&A	Secondary	60.00
	90		UPP	60.00		FLM	Primary	60.00
	91		UPP	60.00		VSL	Primary	60.00
	92		OPEN	60.00		G/CL	Primary	60.00

I'M SENDING YOU A WHITE CHRISTMAS — Plate, Dated — First Issue "Christmas Love" Series

101834	86	Girl Mailing Snowball	Annual	$45.00	8.50"	OLB	Secondary	$75.00
(169)								

SMILE ALONG THE WAY — Figurine

101842	87	Clown Balancing	UPP	$30.00	6.75"	OLB	Retired/Sec	$175.00
(330)	87	Upside Down	UPP	30.00		CED	Retired/Sec	160.00
	88		UPP	35.00		FLW	Retired/Sec	155.00
	89		UPP	40.00		B&A	Retired/Sec	150.00
	90		UPP	45.00		FLM	Retired/Sec	140.00
	91		UPP	45.00		VSL	Retired/Sec	135.00

LORD HELP US KEEP OUR ACT TOGETHER — Figurine

101850	87	Clowns on Unicycle	UPP	$35.00	7.00"	OLB	Retired/Sec	$150.00
(331)	87		UPP	35.00		CED	Retired/Sec	130.00
	88		UPP	40.00		FLW	Retired/Sec	125.00
	89		UPP	45.00		B&A	Retired/Sec	120.00
	90		UPP	50.00		FLM	Retired/Sec	120.00
	91		UPP	50.00		VSL	Retired/Sec	115.00

WORSHIP THE LORD		Figurine						
102229	86	Boy Kneeling at	UPP	$24.00	5.50"	DVE	Secondary	$45.00
(223)	86	Church Window	UPP	24.00		OLB	Secondary	40.00
	87		UPP	24.00		CED	Secondary	35.00
	88		UPP	30.00		FLW	Secondary	35.00
	89		UPP	33.00		B&A	Secondary	35.00
	90		UPP	35.00		FLM	Primary	35.00
	91		UPP	35.00		VSL	Primary	35.00
	92		OPEN	35.00		G/CL	Primary	35.00

Some of these figurines have the title, "Q Worship The Lord."

CONNIE	Doll	Individually Numbered						
102253	86	Doll with Stand	7,500	$160.00	12.00"	OLB	Secondary	$220.00
(291)								

SHEPHERD OF LOVE		Figurine	Mini Nativity Addition					
102261	86	Angel with Black Lamb	UPP	$10.00	3.25"	OLB	Secondary	$22.00
(278)	87		UPP	10.00		CED	Secondary	15.00
	88		UPP	11.00		FLW	Secondary	15.00
	89		UPP	13.50		B&A	Secondary	15.00
	90		UPP	15.00		FLM	Primary	15.00
	91		UPP	15.00		VSL	Primary	15.00
	92		OPEN	15.00		G/CL	Primary	15.00

SHEPHERD OF LOVE		Ornament						
102288	86	Angel with Black Lamb	UPP	$10.00	3.25"	OLB	Secondary	$22.00
(278)	87		UPP	10.00		CED	Secondary	20.00
	88		UPP	11.00		FLW	Secondary	15.00
	89		UPP	13.50		B&A	Secondary	15.00
	90		UPP	15.00		FLM	Primary	15.00
	91		UPP	15.00		VSL	Primary	15.00
	92		OPEN	15.00		G/CL	Primary	15.00

MINI ANIMAL FIGURINES		Figurines	Set of 3	Mini Nativity Addition				
102296	86	Black Sheep, Bunny & Turtle	UPP	$13.50	1.75"	OLB	Secondary	$25.00
(279)	87		UPP	13.50		CED	Secondary	19.00
	88		UPP	15.00		FLW	Secondary	19.00
	89		UPP	17.50		B&A	Secondary	19.00
	90		UPP	19.00		FLM	Primary	19.00
	91		UPP	19.00		VSL	Primary	19.00
	92		OPEN	19.00		G/CL	Primary	19.00

WISHING YOU A COZY CHRISTMAS			Bell, Dated					
102318	86	Girl with Muff	Annual	$20.00	5.50"	OLB	Secondary	$38.00
(280)								

WISHING YOU A COZY CHRISTMAS			Ornament, Dated					
102326	86	Girl with Muff	Annual	$10.00	3.00"	OLB	Secondary	$40.00
(280)								

WISHING YOU A COZY CHRISTMAS			Thimble, Dated					
102334	86	Girl with Muff	Annual	$5.50	2.25"	OLB	Secondary	$20.00
(280)								

WISHING YOU A COZY CHRISTMAS			Figurine, Dated					
102342	86	Girl with Muff	Annual	$17.00	4.75"	OLB	Secondary	$40.00
(280)								

OUR FIRST CHRISTMAS TOGETHER			Ornament, Dated					
102350	86	Boy and Girl in Package	Annual	$10.00	2.74"	OLB	Secondary	$30.00
(277)								

WEDDING ARCH — Figurine

102369	86	Bridal Arch	UPP	$22.50	7.75"	OLB	Secondary	$35.00
(332)	87		UPP	22.50		CED	Secondary	32.00
	88		UPP	25.00		FLW	Secondary	30.00
	89		UPP	27.50		B&A	Secondary	30.00
	90		UPP	30.00		FLM	Primary	30.00
	91		UPP	30.00		VSL	Primary	30.00
	92		OPEN	30.00		G/CL	Primary	30.00

TRUST AND OBEY — Ornament

102377	86	Policeman Writing Ticket	UPP	$10.00	3.00"	OLB	Secondary	$22.00
(237)	87		UPP	10.00		CED	Secondary	15.00
	88		UPP	11.00		FLW	Secondary	15.00
	89		UPP	13.50		B&A	Secondary	15.00
	90		UPP	15.00		FLM	Primary	15.00
	91		UPP	15.00		VSL	Primary	15.00
	92		OPEN	15.00		G/CL	Primary	15.00

LOVE RESCUED ME — Ornament

102385	86	Fireman Holding Puppy	UPP	$10.00	3.00"	OLB	Secondary	$22.00
(281)	87		UPP	10.00		CED	Secondary	15.00
	88		UPP	11.00		FLW	Secondary	15.00
	89		UPP	13.50		B&A	Secondary	15.00
	90		UPP	15.00		FLM	Primary	15.00
	91		UPP	15.00		VSL	Primary	15.00
	92		OPEN	15.00		G/CL	Primary	15.00

LOVE RESCUED ME — Figurine

102393	86	Fireman Holding Puppy	UPP	$22.50	5.50"	OLB	Secondary	$40.00
(281)	87		UPP	22.50		CED	Secondary	35.00
	88		UPP	27.00		FLW	Secondary	32.50
	89		UPP	30.00		B&A	Secondary	32.50
	90		UPP	32.50		FLM	Primary	32.50
	91		UPP	32.50		VSL	Primary	32.50
	92		OPEN	32.50		G/CL	Primary	32.50

ANGEL OF MERCY — Ornament

102407	86	Nurse with Potted Plant	UPP	$10.00	3.00"	OLB	Secondary	$22.00
(282)	87		UPP	10.00		CED	Secondary	18.00
	88		UPP	11.00		FLW	Secondary	15.00
	89		UPP	13.50		B&A	Secondary	15.00
	90		UPP	15.00		FLM	Primary	15.00
	91		UPP	15.00		VSL	Primary	15.00
	92		OPEN	15.00		G/CL	Primary	15.00

IT'S A PERFECT BOY — Ornament

102415	86	Boy Angel with	UPP	$10.00	3.00"	OLB	Susp/Sec	$30.00
(127)	87	Red Cross Bag	UPP	10.00		CED	Susp/Sec	28.00
	88		UPP	11.00		FLW	Susp/Sec	25.00
	89		UPP	13.50		B&A	Susp/Sec	22.00

LORD KEEP ME ON MY TOES — Ornament

102423	86	Ballerina	UPP	$10.00	3.50"	OLB	Retired/Sec	$45.00
(216)	87		UPP	10.00		CED	Retired/Sec	40.00
	88		UPP	11.00		FLW	Retired/Sec	40.00
	89		UPP	13.50		B&A	Retired/Sec	40.00
	90		UPP	15.00		FLM	Retired/Sec	35.00

There are CEDAR TREE pieces with two hooks from the Retailers Wreath, #111465. For further information, see 6th Ed., pg. 209.

SERVE WITH A SMILE — Ornament

102431	86	Tennis Boy	UPP	$10.00	3.25"	OLB	Susp/Sec	$25.00
(222)	87		UPP	10.00		CED	Susp/Sec	22.00
	88		UPP	11.00		FLW	Susp/Sec	20.00

SERVE WITH A SMILE   Ornament

102458	86	Tennis Girl	UPP	$10.00	3.25"	OLB	Susp/Sec	$30.00
(218)	87		UPP	10.00		CED	Susp/Sec	25.00
	88		UPP	11.00		FLW	Susp/Sec	22.00

REINDEER   Ornament, Dated   Birthday Collection

102466	86	Reindeer and Teddy Bear	Annual	$11.00	3.25"	OLB	Secondary	$190.00
(306)								

ROCKING HORSE   Ornament

102474	86	Rocking Horse	UPP	$10.00	2.50"	OLB	Susp/Sec	$28.00
(283)	87		UPP	10.00		CED	Susp/Sec	25.00
	88		UPP	11.00		FLW	Susp/Sec	25.00
	89		UPP	13.50		B&A	Susp/Sec	22.00
	90		UPP	15.00		FLM	Susp/Sec	22.00
	91		UPP	15.00		VSL	Susp/Prim	15.00

There are CEDAR TREE pieces with two hooks from the Retailers Wreath, #111465. For further information, see 6th Ed., pg. 209.

ANGEL OF MERCY   Figurine

102482	86	Nurse with Potted Plant	UPP	$20.00	5.50"	OLB	Secondary	$40.00
(282)	87		UPP	20.00		CED	Secondary	30.00
	88		UPP	24.00		FLW	Secondary	30.00
	89		UPP	27.00		B&A	Secondary	30.00
	90		UPP	30.00		FLM	Primary	30.00
	91		UPP	30.00		VSL	Primary	30.00
	92		OPEN	30.00		G/CL	Primary	30.00

SHARING OUR CHRISTMAS TOGETHER   Figurine

102490	86	Husband & Wife with	UPP	$37.00	5.25"	OLB	Susp/Sec	$68.00
(284)	87	Cookies & Pup	UPP	37.00		CED	Susp/Sec	60.00
	88		UPP	40.00		FLW	Susp/Sec	55.00

BABY'S FIRST CHRISTMAS   Ornament, Dated

102504	86	Girl with Candy Cane	Annual	$10.00	2.75"	OLB	Secondary	$28.00
(285)								

BABY'S FIRST CHRISTMAS   Ornament, Dated

102512	86	Boy with Candy Cane	Annual	$10.00	2.75"	OLB	Secondary	$25.00
(286)								

LET'S KEEP IN TOUCH   Musical   TUNE: Be A Clown

102520	86	Clown on Elephant	UPP	$65.00	7.00"	OLB	Secondary	$95.00
(287)	87		UPP	65.00		CED	Secondary	85.00
	88		UPP	75.00		FLW	Secondary	85.00
	89		UPP	80.00		B&A	Secondary	85.00
	90		UPP	85.00		FLM	Primary	85.00
	91		UPP	85.00		VSL	Primary	85.00
	92		OPEN	85.00		G/CL	Primary	85.00

WE ARE ALL PRECIOUS IN HIS SIGHT   Figurine

102903	87	Girl with Pearl	Annual	$30.00	7.10"	CED	Secondary	$75.00
(373)								

The announcement that "some" figurines were missing the title on the understamp was made in the Fall 1987 GOODNEWSLETTER. However, to date, figurines with the title appear to be nonexistent. Because of the statement in the GOODNEWSLETTER, all who own the piece without the title, and, again, to our knowledge, that's everyone, are under the mistaken impression they own a variation. For more information, see 6th Ed., pg. 223.

GOD BLESS AMERICA   Figurine

102938	86	Uncle Sam Holding Bible	Annual	$30.00	5.50"	OLB	Secondary	$65.00
(292)		with Dog						

MY PEACE I GIVE UNTO THEE   Plate, Dated   Second Issue "Christmas Love" Series

102954	87	Children around Lamppost	Annual	$45.00	8.50"	CED	Secondary	$90.00
(341)								

IT'S THE BIRTHDAY OF A KING — Figurine — Nativity Addition

102962	86	Boy Angel with	UPP	$18.50	5.50"	OLB	Susp/Sec	$42.00
(288)	87	Birthday Cake	UPP	18.50		CED	Susp/Sec	38.00
	88		UPP	21.00		FLW	Susp/Sec	35.00
	89		UPP	25.00		B&A	Susp/Sec	35.00

I WOULD BE SUNK WITHOUT YOU — Figurine

102970	87	Baby Boy in Tub	UPP	$15.00	3.25"	CED	Secondary	$28.00
(342)	88		UPP	16.00		FLW	Secondary	19.00
	89		UPP	17.50		B&A	Secondary	19.00
	90		UPP	19.00		FLM	Primary	19.00
	91		UPP	19.00		VSL	Primary	19.00
	92		OPEN	19.00		G/CL	Primary	19.00

WE BELONG TO THE LORD — Figurine — Damien-Dutton Piece

103004	86	Shepherd & Lambs Figurine	UPP	$50.00	4.90"	DIA	Secondary	$175.00
(338)		w/Leather Bound Bible						

Color photograph: 5th Ed., pg. 195.

MY LOVE WILL NEVER LET YOU GO — Figurine

103497	87	Boy with Hat & Fish	UPP	$25.00	5.50"	CED	Secondary	$40.00
(333)	88		UPP	30.00		FLW	Secondary	35.00
	89		UPP	33.00		B&A	Secondary	35.00
	90		UPP	35.00		FLM	Primary	35.00
	91		UPP	35.00		VSL	Primary	35.00
	92		OPEN	35.00		G/CL	Primary	35.00

I BELIEVE IN THE OLD RUGGED CROSS — Figurine

103632	86	Girl Holding Cross	UPP	$25.00	5.25"	DVE	Secondary	$50.00
(224)	86		UPP	25.00		OLB	Secondary	35.00
	87		UPP	25.00		CED	Secondary	35.00
	88		UPP	30.00		FLW	Secondary	35.00
	89		UPP	33.00		B&A	Secondary	35.00
	90		UPP	35.00		FLM	Primary	35.00
	91		UPP	35.00		VSL	Primary	35.00
	92		OPEN	35.00		G/CL	Primary	35.00

COME LET US ADORE HIM — Figurines — Set of 9

104000	86	Nativity Set with Cassette	UPP	$ 95.00	4.75"	OLB	Secondary	$120.00
(307)	87		UPP	95.00		CED	Secondary	110.00
	88		UPP	100.00		FLW	Secondary	110.00
	89		UPP	110.00		B&A	Secondary	110.00
	90		UPP	110.00		FLM	Primary	110.00
	91		UPP	110.00		VSL	Primary	110.00
	92		OPEN	110.00		G/CL	Primary	110.00

WITH THIS RING I... — Figurine

104019	87	Boy Giving Girl Ring	UPP	$40.00	5.00"	CED	Secondary	$65.00
(343)	88		UPP	45.00		FLW	Secondary	55.00
	89		UPP	50.00		B&A	Secondary	55.00
	90		UPP	55.00		FLM	Primary	55.00
	91		UPP	55.00		VSL	Primary	55.00
	92		OPEN	55.00		G/CL	Primary	55.00

LOVE IS THE GLUE THAT MENDS — Figurine

104027	87	Boy Mending Hobby Horse	UPP	$33.50	4.00"	CED	Susp/Sec	$55.00
(344)	88		UPP	36.00		FLW	Susp/Sec	50.00
	89		UPP	38.50		B&A	Susp/Sec	50.00
	90		UPP	40.00		FLM	Susp/Sec	50.00

CHEERS TO THE LEADER — Figurine

104035	87	Girl Cheerleader	UPP	$22.50	5.25"	CED	Secondary	$40.00
(345)	88		UPP	24.00		FLW	Secondary	30.00
	89		UPP	27.00		B&A	Secondary	30.00
	90		UPP	30.00		FLM	Primary	30.00
	91		UPP	30.00		VSL	Primary	30.00
	92		OPEN	30.00		G/CL	Primary	30.00

HAPPY DAYS ARE HERE AGAIN   Figurine

104396	87	Girl Clown with Books	UPP	$25.00	5.25"	CED	Susp/Sec	$50.00
(346)	88		UPP	27.00		FLW	Susp/Sec	45.00
	89		UPP	30.00		B&A	Susp/Sec	45.00
	90		UPP	32.50		FLM	Susp/Sec	40.00

FRIENDS TO THE END   Figurine   Birthday Collection

104418	88	Rhino with Bird	UPP	$15.00	2.50"	UM	Secondary	$30.00
(420)	88		UPP	17.00		FLW	Secondary	25.00
	89		UPP	17.00		B&A	Secondary	18.50
	90		UPP	18.50		FLM	Primary	18.50
	91		UPP	18.50		VSL	Primary	18.50
	92		OPEN	18.50		G/CL	Primary	18.50

BEAR THE GOOD NEWS OF CHRISTMAS   Ornament, Dated   Birthday Collection

104515	87	Teddy Bear in Cup on Skis	Annual	$11.00	2.10"	CED	Secondary	$22.00
(347)								

"DEALERS ONLY" NATIVITY   Figurines   Set of 9

104523	86	Nativity with Backdrop	UPP	$400.00	9.00"	OLB	Secondary	$485.00
(337)		and Video						

JESUS LOVES ME   Figurine   Easter Seal Raffle Piece   Individually Numbered

104531	88	Girl with Bunny	1,000	$500.00	9.00"	CED	Secondary	$1700.00
(2)								

A TUB FULL OF LOVE   Figurine

104817	87	Baby Boy in Wood Tub	UPP	$22.50	3.75"	CED	Secondary	$35.00
(348)	88		UPP	24.00		FLW	Secondary	30.00
	89		UPP	27.50		B&A	Secondary	30.00
	90		UPP	30.00		FLM	Primary	30.00
	91		UPP	30.00		VSL	Primary	30.00
	92		OPEN	30.00		G/CL	Primary	30.00

SITTING PRETTY   Figurine

104825	87	Girl Angel on Stool	UPP	$22.50	5.50"	CED	Susp/Sec	$50.00
(349)	88		UPP	24.00		FLW	Susp/Sec	48.00
	89		UPP	27.00		B&A	Susp/Sec	45.00
	90		UPP	30.00		FLM	Susp/Sec	42.00
	*					VSL	Susp/Sec	55.00

*Piece was suspended in 1990 yet exists in a VESSEL.

HAVE I GOT NEWS FOR YOU   Figurine   Nativity Addition

105635	87	Boy Reading Scroll	UPP	$22.50	4.75"	CED	Susp/Sec	$45.00
(350)	88		UPP	22.50		FLW	Susp/Sec	42.00
	89		UPP	27.50		B&A	Susp/Sec	40.00
	90		UPP	30.00		FLM	Susp/Sec	35.00
	91		UPP	30.00		VSL	Susp/Prim	30.00

SOMETHING'S MISSING WHEN YOU'RE NOT AROUND   Figurine

105643	88	Girl Holding Doll with Dog	UPP	$32.50	5.50"	FLW	Susp/Sec	$60.00
(421)	89		UPP	36.00		B&A	Susp/Sec	55.00
	90		UPP	37.50		FLM	Susp/Sec	45.00
	91		UPP	37.50		VSL	Susp/Prim	37.50

TO TELL THE TOOTH YOU'RE SPECIAL   Figurine

105813	87	Dentist and Patient with	UPP	$38.50	5.00"	CED	Susp/Sec	$70.00
(351)	88	Pulled Tooth	UPP	42.50		FLW	Susp/Sec	65.00
	89		UPP	47.50		B&A	Susp/Sec	65.00
	90		UPP	50.00		FLM	Susp/Sec	60.00

HALLELUJAH COUNTRY — Figurine

105821	88	Cowboy on Fence with Guitar	UPP	$35.00	5.50"	CED	Secondary	*
(377)	88		UPP	35.00		FLW	Secondary	$50.00
	89		UPP	40.00		B&A	Secondary	45.00
	90		UPP	45.00		FLM	Primary	45.00
	91		UPP	45.00		VSL	Primary	45.00
	92		OPEN	45.00		G/CL	Primary	45.00

* Extremely rare, consider FLOWER as first annual production symbol.

SHOWERS OF BLESSINGS — Figurine — Birthday Collection

105945	87	Elephant Showering	UPP	$16.00	3.25"	CED	Secondary	$30.00
(352)	88	Mouse	UPP	18.50		FLW	Secondary	20.00
	89		UPP	20.00		B&A	Secondary	20.00
	90		UPP	20.00		FLM	Primary	20.00
	91		UPP	20.00		VSL	Primary	20.00
	92		OPEN	20.00		G/CL	Primary	20.00

BRIGHTEN SOMEONE'S DAY — Figurine — Birthday Collection

105953	88	Skunk & Mouse	UPP	$12.50	2.50"	CED	Secondary	$25.00
(395)	88		UPP	12.50		FLW	Secondary	18.00
	89		UPP	13.50		B&A	Secondary	15.00
	90		UPP	15.00		FLM	Primary	15.00
	91		UPP	15.00		VSL	Primary	15.00
	92		OPEN	15.00		G/CL	Primary	15.00

WE'RE PULLING FOR YOU — Figurine

106151	87	Boy with Donkey	UPP	$40.00	5.00"	CED	Susp/Sec	$70.00
(353)	88		UPP	45.00		FLW	Susp/Sec	65.00
	89		UPP	50.00		B&A	Susp/Sec	62.00
	90		UPP	55.00		FLM	Susp/Sec	60.00
	91		UPP	55.00		VSL	Susp/Prim	55.00

GOD BLESS YOU GRADUATE — Figurine

106194	86	Boy Graduate	UPP	$20.00	5.00"	OLB	Secondary	$30.00
(334)	87		UPP	20.00		CED	Secondary	30.00
	88		UPP	24.00		FLW	Secondary	30.00
	89		UPP	27.00		B&A	Secondary	30.00
	90		UPP	30.00		FLM	Primary	30.00
	91		UPP	30.00		VSL	Primary	30.00
	92		OPEN	30.00		G/CL	Primary	30.00

CONGRATULATIONS, PRINCESS — Figurine

106208	86	Girl Graduate	UPP	$20.00	5.50"	OLB	Secondary	$35.00
(318)	87		UPP	20.00		CED	Secondary	32.00
	88		UPP	24.00		FLW	Secondary	30.00
	89		UPP	27.00		B&A	Secondary	30.00
	90		UPP	30.00		FLM	Primary	30.00
	91		UPP	30.00		VSL	Primary	30.00
	92		OPEN	30.00		G/CL	Primary	30.00

LORD HELP ME MAKE THE GRADE — Figurine

106216	87	Schoolboy Clown	UPP	$25.00	5.00"	CED	Susp/Sec	$50.00
(354)	88		UPP	27.00		FLW	Susp/Sec	42.00
	89		UPP	30.00		B&A	Susp/Sec	40.00
	90		UPP	32.50		FLM	Susp/Sec	40.00

HEAVEN BLESS YOUR TOGETHERNESS — Figurine

106755	88	Groom Popping out of	UPP	$65.00	5.50"	CED	Secondary	$85.00
(378)	88	Trunk at Bride	UPP	65.00		FLW	Secondary	80.00
	89		UPP	75.00		B&A	Secondary	80.00
	90		UPP	80.00		FLM	Primary	80.00
	91		UPP	80.00		VSL	Primary	80.00
	92		OPEN	80.00		G/CL	Primary	80.00

PRECIOUS MEMORIES — Figurine

ID	Year	Description		Price	Size	Mark	Market	Value
106763	88	Couple on Couch Looking	UPP	$37.50	4.50"	CED	Secondary	$55.00
(379)	88	at Wedding Album	UPP	37.50		FLW	Secondary	50.00
	89		UPP	45.00		B&A	Secondary	50.00
	90		UPP	50.00		FLM	Primary	50.00
	91		UPP	50.00		VSL	Primary	50.00
	92		OPEN	50.00		G/CL	Primary	50.00

PUPPY LOVE IS FROM ABOVE — Figurine

ID	Year	Description		Price	Size	Mark	Market	Value
106798	88	Anniversary Couple with Dog	UPP	$45.00	5.50"	CED	Secondary	$60.00
(380)	88		UPP	45.00		FLW	Secondary	55.00
	89		UPP	50.00		B&A	Secondary	55.00
	90		UPP	55.00		FLM	Primary	55.00
	91		UPP	55.00		VSL	Primary	55.00
	92		OPEN	55.00		G/CL	Primary	55.00

HAPPY BIRTHDAY POPPY — Figurine

ID	Year	Description		Price	Size	Mark	Market	Value
106836	88	Girl Holding Poppy Plant	UPP	$27.50	5.50"	CED	Secondary	$35.00
(381)	88		UPP	27.50		FLW	Secondary	33.50
	89		UPP	31.50		B&A	Primary	33.50
	90		UPP	33.50		FLM	Primary	33.50
	91		UPP	33.50		VSL	Primary	33.50
	92		OPEN	33.50		G/CL	Primary	33.50

SEW IN LOVE — Figurine

ID	Year	Description		Price	Size	Mark	Market	Value
106844	88	Girl Sewing Boy's Pants	UPP	$45.00	5.50"	CED	Secondary	$70.00
(382)	88		UPP	45.00		FLW	Secondary	60.00
	89		UPP	50.00		B&A	Secondary	55.00
	90		UPP	55.00		FLM	Primary	55.00
	91		UPP	55.00		VSL	Primary	55.00
	92		OPEN	55.00		G/CL	Primary	55.00

HE WALKS WITH ME — Figurine — Special Easter Seal Piece — Easter Seal Lily on Decal

ID	Year	Description		Price	Size	Mark	Market	Value
107999	87	Girl on Crutches	Annual	$25.00	5.50"	OLB	Secondary	$40.00
(319)	87					CED	Secondary	38.00

THEY FOLLOWED THE STAR — Figurines — Set of 3 — Mini Nativity Addition

ID	Year	Description		Price	Size	Mark	Market	Value
108243	87	Kings on Camels	UPP	$75.00	6.50"	CED	Secondary	$110.00
(65)	88		UPP	75.00		FLW	Secondary	100.00
	89		UPP	95.00		B&A	Secondary	100.00
	90		UPP	100.00		FLM	Primary	100.00
	91		UPP	100.00		VSL	Primary	100.00
	92		OPEN	100.00		G/CL	Primary	100.00

THE GREATEST GIFT IS A FRIEND — Figurine

ID	Year	Description		Price	Size	Mark	Market	Value
109231	87	Baby Boy Sitting by Dog	UPP	$30.00	4.25"	CED	Secondary	$50.00
(355)	88		UPP	30.00		FLW	Secondary	42.00
	89		UPP	36.00		B&A	Secondary	38.00
	90		UPP	37.50		FLM	Primary	37.50
	91		UPP	37.50		VSL	Primary	37.50
	92		OPEN	37.50		G/CL	Primary	37.50

BABY'S FIRST CHRISTMAS — Ornament, Dated

ID	Year	Description		Price	Size	Mark	Market	Value
109401	87	Girl on Rocking Horse	Annual	$12.00	3.25"	CED	Secondary	$40.00
(356)								

BABY'S FIRST CHRISTMAS — Ornament, Dated

ID	Year	Description		Price	Size	Mark	Market	Value
109428	87	Boy on Rocking Horse	Annual	$12.00	3.25"	CED	Secondary	$40.00
(357)								

ISN'T EIGHT JUST GREAT — Figurine — "Birthday Circus Train" Series

ID	Year	Description		Price	Size	Mark	Market	Value
109460	88	Ostrich - Age 8	UPP	$18.50	4.50"	CED	Secondary	$30.00
(394)	88		UPP	18.50		FLW	Secondary	25.00
	89		UPP	20.00		B&A	Secondary	23.00
	90		UPP	22.50		FLM	Primary	22.50
	91		UPP	22.50		VSL	Primary	22.50
	92		OPEN	22.50		G/CL	Primary	22.50

WISHING YOU GRRR-EATNESS — Figurine — "Birthday Circus Train" Series

Item	Year	Description		Price	Size	Mark	Status	Value
109479	88	Leopard - Age 7	UPP	$18.50	4.25"	CED	Secondary	$30.00
(393)	88		UPP	18.50		FLW	Secondary	23.00
	89		UPP	20.00		B&A	Secondary	23.00
	90		UPP	22.50		FLM	Primary	22.50
	91		UPP	22.50		VSL	Primary	22.50
	92		OPEN	22.50		G/CL	Primary	22.50

BELIEVE THE IMPOSSIBLE — Figurine

Item	Year	Description		Price	Size	Mark	Status	Value
109487	88	Boy with Barbells	UPP	$35.00	5.50"	CED	Susp/Sec	$100.00
(383)	88		UPP	35.00		FLW	Susp/Sec	65.00
	89		UPP	40.00		B&A	Susp/Sec	60.00
	90		UPP	45.00		FLM	Susp/Sec	50.00
	91		UPP	45.00		VSL	Susp/Prim	45.00

HAPPINESS DIVINE — Figurine

Item	Year	Description		Price	Size	Mark	Status	Value
109584	88	Clown Angel with Flowers	UPP	$25.00	5.50"	FLW	Secondary	$35.00
(384)	89		UPP	27.50		B&A	Secondary	32.00
	90		UPP	30.00		FLM	Primary	30.00
	91		UPP	30.00		VSL	Primary	30.00
	92		OPEN	30.00		G/CL	Primary	30.00

PEACE ON EARTH — Musical — TUNE: Hark! The Herald Angels Sing

Item	Year	Description		Price	Size	Mark	Status	Value
109746	88	Kids with Pup, Kitten,	UPP	$100.00	6.50"	FLW	Secondary	$125.00
(341)	89	and Bird	UPP	110.00		B&A	Secondary	120.00
	90		UPP	120.00		FLM	Primary	120.00
	91		UPP	120.00		VSL	Primary	120.00
	92		OPEN	120.00		G/CL	Primary	120.00

WISHING YOU A YUMMY CHRISTMAS — Figurine

Item	Year	Description		Price	Size	Mark	Status	Value
109754	87	Girl with Ice Cream	UPP	$35.00	5.00"	CED	Secondary	$50.00
(358)	88		UPP	35.00		FLW	Secondary	45.00
	89		UPP	42.50		B&A	Secondary	45.00
	90		UPP	45.00		FLM	Primary	45.00
	91		UPP	45.00		VSL	Primary	45.00
	92		OPEN	45.00		G/CL	Primary	45.00

WE GATHER TOGETHER TO ASK THE LORD'S BLESSING — Figurines — Set of 6

Item	Year	Description		Price	Size	Mark	Status	Value
109762	87	Family Thanksgiving Set	UPP	$130.00	5.00"	CED	Secondary	$170.00
(359)	88		UPP	130.00		FLW	Secondary	150.00
	89		UPP	145.00		B&A	Secondary	150.00
	90		UPP	150.00		FLM	Primary	150.00
	91		UPP	150.00		VSL	Primary	150.00
	92		OPEN	150.00		G/CL	Primary	150.00

LOVE IS THE BEST GIFT OF ALL — Ornament, Dated

Item	Year	Description		Price	Size	Mark	Status	Value
109770	87	Girl with Package and	Annual	$11.00	2.75"	CED	Secondary	$40.00
(360)		Doll						

MEOWIE CHRISTMAS — Figurine

Item	Year	Description		Price	Size	Mark	Status	Value
109800	88	Girl with Kitten	UPP	$30.00	4.50"	FLW	Secondary	$40.00
(423)	89		UPP	33.00		B&A	Secondary	35.00
	90		UPP	35.00		FLM	Primary	35.00
	91		UPP	35.00		VSL	Primary	35.00
	92		OPEN	35.00		G/CL	Primary	35.00

OH WHAT FUN IT IS TO RIDE — Figurine

Item	Year	Description		Price	Size	Mark	Status	Value
109819	87	Grandma on Sled	UPP	$85.00	6.25"	CED	Secondary	$120.00
(361)	88		UPP	85.00		FLW	Secondary	110.00
	89		UPP	100.00		B&A	Secondary	110.00
	90		UPP	110.00		FLM	Primary	110.00
	91		UPP	110.00		VSL	Primary	110.00
	92		OPEN	110.00		G/CL	Primary	110.00

LOVE IS THE BEST GIFT OF ALL   Bell, Dated
| **109835** | 87 | Girl with Package and | Annual | $22.50 | 5.75" | CED | Secondary | $38.00 |
| (360) | | Doll | | | | | | |

LOVE IS THE BEST GIFT OF ALL   Thimble, Dated
| **109843** | 87 | Girl with Package and | Annual | $6.00 | 2.25" | CED | Secondary | $22.00 |
| (360) | | Doll | | | | | | |

WISHING YOU A HAPPY EASTER   Figurine
109886	88	Girl Holding Bunny	UPP	$23.00	5.50"	CED	Secondary	$35.00
(388)	88		UPP	23.00		FLW	Secondary	30.00
	89		UPP	25.00		B&A	Secondary	28.00
	90		UPP	27.50		FLM	Secondary	28.00
	91		UPP	27.50		VSL	Secondary	28.00
	92		OPEN	27.50		G/CL	Primary	27.50

WISHING YOU A BASKET FULL OF BLESSINGS   Figurine
109924	88	Boy Holding Basket	UPP	$23.00	5.50"	CED	Secondary	$32.00
(385)	88		UPP	23.00		FLW	Secondary	30.00
	89		UPP	25.00		B&A	Secondary	28.00
	90		UPP	27.50		FLM	Secondary	28.00
	91		UPP	27.50		VSL	Primary	27.50
	92		OPEN	27.50		G/CL	Primary	27.50

SENDING YOU MY LOVE   Figurine
109967	88	Girl with Hearts in Cloud	UPP	$35.00	5.00"	CED	Secondary	$58.00
(386)	88		UPP	35.00		FLW	Secondary	45.00
	89		UPP	40.00		B&A	Secondary	45.00
	90		UPP	45.00		FLM	Primary	45.00
	91		UPP	45.00		VSL	Primary	45.00
	92		OPEN	45.00		G/CL	Primary	45.00

MOMMY, I LOVE YOU   Figurine
109975	88	Boy with Flower	UPP	$22.50	5.50"	CED	Secondary	$35.00
(387)	88		UPP	22.50		FLW	Secondary	30.00
	89		UPP	25.00		B&A	Secondary	30.00
	90		UPP	27.50		FLM	Secondary	30.00
	91		UPP	27.50		VSL	Secondary	28.00
	92		OPEN	27.50		G/CL	Primary	27.50

JANUARY GIRL   Figurine   "Calendar Girl" Series
109983	88	Girl Pushing Doll in Sleigh	UPP	$37.50	5.50"	CED	Secondary	$65.00
(367)	88		UPP	37.50		FLW	Secondary	50.00
	89		UPP	42.50		B&A	Secondary	45.00
	90		UPP	45.00		FLM	Primary	45.00
	91		UPP	45.00		VSL	Primary	45.00
	92		OPEN	45.00		G/CL	Primary	45.00

FEBRUARY GIRL   Figurine   "Calendar Girl" Series
109991	88	Girl Looking at Plant	UPP	$27.50	5.25"	CED	Secondary	$55.00
(368)	88	Peeking through Snow	UPP	27.50		FLW	Secondary	35.00
	89		UPP	31.50		B&A	Secondary	33.50
	90		UPP	33.50		FLM	Secondary	33.50
	91		UPP	33.50		VSL	Primary	33.50
	92		OPEN	33.50		G/CL	Primary	33.50

MARCH GIRL   Figurine   "Calendar Girl" Series
110019	88	Girl with Kite	UPP	$27.50	5.00"	CED	Secondary	$60.00
(369)	88		UPP	27.50		FLW	Secondary	38.00
	89		UPP	31.50		B&A	Secondary	33.50
	90		UPP	33.50		FLM	Secondary	33.50
	91		UPP	33.50		VSL	Primary	33.50
	92		OPEN	33.50		G/CL	Primary	33.50

APRIL GIRL   Figurine   "Calendar Girl" Series

110027	88	Girl with Umbrella	UPP	$30.00	6.00"	CED	Secondary	$110.00
(370)	88		UPP	30.00		FLW	Secondary	45.00
	89		UPP	33.00		B&A	Secondary	35.00
	90		UPP	35.00		FLM	Secondary	35.00
	91		UPP	35.00		VSL	Primary	35.00
	92		OPEN	35.00		G/CL	Primary	35.00

MAY GIRL   Figurine   "Calendar Girl" Series

110035	88	Girl with Potted Plant	UPP	$25.00	5.75"	CED	Secondary	$150.00
(371)	88		UPP	25.00		FLW	Secondary	35.00
	89		UPP	27.50		B&A	Secondary	30.00
	90		UPP	30.00		FLM	Secondary	30.00
	91		UPP	30.00		VSL	Primary	30.00
	92		OPEN	30.00		G/CL	Primary	30.00

JUNE GIRL   Figurine   "Calendar Girl" Series

110043	88	Girl Dressing Up as Bride	UPP	$40.00	5.50"	CED	Secondary	$110.00
(372)	88		UPP	40.00		FLW	Secondary	60.00
	89		UPP	45.00		B&A	Secondary	50.00
	90		UPP	50.00		FLM	Secondary	50.00
	91		UPP	50.00		VSL	Primary	50.00
	92		OPEN	50.00		G/CL	Primary	50.00

JULY GIRL   Figurine   "Calendar Girl" Series

110051	88	Girl with Puppy in Basket	UPP	$35.00	5.50"	FLW	Secondary	$55.00
(424)	89		UPP	40.00		B&A	Secondary	45.00
	90		UPP	45.00		FLM	Secondary	45.00
	91		UPP	45.00		VSL	Primary	45.00
	92		OPEN	45.00		G/CL	Primary	45.00

AUGUST GIRL   Figurine   "Calendar Girl" Series

110078	88	Girl in Pool	UPP	$40.00	4.00"	FLW	Secondary	$60.00
(425)	89		UPP	45.00		B&A	Secondary	50.00
	90		UPP	50.00		FLM	Secondary	50.00
	91		UPP	50.00		VSL	Primary	50.00
	92		OPEN	50.00		G/CL	Primary	50.00

SEPTEMBER GIRL   Figurine   "Calendar Girl" Series

110086	88	Girl Balancing Books	UPP	$27.50	5.75"	FLW	Secondary	$45.00
(426)	89		UPP	31.50		B&A	Secondary	35.00
	90		UPP	33.50		FLM	Secondary	33.50
	91		UPP	33.50		VSL	Primary	33.50
	92		OPEN	33.50		G/CL	Primary	33.50

OCTOBER GIRL   Figurine   "Calendar Girl" Series

110094	88	Girl with Pumpkins	UPP	$35.00	5.50"	FLW	Secondary	$55.00
(427)	89		UPP	40.00		B&A	Secondary	45.00
	90		UPP	45.00		FLM	Secondary	45.00
	91		UPP	45.00		VSL	Primary	45.00
	92		OPEN	45.00		G/CL	Primary	45.00

NOVEMBER GIRL   Figurine   "Calendar Girl" Series

110108	88	Girl in Pilgrim Suit	UPP	$32.50	5.50"	FLW	Secondary	$50.00
(428)	89		UPP	35.00		B&A	Secondary	37.50
	90		UPP	37.50		FLM	Secondary	37.50
	91		UPP	37.50		VSL	Primary	37.50
	92		OPEN	37.50		G/CL	Primary	37.50

DECEMBER GIRL   Figurine   "Calendar Girl" Series

110116	88	Girl with Christmas Candle	UPP	$27.50	5.50"	FLW	Secondary	$50.00
(429)	89		UPP	31.50		B&A	Secondary	33.50
	90		UPP	33.50		FLM	Secondary	33.50
	91		UPP	33.50		VSL	Primary	33.50
	92		OPEN	33.50		G/CL	Primary	33.50

LOVE IS THE BEST GIFT OF ALL — Figurine, Dated

110930	87	Girl Holding Package with	Annual	$22.50	5.25"	CED	Secondary	$45.00
(360)		Doll						

I'M A POSSIBILITY — Ornament

111120	87	Football Player	UPP	$11.00	3.25"	CED	Susp/Sec	$30.00
(274)	88		UPP	11.00		FLW	Susp/Sec	25.00
	89		UPP	13.50		B&A	Susp/Sec	22.00
	90		UPP	15.00		FLM	Susp/Sec	20.00

There are CEDAR TREE pieces with two hooks from the Retailers Wreath, #111465. For further information, see 6th Ed., pg. 209.

FAITH TAKES THE PLUNGE — Figurine

111155	88	Girl with Plunger	UPP	$27.50	5.50"	CED	Secondary	$55.00
(389)	88		UPP	27.50		FLW	Secondary	35.00
	89		UPP	31.50		B&A	Secondary	33.50
	90		UPP	33.50		FLM	Primary	33.50
	91		UPP	33.50		VSL	Primary	33.50
	92		OPEN	33.50		G/CL	Primary	33.50

At some point during the 1988 production, the expression on the face was changed from a smile to a "determined frown." The smiling piece is often referred to as the "Smiling Plunger."
GREENBOOK Market Prices are smiling with CEDAR TREE (all CED are smiling) annual symbol - $55.00 and smiling with the FLOWER annual symbol - $45.00.

TIS THE SEASON — Figurine

111163	88	Girl Adding Seasoning	UPP	$27.50	5.50"	FLW	Secondary	$40.00
(430)	89		UPP	31.50		B&A	Secondary	33.50
	90		UPP	33.50		FLM	Primary	33.50
	91		UPP	33.50		VSL	Primary	33.50
	92		OPEN	33.50		G/CL	Primary	33.50

O COME LET US ADORE HIM — Figurines — Set of 4

111333	87	Large Nativity	UPP	$200.00	9.00"	CED	Susp/Sec	$240.00
(362)	88		UPP	200.00		FLW	Susp/Sec	220.00
	89		UPP	220.00		B&A	Susp/Sec	220.00
	90		UPP	220.00		FLM	Susp/Prim	220.00
	91		UPP	220.00		VSL	Susp/Prim	220.00

RETAILER'S WREATH — Wreath

111465	87	Christmas Wreath	UPP	$150.00	16.00"	CED	Secondary	$250.00
(410)								

On some wreaths the *Have A Heavenly Christmas* ornament has the inscription "Heaven Bound" upside-down. The GREENBOOK Market Price for the wreath with the upside-down "Heaven Bound" ornament is $310.00. Also see 6th Ed., pg. 209.

MOMMY, I LOVE YOU — Figurine

112143	88	Girl with Flower	UPP	$22.50	5.75"	CED	Secondary	$35.00
(390)	88		UPP	22.50		FLW	Secondary	30.00
	89		UPP	25.00		B&A	Secondary	28.00
	90		UPP	27.50		FLM	Secondary	28.00
	91		UPP	27.50		VSL	Secondary	28.00
	92		OPEN	27.50		G/CL	Primary	27.50

A TUB FULL OF LOVE — Figurine

112313	87	Baby Girl in Wood Tub	UPP	$22.50	3.50"	CED	Secondary	$35.00
(363)	88		UPP	22.50		FLW	Secondary	30.00
	89		UPP	27.50		B&A	Secondary	30.00
	90		UPP	30.00		FLM	Primary	30.00
	91		UPP	30.00		VSL	Primary	30.00
	92		OPEN	30.00		G/CL	Primary	30.00

RETAILER'S WREATH BELL — Bell

112348	87	Retailer's Wreath Bell	UPP	N/A	3.25"	CED	Secondary	$75.00
(415)								

This is the bell from the Retailer's Wreath, #111465. It has its own Enesco Item Number.

YOU HAVE TOUCHED SO MANY HEARTS — Ornament

112356	87	Girl Holding Hearts	UPP	$11.00	3.25"	CED	Secondary	$20.00
(161)	88		UPP	11.00		FLW	Secondary	15.00
	89		UPP	13.50		B&A	Secondary	15.00
	90		UPP	15.00		FLM	Primary	15.00
	91		UPP	15.00		VSL	Primary	15.00
	92		OPEN	15.00		G/CL	Primary	15.00

There are CEDAR TREE pieces with two hooks from the Retailers Wreath, #111465. For further information, see 6th Ed., pg. 209.

WADDLE I DO WITHOUT YOU — Ornament

112364	87	Girl Clown with Goose	UPP	$11.00	3.50"	CED	Secondary	$22.00
(250)	88		UPP	11.00		FLW	Secondary	18.00
	89		UPP	13.50		B&A	Secondary	15.00
	90		UPP	15.00		FLM	Primary	15.00
	91		UPP	15.00		VSL	Primary	15.00
	92		OPEN	15.00		G/CL	Primary	15.00

I'M SENDING YOU A WHITE CHRISTMAS — Ornament

112372	87	Girl Mailing Snowball	UPP	$11.00	3.00"	CED	Secondary	$22.00
(169)	88		UPP	11.00		FLW	Secondary	15.00
	89		UPP	13.50		B&A	Secondary	15.00
	90		UPP	15.00		FLM	Primary	15.00
	91		UPP	15.00		VSL	Primary	15.00
	92		OPEN	15.00		G/CL	Primary	15.00

There are CEDAR TREE pieces with two hooks from the Retailers Wreath, #111465. For further information, see 6th Ed., pg. 209.

HE CLEANSED MY SOUL — Ornament

112380	87	Girl in Old Bathtub	UPP	$12.00	2.75"	CED	Secondary	$25.00
(220)	88		UPP	12.00		FLW	Secondary	18.00
	89		UPP	15.00		B&A	Secondary	18.00
	90		UPP	15.00		FLM	Primary	15.00
	91		UPP	15.00		VSL	Primary	15.00
	92		OPEN	15.00		G/CL	Primary	15.00

There are CEDAR TREE pieces with two hooks from the Retailers Wreath, #111465. For further information, see 6th Ed., pg. 209.

OUR FIRST CHRISTMAS TOGETHER — Ornament, Dated

112399	87	Boy and Girl in Package	Annual	$11.00	2.75"	CED	Secondary	$25.00
(277)								

I'M SENDING YOU A WHITE CHRISTMAS — Musical TUNE: White Christmas

112402	87	Girl Mailing Snowball	UPP	$55.00	6.00"	CED	Secondary	$75.00
(169)	88		UPP	55.00		FLW	Secondary	70.00
	89		UPP	67.50		B&A	Secondary	70.00
	90		UPP	70.00		FLM	Primary	70.00
	91		UPP	70.00		VSL	Primary	70.00
	92		OPEN	70.00		G/CL	Primary	70.00

YOU HAVE TOUCHED SO MANY HEARTS — Musical TUNE: Everybody Loves Somebody

112577	88	Girl with Hearts	UPP	$50.00	6.50"	CED	Secondary	$60.00
(161)	88		UPP	50.00		FLW	Secondary	60.00
	89		UPP	55.00		B&A	Primary	60.00
	90		UPP	60.00		FLM	Primary	60.00
	91		UPP	60.00		VSL	Primary	60.00
	92		OPEN	60.00		G/CL	Primary	60.00

TO MY FOREVER FRIEND — Ornament

113956	88	Girls with Flower Baskets	UPP	$16.00	3.00"	FLW	Secondary	$35.00
(214)	89		UPP	17.50		B&A	Secondary	22.00
	90		UPP	17.50		FLM	Secondary	17.50
	91		UPP	17.50		VSL	Primary	17.50
	92		OPEN	17.50		G/CL	Primary	17.50

SMILE ALONG THE WAY   Ornament

113964	88	Clown Doing Handstand	UPP	$15.00	3.50"	FLW	Secondary	$22.00
(330)	89		UPP	17.00		B&A	Secondary	17.50
	90		UPP	17.50		FLM	Secondary	17.50
	91		UPP	17.50		VSL	Primary	17.50
	92		OPEN	17.50		G/CL	Primary	17.50

GOD SENT YOU JUST IN TIME   Ornament

113972	88	Clown with Jack-in-the-Box	UPP	$13.50	3.00"	FLW	Susp/Sec	$32.00
(256)	89		UPP	15.00		B&A	Susp/Sec	30.00
	90		UPP	15.00		FLM	Susp/Sec	30.00
	91		UPP	15.00		VSL	Susp/Sec	25.00

REJOICE O EARTH   Ornament

113980	88	Angel with Trumpet	UPP	$13.50	3.00"	FLW	Retired/Sec	$42.00
(67)	89		UPP	15.00		B&A	Retired/Sec	40.00
	90		UPP	15.00		FLM	Retired/Sec	38.00
	91		UPP	15.00		VSL	Retired/Sec	35.00

CHEERS TO THE LEADER   Ornament

113999	88	Cheerleader	UPP	$13.50	3.00"	FLW	Susp/Sec	$35.00
(345)	89		UPP	15.00		B&A	Susp/Sec	30.00
	90		UPP	15.00		FLM	Susp/Sec	28.00
	91		UPP	15.00		VSL	Susp/Sec	25.00

MY LOVE WILL NEVER LET YOU GO   Ornament

114006	88	Fisherman	UPP	$13.50	3.25"	FLW	Susp/Sec	$32.00
(333)	89		UPP	15.00		B&A	Susp/Sec	30.00
	90		UPP	15.00		FLM	Susp/Sec	28.00
	91		OPEN	15.00		VSL	Susp/Sec	25.00

THIS TOO SHALL PASS   Figurine

114014	88	Boy with Broken Heart	UPP	$23.00	5.50"	CED	Secondary	$35.00
(391)	88		UPP	23.00		FLW	Secondary	27.50
	89		UPP	25.00		B&A	Secondary	27.50
	90		UPP	27.50		FLM	Primary	27.50
	91		UPP	27.50		VSL	Primary	27.50
	92		OPEN	27.50		G/CL	Primary	27.50

THE GOOD LORD HAS BLESSED US TENFOLD   Figurine   10th Anniversary Commemorative Edition

114022	88	Couple with Dogs	Annual	$90.00	5.75"	CED	Secondary	$135.00
(392)		and Puppies		90.00		FLW	Secondary	120.00

YOU ARE MY MAIN EVENT   Figurine   Special Events Piece

115231	88	Girl Holding Balloons	Annual	$30.00	6.50"	CED	Secondary	$60.00
(397)	88	and Bag		30.00		FLW	Secondary	50.00

The balloon strings on this piece are metal wires covered with colored paper. The first CEDAR TREE pieces produced had pink strings - the rest of the production (balance of CEDAR TREE and all of FLOWER) had white strings. "Pink Strings" is the coveted piece. The GREENBOOK Market Price for "Pink Strings" is $75.00. Color photograph: 4th Ed., pg. 196 or 5th Ed., pg. 201.

SOME BUNNY'S SLEEPING   Figurines   Nativity Addition

115274	88	Bunnies	UPP	$15.00	2.75"	FLW	Secondary	$25.00
(431)	89		UPP	17.00		B&A	Secondary	18.50
	90		UPP	18.50		FLM	Primary	18.50
	91		UPP	18.50		VSL	Primary	18.50
	92		OPEN	18.50		G/CL	Primary	18.50

BABY'S FIRST CHRISTMAS   Ornament, Dated

115282	88	Boy in Sleigh	Annual	$15.00	2.25"	FLW	Secondary	$25.00
(432)								

OUR FIRST CHRISTMAS TOGETHER   Figurine

115290	88	Couple with Gifts	UPP	$50.00	5.50"	FLW	Susp/Sec	$80.00
(433)	89		UPP	55.00		B&A	Susp/Sec	75.00
	90		UPP	60.00		FLM	Susp/Sec	70.00
	91		UPP	60.00		VSL	Susp/Sec	65.00

Item	(Ref)	Year	Title / Description	Type	Issue Price	Size	Mark	Market	Value
TIME TO WISH YOU A MERRY CHRISTMAS — Bell, Dated									
115304 (434)		88	Girl Holding Clock with Mouse	Annual	$25.00	6.00"	FLW	Secondary	$40.00
TIME TO WISH YOU A MERRY CHRISTMAS — Thimble, Dated									
115312 (434)		88	Girl with Clock and Mouse	Annual	$7.00	2.00"	FLW	Secondary	$20.00
TIME TO WISH YOU A MERRY CHRISTMAS — Ornament, Dated									
115320 (434)		88	Girl with Clock and Mouse	Annual	$13.00	3.00"	FLW	Secondary	$50.00
TIME TO WISH YOU A MERRY CHRISTMAS — Figurine, Dated									
115339 (434)		88	Girl Holding Clock with Mouse	Annual	$24.00	5.00"	FLW	Secondary	$35.00
BLESSED ARE THEY THAT OVERCOME — Figurine — Special Easter Seal Piece									
115479 (396)		88	Boy on Crutches at	Annual	$27.50	5.50"	CED	Secondary	$35.00
		88	Finish Line		27.50		FLW	Secondary	35.00
Easter Seal Lily missing on all decals.									
THE VOICE OF SPRING — Musical Jack-in-the-Box — "The Four Seasons" Series — TUNE: April Love									
408735 (226)		90	Spring Girl	2yr	$200.00	13.00"	FLM	Primary	$200.00
		91			200.00		VSL	Primary	200.00
SUMMER'S JOY — Musical Jack-in-the-Box — "The Four Seasons" Series — TUNE: You Are My Sunshine									
408743 (227)		90	Summer Girl	2yr	$200.00	13.00"	FLM	Primary	$200.00
		91			200.00		VSL	Primary	200.00
AUTUMN'S PRAISE — Musical Jack-in-the-Box — "The Four Seasons" Series — TUNE: Autumn Leaves									
408751 (228)		90	Autumn Girl	2yr	$200.00	13.00"	FLM	Primary	$200.00
		91			200.00		VSL	Primary	200.00
WINTER'S SONG — Musical Jack-in-the-Box — "The Four Seasons" Series — TUNE: Thru The Eyes Of Love									
408778 (229)		90	Winter Girl	2yr	$200.00	13.00"	FLM	Primary	$200.00
		91			200.00		VSL	Primary	200.00
THE VOICE OF SPRING — Doll — "The Four Seasons" Series									
408786 (226)		90	Spring Girl	2yr	$150.00	15.00"	FLM	Primary	$150.00
		91			150.00		VSL	Primary	150.00
SUMMER'S JOY — Doll — "The Four Seasons" Series									
408794 (227)		90	Summer Girl	2yr	$150.00	15.00"	FLM	Primary	$150.00
		91			150.00		VSL	Primary	150.00
AUTUMN'S PRAISE — Doll — "The Four Seasons" Series									
408808 (228)		90	Autumn Girl	2yr	$150.00	15.00"	FLM	Primary	$150.00
		91			150.00		VSL	Primary	150.00
WINTER'S SONG — Doll — "The Four Seasons" Series									
408816 (229)		90	Winter Girl	2yr	$150.00	15.00"	FLM	Primary	$150.00
		91			150.00		VSL	Primary	150.00
MAY YOU HAVE AN OLD FASHIONED CHRISTMAS — Musical Jack-in-the-Box — TUNE: Have Yourself A Merry Little Christmas									
417777 (548)		91	Christmas Girl in Plaid Dress	2yr	$200.00	12.00"	VSL	Primary	$200.00
		92			200.00		G/CL	Primary	200.00
MAY YOU HAVE AN OLD FASHIONED CHRISTMAS — Doll									
417785 (548)		91	Christmas Girl in Plaid Dress	2yr	$150.00	12.00"	VSL	Primary	$150.00
		92			150.00		G/CL	Primary	150.00
YOU HAVE TOUCHED SO MANY HEARTS — Musical Jack-in-the-Box — TUNE: Everybody Loves Somebody									
422282 (161)		91	Girl with String of Hearts	2yr	$175.00	12.00"	FLM	Primary	$175.00
		91			175.00		VSL	Primary	175.00
		92			175.00		G/CL	Primary	175.00

YOU HAVE TOUCHED SO MANY HEARTS   Doll
427527   91   Girl with String of Hearts   2yr $90.00   12.00"   VSL   Primary $90.00
(161)   92   90.00   G/CL   Primary   90.00

THE EYES OF THE LORD ARE UPON YOU   Motion Musical Doll   TUNE: Brahm's Lullaby
429570   91   Baby Boy on Pillow   UPP $65.00   10.00"   VSL   Primary $65.00
((522)   92   OPEN   65.00   G/CL   Primary   65.00

THE EYES OF THE LORD ARE UPON YOU   Motion Musical Doll   TUNE: Brahm's Lullaby
429589   91   Baby Girl on Pillow   UPP $65.00   10.00"   VSL   Primary $65.00
(523)   92   OPEN   65.00   G/CL   Primary   65.00

OUR FIRST CHRISTMAS TOGETHER   Ornament, Dated
520233   88   Boy and Girl in Package   Annual $13.00   2.50"   FLW   Secondary $20.00
(277)

BABY'S FIRST CHRISTMAS   Ornament, Dated
520241   88   Girl in Sleigh   Annual $15.00   2.25"   FLW   Secondary $25.00
(435)

REJOICE O EARTH   Figurine   Mini Nativity Addition
520268   88   Angel with Trumpet   UPP $13.00   3.00"   FLW   Secondary $22.00
(67)   89   UPP   15.00   B&A   Secondary   15.00
   90   UPP   15.00   FLM   Primary   15.00
   91   UPP   15.00   VSL   Primary   15.00
   92   OPEN   15.00   G/CL   Primary   15.00

YOU ARE MY GIFT COME TRUE   Ornament, Dated   10th Anniversary Commemorative Piece
520276   88   Puppy in Sock   Annual $12.50   2.50"   FLW   Secondary $22.00
(436)

MERRY CHRISTMAS, DEER   Plate, Dated   Third Issue "Christmas Love" Series
520284   88   Girl Decorating Reindeer   Annual $50.00   8.25"   FLW   Secondary $75.00
(438)

HANG ON FOR THE HOLLY DAYS   Ornament, Dated   Birthday Collection
520292   88   Kitten Hanging on to   Annual $13.00   3.50"   FLW   Secondary $30.00
(400)   Wreath

MAKE A JOYFUL NOISE   Figurine   Easter Seal Raffle Piece   Individually Numbered
520322   89   Girl with Goose   1,500 $500.00   9.00"   B&A   Secondary $950.00
(5)

JESUS THE SAVIOR IS BORN   Figurine   Nativity Addition
520357   88   Angel with Newspaper   UPP $25.00   4.50"   FLW   Secondary $35.00
(437)   89   and Dog   UPP   30.00   B&A   Secondary   32.50
   90   UPP   32.50   FLM   Primary   32.50
   91   UPP   32.50   VSL   Primary   32.50
   92   OPEN   32.50   G/CL   Primary   32.50

I'M NUTS ABOUT YOU   Ornament, Dated   Birthday Collection
520411   92   Squirrel Decorating Tree   Annual $16.00   2.50"   G/CL   Primary $16.00
(570)   atop Log Filled w/Nuts

SNO-BUNNY FALLS FOR YOU LIKE I DO   Ornament, Dated   Birthday Collection
520438   91   Rabbit on Skates   Annual $15.00   3.25"   VSL   Secondary $28.00
(549)

CHRISTMAS IS RUFF WITHOUT YOU   Ornament, Dated   Birthday Collection
520462   89   Puppy Resting on Elbow   Annual $13.00   2.75"   B&A   Secondary $35.00
(470)

WISHING YOU A PURR-FECT HOLIDAY   Ornament, Dated   Birthday Collection
520497   90   Kitten with Ornament   Annual $15.00   2.75"   FLM   Secondary $32.00
(521)

THE LORD TURNED MY LIFE AROUND — Figurine

520535	92	Ballerina on Pointe	OPEN	$35.00	5.75"	G/CL	Primary	$35.00
(571)								

IN THE SPOTLIGHT OF HIS GRACE — Figurine

520543	91	Ballerina on Pointe	UPP	$35.00	5.75"	VSL	Secondary	$38.00
(524)	92		OPEN	35.00		G/CL	Primary	35.00

LORD, TURN MY LIFE AROUND — Figurine

520551	90	Ballerina	UPP	$35.00	5.75"	B&A	Secondary	$45.00
(493)	90		UPP	35.00		FLM	Primary	35.00
	91		UPP	35.00		VSL	Primary	35.00
	92		OPEN	35.00		G/CL	Primary	35.00

YOU DESERVE AN OVATION — Figurine

520578	92	Ballerina on Pointe	OPEN	$35.00	5.75"	G/CL	Primary	$35.00
(572)								

MY HEART IS EXPOSED WITH LOVE — Figurine

520624	89	Nurse X-raying Boy's Heart	UPP	$45.00	5.25"	FLW	Secondary	$55.00
(458)	89		UPP	45.00		B&A	Secondary	50.00
	90		UPP	50.00		FLM	Primary	50.00
	91		UPP	50.00		VSL	Primary	50.00
	92		OPEN	50.00		G/CL	Primary	50.00

A FRIEND IS SOMEONE WHO CARES — Figurine

520632	89	Mouse Wiping	UPP	$30.00	4.25"	FLW	Secondary	$42.00
(449)	89	Clown's Tears	UPP	30.00		B&A	Secondary	32.50
	90		UPP	32.50		FLM	Primary	32.50
	91		UPP	32.50		VSL	Primary	32.50
	92		OPEN	32.50		G/CL	Primary	32.50

I'M SO GLAD YOU FLUTTERED INTO MY LIFE — Figurine

520640	89	Angel with Butterfly Net	UPP	$40.00	5.75"	FLW	Retired/Sec	$375.00
(447)	89		UPP	40.00		B&A	Retired/Sec	275.00
	90		UPP	45.00		FLM	Retired/Sec	265.00
	91		UPP	45.00		VSL	Retired/Sec	250.00

EGGSPECIALLY FOR YOU — Figurine

520667	89	Girl with Hen & Easter Egg	UPP	$45.00	4.75"	FLW	Secondary	$60.00
(455)	89		UPP	45.00		B&A	Secondary	50.00
	90		UPP	50.00		FLM	Primary	50.00
	91		UPP	50.00		VSL	Primary	50.00
	92		OPEN	50.00		G/CL	Primary	50.00

YOUR LOVE IS SO UPLIFTING — Figurine

520675	89	Boy Holding Girl at Fountain	UPP	$60.00	6.50"	FLW	Secondary	$75.00
(454)	89		UPP	60.00		B&A	Secondary	65.00
	90		UPP	65.00		FLM	Primary	65.00
	91		UPP	65.00		VSL	Primary	65.00
	92		OPEN	65.00		G/CL	Primary	65.00

SENDING YOU SHOWERS OF BLESSINGS — Figurine

520683	89	Boy with Newspaper	UPP	$32.50	5.50"	FLW	Secondary	$42.00
(450)	89	over Head	UPP	32.50		B&A	Secondary	35.00
	90		UPP	35.00		FLM	Primary	35.00
	91		UPP	35.00		VSL	Primary	35.00
	92		OPEN	35.00		G/CL	Primary	35.00

LORD, KEEP MY LIFE IN BALANCE — Musical — TUNE: Music Box Dancer

520691	91	Ballerina at Barre	UPP	$60.00	7.00"	VSL	Secondary	$68.00
(525)	92		OPEN	60.00		G/CL	Primary	60.00

BABY'S FIRST PET — Figurine — Fifth Issue "Baby's First" Series

520705	89	Boy with Baby Feeding Dog	UPP	$45.00	5.25"	FLW	Secondary	$60.00
(461)	89		UPP	45.00		B&A	Secondary	52.00
	90		UPP	50.00		FLM	Primary	50.00
	91		UPP	50.00		VSL	Primary	50.00
	92		OPEN	50.00		G/CL	Primary	50.00

JUST A LINE TO WISH YOU A HAPPY DAY — Figurine

520721	89	Dog Pulling Boy's	UPP	$65.00	6.50"	FLW	Secondary	$80.00
(456)	89	Fishing Line	UPP	65.00		B&A	Secondary	75.00
	90		UPP	70.00		FLM	Primary	70.00
	91		UPP	70.00		VSL	Primary	70.00
	92		OPEN	70.00		G/CL	Primary	70.00

FRIENDSHIP HITS THE SPOT — Figurine

520748	89	Two Girls Having Tea	UPP	$55.00	5.25"	FLW	Secondary	$70.00
(453)	89		UPP	55.00		B&A	Secondary	60.00
	90		UPP	60.00		FLM	Primary	60.00
	91		UPP	60.00		VSL	Primary	60.00
	92		OPEN	60.00		G/CL	Primary	60.00

JESUS IS THE ONLY WAY — Figurine

520756	89	Boy at Crossroads	UPP	$40.00	6.00"	FLW	Secondary	$50.00
(464)	89		UPP	40.00		B&A	Secondary	45.00
	90		UPP	45.00		FLM	Primary	45.00
	91		UPP	45.00		VSL	Primary	45.00
	92		OPEN	45.00		G/CL	Primary	45.00

PUPPY LOVE — Figurine

520764	89	Two Puppies	UPP	$12.50	2.10"	FLW	Secondary	$23.00
(465)	89		UPP	12.50		B&A	Secondary	14.00
	90		UPP	13.50		FLM	Secondary	14.00
	91		UPP	13.50		VSL	Primary	13.50
	92		OPEN	13.50		G/CL	Primary	13.50

MANY MOONS IN SAME CANOE, BLESSUM YOU — Figurine

520772	89	Indians in Canoe	UPP	$50.00	5.00"	FLW	Retired/Sec	$225.00
(457)	89		UPP	50.00		B&A	Retired/Sec	195.00
	90		UPP	55.00		FLM	Retired/Sec	175.00

WISHING YOU ROADS OF HAPPINESS — Figurine

520780	89	Bride & Groom in Car	UPP	$60.00	4.50"	FLW	Secondary	$75.00
(460)	89		UPP	60.00		B&A	Secondary	65.00
	90		UPP	65.00		FLM	Secondary	65.00
	91		UPP	65.00		VSL	Primary	65.00
	92		OPEN	65.00		G/CL	Primary	65.00

SOMEDAY MY LOVE — Figurine

520799	89	Bride with Dress	UPP	$40.00	5.50"	FLW	Secondary	$52.00
(446)	89		UPP	40.00		B&A	Secondary	45.00
	90		UPP	45.00		FLM	Primary	45.00
	91		UPP	45.00		VSL	Primary	45.00
	92		OPEN	45.00		G/CL	Primary	45.00

MY DAYS ARE BLUE WITHOUT YOU — Figurine

520802	89	Girl with Paint & Ladder	UPP	$65.00	7.00"	FLW	Susp/Sec	$95.00
(462)	89		UPP	65.00		B&A	Susp/Sec	90.00
	90		UPP	70.00		FLM	Susp/Sec	80.00
	91		UPP	70.00		VSL	Susp/Prim	70.00

Exists with three variations of the mouth - smiling, frowning, and "O."

WE NEED A GOOD FRIEND THROUGH THE RUFF TIMES — Figurine

520810	89	Grandpa with Cane & Dog	UPP	$35.00	5.00"	FLW	Susp/Sec	$50.00
(452)	89		UPP	35.00		B&A	Susp/Sec	45.00
	90		UPP	37.50		FLM	Susp/Prim	37.50
	91		UPP	37.50		VSL	Susp/Prim	37.50

YOU ARE MY NUMBER ONE   Figurine

520829	89	Girl Holding Trophy	UPP	$25.00	6.00"	FLW	Secondary	$35.00
(448)	89		UPP	25.00		B&A	Secondary	27.50
	90		UPP	27.50		FLM	Primary	27.50
	91		UPP	27.50		VSL	Primary	27.50
	92		OPEN	27.50		G/CL	Primary	27.50

THE LORD IS YOUR LIGHT TO HAPPINESS   Figurine

520837	89	Bridal Couple Lighting	UPP	$50.00	4.75"	FLW	Secondary	$62.00
(466)	89	Candle	UPP	50.00		B&A	Secondary	55.00
	90		UPP	55.00		FLM	Primary	55.00
	91		UPP	55.00		VSL	Primary	55.00
	92		OPEN	55.00		G/CL	Primary	55.00

WISHING YOU A PERFECT CHOICE   Figurine

520845	89	Boy Proposing to Girl	UPP	$55.00	5.80"	FLW	Secondary	$70.00
(459)	89		UPP	55.00		B&A	Secondary	60.00
	90		UPP	60.00		FLM	Primary	60.00
	91		UPP	60.00		VSL	Primary	60.00
	92		OPEN	60.00		G/CL	Primary	60.00

I BELONG TO THE LORD   Figurine

520853	89	Orphan Girl	UPP	$25.00	5.10"	FLW	Susp/Sec	$38.00
(463)	89		UPP	25.00		B&A	Susp/Prim	27.50
	90		UPP	27.50		FLM	Susp/Prim	27.50
	91		UPP	27.50		VSL	Susp/Prim	27.50

SHARING BEGINS IN THE HEART   Figurine   Special Events Piece

520861	89	Girl with Chalkboard	Annual	$25.00	5.75"	FLW	Secondary	$75.00
(467)	89			25.00		B&A	Secondary	45.00

HEAVEN BLESS YOU   Figurine

520934	90	Baby with Bunny and	UPP	$35.00	3.50"	B&A	Secondary	$150.00
(221)	90	Turtle	UPP	35.00		FLM	Secondary	40.00
	91		UPP	35.00		VSL	Primary	35.00
	92		OPEN	35.00		G/CL	Primary	35.00

TO MY FAVORITE FAN   Figurine   Birthday Collection

521043	90	Gorilla and Parrot	UPP	$16.00	2.50"	B&A	Secondary	$45.00
(501)	90		UPP	16.00		FLM	Secondary	20.00
	91		UPP	16.00		VSL	Primary	16.00
	92		OPEN	16.00		G/CL	Primary	16.00

HELLO WORLD!   Figurine   Birthday Collection

521175	89	Kangaroo with Baby	UPP	$13.50	3.25"	FLW	Secondary	$22.00
(451)	89		UPP	13.50		B&A	Secondary	15.00
	90		UPP	15.00		FLM	Primary	15.00
	91		UPP	15.00		VSL	Primary	15.00
	92		OPEN	15.00		G/CL	Primary	15.00

THAT'S WHAT FRIENDS ARE FOR   Figurine

521183	90	Crying Girls Hugging	UPP	$45.00	6.00"	FLM	Secondary	$50.00
(520)	91		UPP	45.00		VSL	Primary	45.00
	92		OPEN	45.00		G/CL	Primary	45.00

HOPE YOU'RE UP AND ON THE TRAIL AGAIN   Figurine

521205	90	Girl on Hobby Horse	UPP	$35.00	5.50"	B&A	Secondary	$45.00
(494)	90		UPP	35.00		FLM	Primary	35.00
	91		UPP	35.00		VSL	Primary	35.00
	92		OPEN	35.00		G/CL	Primary	35.00

TAKE HEED WHEN YOU STAND   Figurine

521272	91	Boy on Rocking Horse	UPP	$55.00	6.00"	VSL	Primary	$55.00
(550)	92		OPEN	55.00		G/CL	Primary	55.00

HAPPY TRIP   Figurine

521280	90	Girl on Roller Skates	UPP	$35.00	5.75"	B&A	Secondary	$75.00
(499)	90		UPP	35.00		FLM	Secondary	40.00
	91		UPP	35.00		VSL	Primary	35.00
	92		OPEN	35.00		G/CL	Primary	35.00

HUG ONE ANOTHER   Figurine

521299	91	Girl and Boy Hugging	UPP	$45.00	5.50"	FLM	Secondary	$50.00
(526)	91		UPP	45.00		VSL	Primary	45.00
	92		OPEN	45.00		G/CL	Primary	45.00

MAY ALL YOUR CHRISTMASES BE WHITE   Ornament

521302	89	Girl Tying Snowball with	UPP	$13.50	3.25"	B&A	Secondary	$18.00
(477)	90	Ribbon	UPP	15.00		FLM	Primary	15.00
	91		UPP	15.00		VSL	Primary	15.00
	92		OPEN	15.00		G/CL	Primary	15.00

YIELD NOT TO TEMPTATION   Figurine

521310	90	Girl with Apple	UPP	$27.50	5.50"	B&A	Secondary	$38.00
(505)	90		UPP	27.50		FLM	Secondary	30.00
	91		UPP	27.50		VSL	Primary	27.50
	92		OPEN	27.50		G/CL	Primary	27.50

FAITH IS A VICTORY   Figurine

521396	90	Girl Wearing Boxing Gloves	UPP	$25.00	5.50"	B&A	Secondary	$35.00
(496)	90		UPP	25.00		FLM	Secondary	28.00
	91		UPP	25.00		VSL	Primary	25.00
	92		OPEN	25.00		G/CL	Primary	25.00

I'LL NEVER STOP LOVING YOU   Figurine

521418	90	Girl with Letters Y O U	UPP	$37.50	5.50"	B&A	Secondary	$50.00
(511)	90		UPP	37.50		FLM	Secondary	40.00
	91		UPP	37.50		VSL	Primary	37.50
	92		OPEN	37.50		G/CL	Primary	37.50

TO A VERY SPECIAL MOM AND DAD   Figurine

521434	91	Girl Holding Picture Frame	UPP	$35.00	5.75"	VSL	Primary	$35.00
(551)	92		OPEN	35.00		G/CL	Primary	35.00

LORD, HELP ME STICK TO MY JOB   Figurine

521450	90	Girl with Account Books	UPP	$30.00	5.75"	B&A	Secondary	$38.00
(503)	90	and Glue	UPP	30.00		FLM	Primary	30.00
	91		UPP	30.00		VSL	Primary	30.00
	92		OPEN	30.00		G/CL	Primary	30.00

TELL IT TO JESUS   Figurine

521477	89	Girl on Telephone	UPP	$35.00	5.25"	B&A	Secondary	$45.00
(476)	90		UPP	37.50		FLM	Secondary	40.00
	91		UPP	37.50		VSL	Primary	37.50
	92		OPEN	37.50		G/CL	Primary	37.50

THERE'S A LIGHT AT THE END OF THE TUNNEL   Figurine

521485	91	Girl Peeking at Bunny	UPP	$55.00	4.00"	VSL	Secondary	$60.00
(527)	92	thru Log	OPEN	55.00		G/CL	Primary	55.00

A SPECIAL DELIVERY   Figurine

521493	91	Girl with Baby	UPP	$30.00	5.75"	VSL	Primary	$30.00
(552)	92		OPEN	30.00		G/CL	Primary	30.00

THE LIGHT OF THE WORLD IS JESUS   Musical   TUNE: White Christmas

521507	89	Girl by Lamppost	UPP	$60.00	7.00"	B&A	Secondary	$80.00
(475)	90		UPP	65.00		FLM	Secondary	70.00
	91		UPP	65.00		VSL	Primary	65.00
	92		OPEN	65.00		G/CL	Primary	65.00

OUR FIRST CHRISTMAS TOGETHER — Ornament, Dated

No.	Year	Description	Edition	Price	Size	Mark	Market	Value
521558 (460)	89	Bride and Groom in Car	Annual	$17.50	2.75"	B&A	Secondary	$30.00

GLIDE THROUGH THE HOLIDAYS — Ornament

No.	Year	Description	Edition	Price	Size	Mark	Market	Value
521566 (499)	90	Girl on Roller Skates	UPP	$13.50	3.50"	FLM	Secondary	$20.00
	91		UPP	13.50		VSL	Secondary	15.00
	92		OPEN	13.50		G/CL	Primary	13.50

DASHING THROUGH THE SNOW — Ornament

No.	Year	Description	Edition	Price	Size	Mark	Market	Value
521574 (367)	90	Girl Pushing Doll in Sled	UPP	$15.00	3.00"	FLM	Secondary	$18.00
	91		UPP	15.00		VSL	Primary	15.00
	92		OPEN	15.00		G/CL	Primary	15.00

DON'T LET THE HOLIDAYS GET YOU DOWN — Ornament

No.	Year	Description	Edition	Price	Size	Mark	Market	Value
521590 (471)	90	Boy with Christmas Tree	UPP	$15.00	2.25"	FLM	Secondary	$20.00
	91		UPP	15.00		VSL	Primary	15.00
	92		OPEN	15.00		G/CL	Primary	15.00

THUMB-BODY LOVES YOU — Figurine

No.	Year	Description	Edition	Price	Size	Mark	Market	Value
521698 (528)	91	Girl Misses Nail,	UPP	$55.00	5.25"	FLM	Secondary	$60.00
	91	Hits Boy's Thumb	UPP	55.00		VSL	Primary	55.00
	92		OPEN	55.00		G/CL	Primary	55.00

SWEEP ALL YOUR WORRIES AWAY — Figurine

No.	Year	Description	Edition	Price	Size	Mark	Market	Value
521779 (502)	90	Girl Sweeping Dust under	UPP	$40.00	5.25"	B&A	Secondary	$125.00
	90	Rug	UPP	40.00		FLM	Secondary	45.00
	91		UPP	40.00		VSL	Primary	40.00
	92		OPEN	40.00		G/CL	Primary	40.00

GOOD FRIENDS ARE FOREVER — Figurine

No.	Year	Description	Edition	Price	Size	Mark	Market	Value
521817 (492)	90	Girls with Flower	UPP	$50.00	5.50"	B&A	Secondary	$55.00
	90		UPP	50.00		FLM	Primary	50.00
	91		UPP	50.00		VSL	Primary	50.00
	92		OPEN	50.00		G/CL	Primary	50.00

MAY YOUR BIRTHDAY BE MAMMOTH — Figurine — "Birthday Circus Train" Series

No.	Year	Description	Edition	Price	Size	Mark	Market	Value
521825 (573)	92	Whale Riding Wave Wearing Sailor Hat (10)	OPEN	$25.00	4.12"	G/CL	Primary	$25.00

BEING NINE IS JUST DIVINE — Figurine — "Birthday Circus Train" Series

No.	Year	Description	Edition	Price	Size	Mark	Market	Value
521833 (574)	92	Curly Maned Prancing Pony (9)	OPEN	$25.00	4.25"	G/CL	Primary	$25.00

LOVE IS FROM ABOVE — Figurine

No.	Year	Description	Edition	Price	Size	Mark	Market	Value
521841 (510)	90	Boy Whispering to Girl	UPP	$45.00	5.50"	B&A	Secondary	$55.00
	90		UPP	45.00		FLM	Primary	45.00
	91		UPP	45.00		VSL	Primary	45.00
	92		OPEN	45.00		G/CL	Primary	45.00

THE GREATEST OF THESE IS LOVE — Figurine

No.	Year	Description	Edition	Price	Size	Mark	Market	Value
521868 (483)	89	Angel Holding	UPP	$27.50	5.25"	B&A	Susp/Sec	$45.00
	90	Commandments	UPP	30.00		FLM	Susp/Sec	42.00
	91		UPP	30.00		VSL	Susp/Prim	30.00

EASTER'S ON ITS WAY — Figurine

No.	Year	Description	Edition	Price	Size	Mark	Market	Value
521892 (508)	90	Boy Pulling Girl and Lily	UPP	$60.00	5.25"	B&A	Secondary	$70.00
	90	in Wagon	UPP	60.00		FLM	Primary	60.00
	91		UPP	60.00		VSL	Primary	60.00
	92		OPEN	60.00		G/CL	Primary	60.00

HOPPY EASTER FRIEND — Figurine

No.	Year	Description	Edition	Price	Size	Mark	Market	Value
521906 (529)	91	Girl Collecting Eggs	UPP	$40.00	5.25"	FLM	Secondary	$40.00
	91	with Frog's Help	UPP	40.00		VSL	Primary	40.00
	92		OPEN	40.00		G/CL	Primary	40.00

WISHING YOU A COZY SEASON   Figurine

521949	89	Boy by Stump	UPP	$42.50	5.25"	B&A	Secondary	$52.00
(480)	90		UPP	45.00		FLM	Primary	45.00
	91		UPP	45.00		VSL	Primary	45.00
	92		OPEN	45.00		G/CL	Primary	45.00

All have "SWeet" decal error inside stump.

HIGH HOPES   Figurine

521957	90	Boy with Kite	UPP	$30.00	5.25"	B&A	Secondary	$40.00
(498)	90		UPP	30.00		FLM	Secondary	35.00
	91		UPP	30.00		VSL	Primary	30.00
	92		OPEN	30.00		G/CL	Primary	30.00

TO A SPECIAL MUM   Figurine

521965	91	Boy Looking at Bee	UPP	$30.00	5.25"	FLM	Secondary	$35.00
(530)	91	on Flower Pot for Mom	UPP	30.00		VSL	Primary	30.00
	92		OPEN	30.00		G/CL	Primary	30.00

MAY YOUR LIFE BE BLESSED WITH TOUCHDOWNS   Figurine

522023	89	Boy Playing Football	UPP	$45.00	4.25"	B&A	Secondary	$55.00
(473)	90		UPP	50.00		FLM	Primary	50.00
	91		UPP	50.00		VSL	Primary	50.00
	92		OPEN	50.00		G/CL	Primary	50.00

THANK YOU LORD FOR EVERYTHING   Figurine

522031	89	Boy Having Dinner	UPP	$60.00	5.25"	B&A	Secondary	$65.00
(472)	90	with Turkey	UPP	60.00		FLM	Primary	60.00
	91		UPP	60.00		VSL	Primary	60.00
	92		OPEN	60.00		G/CL	Primary	60.00

MAY YOUR WORLD BE TRIMMED WITH JOY   Figurine

522082	91	Boy Decorating Globe	UPP	$55.00	5.50"	VSL	Primary	$55.00
(553)	92		OPEN	55.00		G/CL	Primary	55.00

THERE SHALL BE SHOWERS OF BLESSINGS   Figurine

522090	90	Boy and Girl in Garden	UPP	$60.00	5.50"	B&A	Secondary	$65.00
(500)	90		UPP	60.00		FLM	Primary	60.00
	91		UPP	60.00		VSL	Primary	60.00
	92		OPEN	60.00		G/CL	Primary	60.00

IT'S NO YOLK WHEN I SAY I LOVE YOU   Figurine

522104	92	Hens Laugh cause Girl Drop'd	UPP	$60.00	5.25"	VSL	Primary	$60.00
(575)	92	Egg on Puppy's Head	OPEN	60.00		G/CL	Primary	60.00

DON'T LET THE HOLIDAYS GET YOU DOWN   Figurine

522112	89	Boy with Christmas Tree	UPP	$42.50	4.25"	B&A	Secondary	$50.00
(471)	90		UPP	45.00		FLM	Primary	45.00
	91		UPP	45.00		VSL	Primary	45.00
	92		OPEN	45.00		G/CL	Primary	45.00

WISHING YOU A VERY SUCCESSFUL SEASON   Figurine

522120	89	Boy with Box, Puppy & Bat	UPP	$60.00	6.00"	B&A	Secondary	$72.00
(478)	90		UPP	65.00		FLM	Primary	65.00
	91		UPP	65.00		VSL	Primary	65.00
	92		OPEN	65.00		G/CL	Primary	65.00

BON VOYAGE!   Figurine

522201	89	Boy & Girl on Motorcycle	UPP	$75.00	6.50"	B&A	Secondary	$85.00
(474)	90		UPP	80.00		FLM	Primary	80.00
	91		UPP	80.00		VSL	Primary	80.00
	92		OPEN	80.00		G/CL	Primary	80.00

DO NOT OPEN TILL CHRISTMAS   Musical   TUNE: Toyland

522244	92	Boy Peeking into Opened	OPEN	$75.00	6.50"	G/CL	Primary	$75.00
(576)		Christmas Present						

HE IS THE STAR OF THE MORNING — Figurine

522252	89	Angel on Cloud	UPP	$55.00	6.00"	B&A	Secondary	$65.00
(481)	90	with Manger	UPP	60.00		FLM	Primary	60.00
	91		UPP	60.00		VSL	Primary	60.00
	92		OPEN	60.00		G/CL	Primary	60.00

TO BE WITH YOU IS UPLIFTING — Figurine

522260	89	Giraffe with Baby Bear	UPP	$20.00	4.25"	B&A	Secondary	$28.00
(484)	90		UPP	22.50		FLM	Primary	22.50
	91		UPP	22.50		VSL	Primary	22.50
	92		OPEN	22.50		G/CL	Primary	22.50

A REFLECTION OF HIS LOVE — Figurine

522279	91	Girl and Bird	UPP	$50.00	5.50"	VSL	Primary	$50.00
(531)	92	at Bird Bath	OPEN	50.00		G/CL	Primary	50.00

Title originally announced as "God Has Sent You My Way."

THINKING OF YOU IS WHAT I REALLY LIKE TO DO — Figurine

522287	90	Kneeling Girl with Bouquet	UPP	$30.00	4.50"	B&A	Secondary	$30.00
(504)	90			30.00		FLM	Primary	30.00
	91		UPP	30.00		VSL	Primary	30.00
	92		OPEN	30.00		G/CL	Primary	30.00

MERRY CHRISTMAS, DEER — Figurine

522317	89	Girl Decorating Reindeer	UPP	$50.00	5.50"	B&A	Secondary	$60.00
(438)	90		UPP	55.00		FLM	Primary	55.00
	91		UPP	55.00		VSL	Primary	55.00
	92		OPEN	55.00		G/CL	Primary	55.00

HIS LOVE WILL SHINE ON YOU — Figurine — Special Easter Seal Piece — Easter Seal Lily on Decal

522376	89	Girl Holding Easter Lily	Annual	$30.00	5.75"	FLW	Secondary	$50.00
(443)	89			30.00		B&A	Secondary	45.00

OH HOLY NIGHT — Figurine, Dated

522546	89	Girl Playing Violin	Annual	$25.00	4.75"	B&A	Secondary	$35.00
(482)								

OH HOLY NIGHT — Thimble, Dated

522554	89	Girl Playing Violin	Annual	$7.50	2.25"	B&A	Secondary	$15.00
(482)								

OH HOLY NIGHT — Bell, Dated

522821	89	Girl Playing Violin	Annual	$25.00	5.50"	B&A	Secondary	$35.00
(482)								

OH HOLY NIGHT — Ornament, Dated

522848	89	Girl Playing Violin	Annual	$13.50	3.25"	B&A	Secondary	$35.00
(482)								

HAVE A BEARY MERRY CHRISTMAS — Figurine — "Family Christmas Scene" Series

522856	89	Teddy in Rocker	UPP	$15.00	3.75"	B&A	Secondary	$22.00
(469)	90		UPP	16.50		FLM	Primary	16.50
	91		UPP	16.50		VSL	Primary	16.50
	92		OPEN	16.50		G/CL	Primary	16.50

MAKE A JOYFUL NOISE — Ornament

522910	89	Girl with Goose	UPP	$15.00	3.25"	B&A	Secondary	$22.00
(5)	90		UPP	15.00		FLM	Secondary	18.00
	91		UPP	15.00		VSL	Secondary	16.00
	92		OPEN	15.00		G/CL	Primary	15.00

LOVE ONE ANOTHER — Ornament

522929	89	Boy & Girl on Stump	UPP	$17.50	3.50"	B&A	Secondary	$24.00
(8)	90		UPP	17.50		FLM	Secondary	18.00
	91		UPP	17.50		VSL	Secondary	18.00
	92		OPEN	17.50		G/CL	Primary	17.50

FRIENDS NEVER DRIFT APART		Ornament						
522937	90	Kids in Boat	UPP	$17.50	2.50"	FLM	Secondary	$22.00
(219)	91		UPP	17.50		VSL	Secondary	18.00
	92		OPEN	17.50		G/CL	Primary	17.50

OUR FIRST CHRISTMAS TOGETHER		Ornament, Dated						
522945	91	Groom Popping out	Annual	$17.50	3.00"	VSL	Secondary	$25.00
(378)		of Trunk/Bride						

I BELIEVE IN THE OLD RUGGED CROSS		Ornament						
522953	89	Girl with Cross	UPP	$15.00	3.50"	B&A	Secondary	$18.00
(224)	90		UPP	15.00		FLM	Secondary	15.00
	91		UPP	15.00		VSL	Primary	15.00
	92		OPEN	15.00		G/CL	Primary	15.00

ISN'T HE PRECIOUS	Figurine	Mini Nativity Addition						
522988	89	Girl with Broom	UPP	$15.00	3.75"	B&A	Secondary	$22.00
(189)	90		UPP	16.50		FLM	Secondary	17.00
	91		UPP	16.50		VSL	Primary	16.50
	92		OPEN	16.50		G/CL	Primary	16.50

SOME BUNNIES SLEEPING	Figurine	Mini Nativity Addition						
522996	90	Bunnies	UPP	$12.00	1.75"	FLM	Secondary	$18.00
(431)	91		UPP	12.00		VSL	Primary	12.00
	92		OPEN	12.00		G/CL	Primary	12.00

MAY YOUR CHRISTMAS BE A HAPPY HOME		Plate, Dated	Fourth Issue "Christmas Love" Series					
523003	89	Family Christmas Scene	Annual	$50.00	8.50"	B&A	Secondary	$75.00
(479)								

THERE'S A CHRISTIAN WELCOME HERE		Figurine						
523011	89	Angel outside Chapel	UPP	$45.00	4.00"	UM	Secondary	$95.00
(491)	91		UPP	45.00		VSL	Secondary	45.00
	92		OPEN	45.00		G/CL	Primary	45.00

Available exclusively at PRECIOUS MOMENTS Chapel or through the Chapel mail order catalog. UNMARKED pieces of this figurine exist with and without an eyebrow on the angel boy (bangs cover where the second eyebrow would be). The GREENBOOK Market Price for the "Without Eyebrow" piece is $135.00.

HE IS MY INSPIRATION	Figurine							
523038	91	Sam Butcher as artist	OPEN	$60.00	5.00"	UM	Primary	$60.00
(563)		Painting/Animals						

Available exclusively at PRECIOUS MOMENTS Chapel or through the Chapel mail order catalog.

PEACE ON EARTH		Ornament, Dated	First Issue "Masterpiece Ornaments" Series					
523062	89	Kids with Pup, Kitten,	Annual	$25.00	4.25"	B&A	Secondary	$80.00
(341)		and Bird						

JESUS IS THE SWEETEST NAME I KNOW		Figurine	Nativity Addition					
523097	89	Angel with Baby	UPP	$22.50	4.75"	B&A	Secondary	$30.00
(468)	90	Name Book	UPP	25.00		FLM	Secondary	25.00
	91		UPP	25.00		VSL	Primary	25.00
	92		OPEN	25.00		G/CL	Primary	25.00

JOY ON ARRIVAL	Figurine							
523178	91	Stork Delivering Baby	UPP	$50.00	5.50"	VSL	Primary	$50.00
(532)	92	to Mother	OPEN	50.00		G/CL	Primary	50.00

BABY'S FIRST CHRISTMAS		Ornament, Dated						
523194	89	Boy in Sleigh	Annual	$15.00	2.50"	B&A	Secondary	$25.00
(432)								

BABY'S FIRST CHRISTMAS		Ornament, Dated						
523208	89	Girl in Sleigh	Annual	$15.00	2.50"	B&A	Secondary	$25.00
(435)								

HAPPY TRAILS IS TRUSTING JESUS — Ornament

523224	91	Girl on Hobby Horse	UPP	$15.00	3.25"	VSL	Secondary	$18.00
(494)	92		OPEN	15.00		G/CL	Primary	15.00

YOU HAVE TOUCHED SO MANY HEARTS — Figurine — Easter Seal Raffle Piece — Individually Numbered

523283	90	Girl with Hearts	2,000	$500.00	9.00"	B&A	Secondary	$650.00
(161)								

BLESSED ARE THE ONES WHO MOURN — Wall Hanging
Chapel Window Collection - Second Issue "Beatitude" Series

523380	92	Girl Crying over Spilled	Annual	$55.00	6.50"	G/CL	Primary	$55.00
(609)		Milk/Kitten						

Available exclusively at PRECIOUS MOMENTS Chapel or through Chapel mail order catalog.
First 500 pieces signed by Sam Butcher.

BLESSED ARE THE HUMBLE — Wall Hanging
Chapel Window Collection - First Issue "Beatitude" Series

523437	92	Princess Washing	Annual	$55.00	6.50"	G/CL	Primary	$55.00
(610)		Servant's Feet						

Available exclusively at PRECIOUS MOMENTS Chapel or through Chapel mail order catalog.
First 500 pieces signed by Sam Butcher.

THE GOOD LORD ALWAYS DELIVERS — Figurine

523453	90	Mother-to-Be with Baby	UPP	$27.50	5.50"	B&A	Secondary	$35.00
(497)	90	Book	UPP	27.50		FLM	Primary	27.50
	91		UPP	27.50		VSL	Primary	27.50
	92		OPEN	27.50		G/CL	Primary	27.50

THIS DAY HAS BEEN MADE IN HEAVEN — Figurine

523496	90	Girl Holding Bible and	UPP	$30.00	5.50"	B&A	Secondary	$35.00
(506)	90	Cross	UPP	30.00		FLM	Secondary	32.00
	91		UPP	30.00		VSL	Primary	30.00
	92		OPEN	30.00		G/CL	Primary	30.00

GOD IS LOVE DEAR VALENTINE — Figurine

523518	90	Girl Hiding Valentine behind	UPP	$27.50	5.50"	B&A	Secondary	$30.00
(509)	90	Her Back	UPP	27.50		FLM	Primary	27.50
	91		UPP	27.50		VSL	Primary	27.50
	92		OPEN	27.50		G/CL	Primary	27.50

I'M A PRECIOUS MOMENTS FAN — Figurine — Special Events Piece

523526	90	Girl with Fan	Annual	$30.00	5.50"	B&A	Secondary	$50.00
(490)	90			30.00		FLM	Secondary	35.00

I WILL CHERISH THE OLD RUGGED CROSS — Egg, Dated

523534	91	Girl Holding Cross	Annual	$27.50	4.75"	FLM	Secondary	$42.00
(224)	91			27.50		VSL	Secondary	40.00

YOU ARE THE TYPE I LOVE — Figurine

523542	92	Girl Typing Message	UPP	$40.00	5.40"	VSL	Primary	$40.00
(577)	92	on Typewriter	OPEN	40.00		G/CL	Primary	40.00

GOOD NEWS IS SO UPLIFTING — Figurine

523615	91	Girl on Ladder	UPP	$60.00	6.50"	VSL	Primary	$60.00
(554)	92	by Mailboxes	OPEN	60.00		G/CL	Primary	60.00

THIS DAY HAS BEEN MADE IN HEAVEN — Musical — TUNE: Amazing Grace

523682	92	Girl Holding Bible & Cross	UPP	$60.00	6.60"	VSL	Primary	$60.00
(506)			OPEN	60.00		G/CL	Primary	60.00

MAY YOUR CHRISTMAS BE A HAPPY HOME — Ornament, Dated
Second Issue "Masterpiece Ornament" Series

523704	90	Family Christmas Scene	Annual	$27.50	4.50"	FLM	Secondary	$45.00
(479)								

Variation. Sitting boy with yellow (usual color is blue) shirt - GREENBOOK Price is $65.00.

TIME HEALS   Figurine
523739 90 Nurse at Desk with Clock   UPP $37.50   5.50"   FLM   Secondary $45.00
(518)   91   UPP   37.50   VSL   Primary   37.50
            92   OPEN   37.50   G/CL Primary   37.50

BLESSINGS FROM ABOVE   Figurine
523747 90 Boy and Girl Kissing under   UPP $45.00   6.50"   FLM   Secondary $50.00
(495)   91   Mistletoe   UPP   45.00   VSL   Primary   45.00
            92   OPEN   45.00   G/CL Primary   45.00

I CAN'T SPELL SUCCESS WITHOUT YOU   Figurine
523763 91 Boy and Dog Using   UPP $40.00   5.00"   FLM   Secondary $60.00
(533)   91   Blocks to Spell UPP   40.00   VSL   Secondary   52.00
            92   OPEN   40.00   G/CL Primary   40.00

BABY'S FIRST CHRISTMAS   Ornament, Dated
523771 90 Baby Girl with Pie   Annual $15.00   2.75"   FLM   Secondary $25.00
(516)

BABY'S FIRST CHRISTMAS   Ornament, Dated
523798 90 Baby Boy with Pie   Annual $15.00   2.75"   FLM   Secondary $25.00
(517)

WISHING YOU A YUMMY CHRISTMAS   Plate, Dated   First Issue "Christmas Blessings" Series
523801 90 Boy and Girl at Ice Cream   Annual $50.00   8.25"   FLM   Secondary $70.00
(358)   Stand

ONCE UPON A HOLY NIGHT   Bell, Dated
523828 90 Girl with Book and Candle   Annual $25.00   5.75"   FLM   Secondary $35.00
(519)

ONCE UPON A HOLY NIGHT   Figurine, Dated
523836 90 Girl with Book and Candle   Annual $25.00   5.50"   FLM   Secondary $35.00
(519)

ONCE UPON A HOLY NIGHT   Thimble, Dated
523844 90 Girl with Book and Candle   Annual $8.00   1.50"   FLM   Secondary $15.00
(519)

ONCE UPON A HOLY NIGHT   Ornament, Dated
523852 90 Girl with Book and Candle   Annual $15.00   3.25"   FLM   Secondary $30.00
(519)

BLESSINGS FROM ME TO THEE   Plate, Dated   2nd Issue "Christmas Blessings" Series
523860 91 Girl at Birdhouse   Annual $50.00   8.50"   VSL   Secondary $60.00
(120)

WE ARE GOD'S WORKMANSHIP   Figurine   Easter Seal Raffle Piece   Individually Numbered
523879 91 Bonnet Girl with   2,000 $500.00   9.00"   FLM   Secondary $650.00
(140)   Butterfly

BABY'S FIRST MEAL   Figurine   Sixth Issue in "Baby's First" Series
524077 91 Baby in Highchair   UPP $35.00   5.25"   VSL   Secondary $35.00
(534)   92   with Cereal Bowl OPEN   35.00   G/CL Primary   35.00

MY WARMEST THOUGHTS ARE YOU   Figurine
524085 92 Little Bird Watching Girl   UPP $55.00   5.75"   VSL   Primary $55.00
(578)   92   on Tree Swing   OPEN   55.00   G/CL Primary   55.00

GOOD FRIENDS ARE FOR ALWAYS   Figurine
524123 91 Girl in Snowsuit   UPP $27.50   5.50"   VSL   Secondary $28.00
(555)   92   Holding Bunny   OPEN   27.50   G/CL Primary   27.50

GOOD FRIENDS ARE FOR ALWAYS   Ornament
524131 92 Girl in Snowsuit   OPEN $15.00   3.50"   G/CL   Primary $15.00
(555)   Holding Bunny

MAY YOUR CHRISTMAS BE MERRY		Figurine, Dated							
524166	91	Girl Holding Bird	Annual	$27.50	5.25"	VSL	Secondary	$32.00
(556)								
MAY YOUR CHRISTMAS BE MERRY		Ornament, Dated						
524174	91	Girl Holding Bird	Annual	$15.00	3.50"	VSL	Secondary	$25.00
(556)								
MAY YOUR CHRISTMAS BE MERRY		Bell, Dated						
524182	91	Girl Holding Bird	Annual	$25.00	5.75"	VSL	Secondary	$32.00
(556)								
MAY YOUR CHRISTMAS BE MERRY		Thimble, Dated						
524190	91	Girl Holding Bird	Annual	$8.00	2.25"	VSL	Secondary	$15.00
(556)								
HE LOVES ME		Figurine						
524263	91	Girl Holding Flower	Annual	$35.00	6.25"	FLM	Secondary	$45.00
(535)	91			35.00		VSL	Secondary	35.00
FRIENDSHIP GROWS WHEN YOU PLANT A SEED			Figurine					
524271	92	Girl in Sunbonnet Watering	UPP	$40.00	4.10"	VSL	Primary	$40.00
(579)	92	a Seedling	OPEN	40.00		G/CL	Primary	40.00
MAY YOUR BIRTHDAY BE A BLESSING			Figurine					
524301	91	Girl with Cake and Candles	UPP	$30.00	5.75"	FLM	Primary	$30.00
(536)	91		UPP	30.00		VSL	Primary	30.00
	92		OPEN	30.00		G/CL	Primary	30.00
WHAT THE WORLD NEEDS NOW		Figurine						
524352	92	Girl Gazing at Globe Praying	UPP	$50.00	5.75"	VSL	Primary	$50.00
(580)	92	for Peace & Love	OPEN	50.00		G/CL	Primary	50.00
MAY ONLY GOOD THINGS COME YOUR WAY			Figurine					
524425	91	Girl Holding Net	UPP	$30.00	5.50"	FLM	Secondary	$35.00
(537)	91	for Butterfly	UPP	30.00		VSL	Primary	30.00
	92		OPEN	30.00		G/CL	Primary	30.00
NOT A CREATURE WAS STIRRING		Figurine	Set of 2					
524484	90	Mouse on Cheese and Kitten	UPP	$17.00	2.75"	FLM	Secondary	$22.00
(514)	91		UPP	17.00		VSL	Secondary	20.00
	92		OPEN	17.00		G/CL	Primary	17.00
CAN'T BE WITHOUT YOU		Figurine	Birthday Collection					
524492	91	Bird on Cage Door	UPP	$16.00	2.50"	VSL	Secondary	$16.00
(538)	92	and Cat	OPEN	16.00		G/CL	Primary	16.00
ALWAYS IN HIS CARE		Figurine	Special Easter Seal Piece		Easter Seal Lily on Decal			
524522	90	Girl Looking at Sleeping	Annual	$30.00	5.00"	B&A	Secondary	$40.00
(507)	90	Chick in Egg		30.00		FLM	Secondary	35.00
HAPPY BIRTHDAY DEAR JESUS		Figurine	Nativity Addition					
524875	90	Teddy Bear in Package	UPP	$13.50	2.25"	FLM	Secondary	$15.00
(513)	91		UPP	13.50		VSL	Primary	13.50
	92		OPEN	13.50		G/CL	Primary	13.50
CHRISTMAS FIREPLACE		Figurine	"Family Christmas Scene" Series					
524883	90	Fireplace with Stockings	UPP	$37.50	4.50"	FLM	Secondary	$45.00
(512)	91		UPP	37.50		VSL	Primary	37.50
	92		OPEN	37.50		G/CL	Primary	37.50
IT'S SO UPLIFTING TO HAVE A FRIEND LIKE YOU			Figurine					
524905	92	Girl on Skis Startled by	OPEN	$40.00	6.00"	G/CL	Primary	$40.00
(581)		Ski Jump						

WE'RE GOING TO MISS YOU   Figurine

524913	90	Girl and Melting Snowman	UPP	$50.00	5.50"	FLM	Secondary	$55.00
(515)	91		UPP	50.00		VSL	Primary	50.00
	92		OPEN	50.00		G/CL	Primary	50.00

ANGELS WE HAVE HEARD ON HIGH   Figurine

524921	91	Two Angels on Stool	UPP	$60.00	7.25"	VSL	Primary	$60.00
(557)	92	Afraid of Mouse	OPEN	60.00		G/CL	Primary	60.00

Production error: Mismatched painting of hands and feet!

GOOD FRIENDS ARE FOREVER   Figurine   Special Events Piece   Rosebud Decal Understamp

525049	90	Girls with Flower	Annual		5.50"	B&A	Secondary	750.00
(492)								

Identical to 521817 with exception of Rosebud decal.
One per Center for 1990 Events, see 6th Ed., pg. 213.

BUNDLES OF JOY   Ornament   Limited to Centers

525057	90	Girl with Presents	Annual	$15.00	3.25"	FLM	Secondary	$35.00
(96)								

TUBBY'S FIRST CHRISTMAS   Figurine   Mini Nativity Addition

525278	92	Rooster Sitting on	OPEN	$10.00	1.75"	G/CL	Primary	$10.00
(126)		Pig's Back						

IT'S A PERFECT BOY   Figurine   Mini Nativity Addition

525286	91	Boy Angel with	UPP	$16.50	3.50"	VSL	Primary	$16.50
(127)	92	Red Cross Bag	OPEN	16.50		G/CL	Primary	16.50

OUR FIRST CHRISTMAS TOGETHER   Ornament, Dated

525324	90	Bride and Groom in Car	Annual	$17.50	2.50"	FLM	Secondary	$25.00
(460)								

LORD KEEP ME ON MY TOES   Ornament

525332	92	Ballerina on Pointe	OPEN	$15.00	3.75"	G/CL	Primary	$15.00
(582)								

RING THOSE CHRISTMAS BELLS   Figurine

525898	92	Angel Ringing Bell, Angel	OPEN	$95.00	6.25"	G/CL	Primary	$95.00
(583)		Pray'g, Bunny Cover'g Ears						

WE ARE GOD'S WORKMANSHIP   Egg, Dated

525960	92	Bonnet Girl with Butterfly	Annual	$27.50	4.10"	VSL	Secondary	$30.00
(140)	92			27.50		G/CL	Primary	27.50

GOING HOME   Figurine

525979	92	Angel Stopping to Take	UPP	$60.00	4.60"	VSL	Primary	$60.00
(584)	92	God's Child to Heaven	OPEN	60.00		G/CL	Primary	60.00

YOU ARE SUCH A PURR-FECT FRIEND   Figurine   Individually Numbered

526010	92	Little Girl Cuddling Kitten	2,000	$500.00	9.00"	VSL	Primary	$500.00
(585)		in Arms				G/CL	Primary	500.00

All are signed by Artist Sam Butcher, Enesco President Eugene Freedman, and Sculptor
Fujioka-San. Benefits Easter Seal Society.

I WOULD BE LOST WITHOUT YOU   Figurine

526142	92	Girl Checking Roadmap	UPP	$27.50	5.75"	VSL	Primary	$27.50
(586)	92		OPEN	27.50		G/CL	Primary	27.50

YOU ARE MY HAPPINESS   Figurine

526185	92	Bluebird Sitting on Bouquet	Annual	$37.50	6.75"	VSL	Primary	$37.50
(587)	92	of Roses Held by Girl				G/CL	Primary	$37.50

BLESS THOSE WHO SERVE THEIR COUNTRY - NAVY   Figurine

526568	91	Boy in Sailor Suit & Hat	UPP	$32.50	5.50"	FLG	Primary	$32.50
(588)	92	with Duffel Bag	OPEN	32.50		FLG/*	Primary	32.50

BLESS THOSE WHO SERVE THEIR COUNTRY - ARMY Figurine

526576	91	Boy in Dress Uniform with	UPP	$32.50	5.50"	FLG	Primary	$32.50
(589)	92	Duffel, Saluting	OPEN	32.50		FLG/*	Primary	32.50

BLESS THOSE WHO SERVE THEIR COUNTRY - AIR FORCE Figurine

526584	91	Boy in Dress Uniform, Hand	UPP	$32.50	5.50"	FLG	Primary	$32.50
(590)	92	Resting on Duffel	OPEN	32.50		FLG/*	Primary	32.50

HOW CAN I EVER FORGET YOU Figurine Birthday Collection

526924	91	Elephant with Knot	UPP	$15.00	3.00"	VSL	Secondary	$18.00
(558)	92	in Trunk	OPEN	15.00		G/CL	Primary	15.00

MAY YOUR CHRISTMAS BE MERRY Ornament, Dated Third Issue "Masterpiece Ornament" Series

526940	91	Girl Holding Bird	Annual	$30.00	4.25"	VSL	Secondary	$40.00
(556)								

WE HAVE COME FROM AFAR Figurine Nativity Addition

526959	91	Penguins	UPP	$17.50	2.50"	VSL	Secondary	$18.00
(559)	92		OPEN	17.50		G/CL	Primary	17.50

BABY'S FIRST CHRISTMAS Ornament, Dated

527084	91	Boy with Drum	Annual	$15.00	2.50"	VSL	Secondary	$20.00
(560)								

BABY'S FIRST CHRISTMAS Ornament, Dated

527092	91	Girl with Drum	Annual	$15.00	2.50"	VSL	Secondary	$20.00
(561)								

SHARING A GIFT OF LOVE Figurine Special Easter Seal Piece Easter Seal Lily on Decal

527114	91	Girl Helping Bird to Fly	Annual	$30.00	5.75"	FLM	Secondary	$50.00
(539)	91			30.00		VSL	Secondary	40.00

YOU CAN ALWAYS BRING A FRIEND Figurine Special Events Piece

527122	91	Girl Holding Puppy	Annual	$30.00	5.75"	FLM	Secondary	$48.00
(546)	91			30.00		VSL	Secondary	42.00

THE GOOD LORD ALWAYS DELIVERS Ornament

527165	91	Expectant Mother	UPP	$15.00	3.50"	VSL	Primary	$15.00
(497)	92		OPEN	15.00		G/CL	Primary	15.00

A UNIVERSAL LOVE Figurine Special Easter Seal Piece Easter Seal Lily on Decal

527173	92	Seated Child Signing	UPP	$32.50	5.10"	VSL	Secondary	$35.00
(591)	92	Message	OPEN	32.50		G/CL	Primary	32.50

BABY'S FIRST WORD Figurine Seventh Issue in "Baby's First" Series

527238	92	Baby/Footed Sleepers Talk'g	OPEN	$25.00	4.50"	G/CL	Primary	$25.00
(592)		into a Microphone						

LET'S BE FRIENDS Figurine Birthday Collection

527270	92	Pup w/Bow & Pup w/Party	UPP	$15.00	3.00"	VSL	Primary	$15.00
(593)		Hat Hugging Each Other	OPEN	15.00		G/CL	Primary	15.00

BLESS THOSE WHO SERVE THEIR COUNTRY - GIRL SOLDIER Figurine

527289	91	Girl Soldier in Dress Uniform,	UPP	$32.50	5.50"	FLG	Primary	$32.50
(594)	92	Saluting	OPEN	32.50		FLG/*	Primary	32.50

BLESS THOSE WHO SERVE THEIR COUNTRY - AFRICAN-AMERICAN SOLDIER Figurine

527297	91	African-American Soldier in	UPP	$32.50	5.50"	FLG	Primary	$32.50
(595)	92	Dress Uniform w/Duffel	OPEN	32.50		FLG/*	Primary	32.50

AN EVENT WORTH WADING FOR Figurine Special Events Piece

527319	92	Girl Wading to View	Annual	$32.50	5.12"	VSL	Secondary	$35.00
(596)	92	Mother Duck w/Eggs		32.50		G/CL	Primary	32.50

HAPPY BIRDIE Figurine Birthday Collection

527343	92	Bird in Party Hat Blowing	OPEN	$16.00	3.25"	G/CL	Primary	$16.00
(597)		Lit Candle on B/Day Cake						

YOU ARE MY FAVORITE STAR   Figurine
527378   92   Girl Placing Star on   OPEN $60.00   5.50"   G/CL   Primary $60.00
(598)   Decorated Boy's Head

527386   THIS LAND IS OUR LAND   See The Enesco PRECIOUS MOMENTS Collectors' Club, page 223.

BABY'S FIRST CHRISTMAS - GIRL   Ornament, Dated
527475   92   Girl Sitting on Upside-down   Annual $15.00   3.50"   G/CL   Primary $15.00
(600)   Candy Cane

BABY'S FIRST CHRISTMAS - BOY   Ornament, Dated
527483   92   Boy Sitting on Upside-down   Annual $15.00   3.50"   G/CL   Primary $15.00
(601)   Candy Cane

BLESS THOSE WHO SERVE THEIR COUNTRY - MARINE   Figurine
527521   91   Boy Marine in Full Dress   UPP $32.50   5.50"   FLG   Primary $32.50
(602)   92   Stands at Attention   OPEN   32.50   FLG/*   Primary   32.50

BRING THE LITTLE ONES TO JESUS   Figurine   Child Evangelism Fellowship Piece
527556   92   Mom Reading "Wordless   UPP $90.00   5.00"   VSL   Primary $90.00
(603)   92   Book" to Children   OPEN   90.00   G/CL   Primary   90.00

GOD BLESS THE USA   Figurine
527564   92   Uncle Sam Kneeling   Annual $32.50   4.75"   VSL   Secondary $35.00
(604)   92   in Prayer   32.50   G/CL   Primary   32.50
             National Day Of Prayer Figurine. Original 9" accepted by President Bush May 2, 1991 during
             National Day Of Prayer ceremonies.

WISHING YOU A HO HO HO   Figurine
527629   92   Boy in Santa Suit Look'g at OPEN $40.00   5.75"   G/CL   Primary $40.00
(605)   Pup Hold'g Santa Whiskers

YOU HAVE TOUCHED SO MANY HEARTS   Figurine   Available at Distinguished Service Retailers (DSR) Only
527661   91   Girl with Hearts   UPP $35.00   5.50"   VSL   Primary $35.00
(161)   92   OPEN   35.00   G/CL   Primary   35.00
             "Especially For You" version with letter transfer kit so collectors may personalize figurine.

BUT THE GREATEST OF THESE IS LOVE   Figurine, Dated
527688   92   Girl Holding Her List to   Annual $27.50   5.50"   G/CL   Primary $27.50
(606)   Santa Claus

BUT THE GREATEST OF THESE IS LOVE   Ornament, Dated
527696   92   Girl Holding Her List to   Annual $15.00   4.00"   G/CL   Primary $15.00
(606)   Santa Claus

BUT THE GREATEST OF THESE IS LOVE   Thimble, Dated
527718   92   Girl Holding Her List to   Annual $8.00   2.50"   G/CL   Primary $8.00
(606)   Santa Claus

BUT THE GREATEST OF THESE IS LOVE   Bell, Dated
527726   92   Girl Holding Her List to   Annual $25.00   6.50"   G/CL   Primary $25.00
(606)   Santa Claus

BUT THE GREATEST OF THESE IS LOVE   Ball Ornament, Dated
                                      Fourth Issue, "Masterpiece Ornament" Series
527734   92   Girl Holding Her List to   Annual $30.00   4.00"   G/CL   Primary $30.00
(606)   Santa Claus

BUT THE GREATEST OF THESE IS LOVE   Plate, Dated   Third Issue "Christmas Blessings" Series
527742   92   Girl Holding Her List to   Annual $50.00   8.50"   G/CL   Primary $50.00
(606)   Santa Claus

WISHING YOU A COMFY CHRISTMAS   Figurine   Nativity Addition
527750   92   Angel Holding Favorite   OPEN $27.50   5.50"   G/CL   Primary $27.50
(607)   Patched Blanket

THIS LAND IS OUR LAND   Figurine
527777   92   Explorer on One Knee   Annual $35.00   4.88"   G/CL   Primary $35.00
(608)   Hold'g Flag & Teddy

OUR FIRST CHRISTMAS TOGETHER   Ornament, Dated
528870   92   Groom Popping out of   Annual $17.50   3.00"   G/CL   Primary $17.50
(378)   Trunk/Bride

REJOICE, O EARTH   Musical Tree Topper   TUNE: Hark! The Herald Angels Sing
617334   90   Angel   Annual $125.00 14.00"   FLM   Secondary $125.00
(545)

NOTES

THE ENESCO PRECIOUS MOMENTS COLLECTORS' CLUB

SYMBOLS OF CHARTER MEMBERSHIP

BUT LOVE GOES ON FOREVER   Figurine
E-0001	81	Boy & Girl Angels	MemOnly	$20.00	5.00"	NM	Secondary	$190.00
(39)		on Cloud				TRI	Secondary	165.00
						HRG	Secondary	160.00

BUT LOVE GOES ON FOREVER   Plaque
E-0102	82	Boy & Girl Angels	MemOnly	$15.00	5.00"	UM	Secondary	$100.00
(39)		on Cloud				TRI	Secondary	80.00
						HRG	Secondary	70.00

LET US CALL THE CLUB TO ORDER   Figurine
| E-0103 | 83 | Club Meeting | MemOnly | $25.00 | 5.75" | HRG | Secondary | $65.00 |
| (158) | | | | | | FSH | Secondary | 60.00 |

JOIN IN ON THE BLESSINGS   Figurine
E-0104	84	Girl with Dues Bank	MemOnly	$25.00	4.50"	HRG	Secondary	$100.00
(205)						FSH	Secondary	60.00
						CRS	Secondary	55.00

SEEK AND YE SHALL FIND   Figurine
E-0105	85	Girl with Shopping	MemOnly	$25.00	5.25"	FSH	Secondary	$50.00
(104)		Bag				CRS	Secondary	45.00
						DVE	Secondary	45.00

BIRDS OF A FEATHER COLLECT TOGETHER   Figurine
| E-0106 | 86 | Girl with Embroidery | MemOnly | $25.00 | 5.75" | DVE | Secondary | $50.00 |
| (295) | | Hoop and Bird | | | | OLB | Secondary | 48.00 |

SHARING IS UNIVERSAL   Figurine
| E-0107 | 87 | Girl Sending Package | MemOnly | $25.00 | 5.00" | OLB | Secondary | $45.00 |
| (336) | | to Friend | | | | CED | Secondary | 45.00 |

A GROWING LOVE   Figurine
| E-0108 | 88 | Girl with Flowerpot | MemOnly | $25.00 | 4.50" | CED | Secondary | $45.00 |
| (399) | | and Sunflower | | | | FLW | Secondary | 42.00 |

ALWAYS ROOM FOR ONE MORE   Figurine
| C-0109 | 89 | Girl with Puppies | MemOnly | $35.00 | 4.50" | FLW | Secondary | $45.00 |
| (444) | | in Box | | | | B&A | Secondary | 40.00 |

MY HAPPINESS   Figurine
| C-0110 | 90 | Girl at Table with Figurine | MemOnly | $35.00 | 4.50" | B&A | Secondary | $35.00 |
| (489) | | | | | | FLM | Secondary | 35.00 |

SHARING THE GOOD NEWS TOGETHER   Figurine
| C-0111 | 91 | Girl at Mailbox | MemOnly | $40.00 | 5.25" | FLM | Secondary | $40.00 |
| (562) | | with Club Newsletter | | 40.00 | | VSL | Secondary | 40.00 |

THE CLUB THAT'S OUT OF THIS WORLD   Figurine
| C-0112 | 92 | Girl in Spacesuit | MemOnly | $40.00 | 5.00" | VSL | Primary | $40.00 |
| (569) | | Holding Space Helmet | | | | G/CL | Primary | 40.00 |

SYMBOLS OF MEMBERSHIP

BUT LOVE GOES ON FOREVER   Plaque
E-0202   82   Boy & Girl Angels   MemOnly $15.00   5.00"   UM   Secondary $85.00
(39)   on Cloud   TRI   Secondary   70.00
                                                                                                   HRG   Secondary   65.00

Termed the "Canadian Plaque Error," approximately 750 pieces of this 1982 Symbol Of Membership piece were produced in 1985 and shipped to Canada. These pieces are stamped "TAIWAN" and have a DOVE Annual Symbol. The GREENBOOK Market Price for the "Canadian Plaque Error is $125.00. Photograph: 6th Ed., pg. 225.

LET US CALL THE CLUB TO ORDER   Figurine
E-0303   83   Club Meeting   MemOnly $25.00   5.75"   HRG   Secondary $60.00
(158)   FSH   Secondary   55.00

JOIN IN ON THE BLESSINGS   Figurine
E-0404   84   Girl with Dues Bank   MemOnly $25.00   4.50"   HRG   Secondary $100.00
(205)   FSH   Secondary   50.00
                                                                              CRS   Secondary   40.00

SEEK AND YE SHALL FIND   Figurine
E-0005   85   Girl with Shopping   MemOnly $25.00   5.25"   CRS   Secondary $45.00
(104)   Bag   DVE   Secondary   40.00

BIRDS OF A FEATHER COLLECT TOGETHER   Figurine
E-0006   86   Girl with Embroidery   MemOnly $25.00   5.75"   DVE   Secondary $40.00
(295)   Hoop and Bird   OLB   Secondary   35.00

SHARING IS UNIVERSAL   Figurine
E-0007   87   Girl Sending Package   MemOnly $25.00   5.00"   OLB   Secondary $45.00
(336)   to Friend   CED   Secondary   35.00

A GROWING LOVE   Figurine
E-0008   88   Girl with Flowerpot   MemOnly $25.00   4.50"   CED   Secondary $38.00
(399)   and Sunflower   FLW   Secondary   35.00

ALWAYS ROOM FOR ONE MORE   Figurine
C-0009   89   Girl with Puppies   MemOnly $35.00   4.50"   FLW   Secondary $35.00
(444)   in Box   B&A   Secondary   35.00
                                                                              FLM   Secondary   35.00

MY HAPPINESS   Figurine
C-0010   90   Girl at Table with Figurine   MemOnly $35.00   4.50"   B&A   Secondary $35.00
(489)   FLM   Secondary   35.00

SHARING THE GOOD NEWS TOGETHER
C-0011   91   Girl at Mailbox   MemOnly $40.00   5.25"   FLM   Secondary $40.00
(562)   with Club Newsletter   VSL   Secondary   40.00

THE CLUB THAT'S OUT OF THIS WORLD   Figurine
C-0012   92   Girl in Spacesuit   MemOnly $40.00   5.00"   VSL   Primary $40.00
(569)   Holding Space Helmet   G/CL   Primary   40.00

MEMBERSHIP PIECES

HELLO LORD, IT'S ME AGAIN		Figurine						
PM-811	81	Boy on Telephone	MemOnly	$25.00	4.75"	TRI	Secondary	$435.00
(78)						HRG	Secondary	425.00
SMILE, GOD LOVES YOU		Figurine						
PM-821	82	Girl with Curlers	MemOnly	$25.00	5.25"	HRG	Secondary	$250.00
(117)						FSH	Secondary	240.00
PUT ON A HAPPY FACE		Figurine						
PM-822	83	Boy Clown Holding	MemOnly	$25.00	5.50"	HRG	Secondary	$205.00
(159)		Mask				FSH	Secondary	190.00
						CRS	Secondary	185.00
DAWN'S EARLY LIGHT		Figurine						
PM-831	83	Girl Covering Kitten	MemOnly	$25.00	4.50"	FSH	Secondary	$90.00
(160)						CRS	Secondary	85.00
GOD'S RAY OF MERCY		Figurine						
PM-841	84	Boy Angel with	MemOnly	$25.00	4.75"	FSH	Secondary	$85.00
(206)		Flashlight				CRS	Secondary	55.00
						DVE	Secondary	55.00
TRUST IN THE LORD TO THE FINISH		Figurine						
PM-842	84	Boy with Racing Cup	MemOnly	$25.00	5.50"	CRS	Secondary	$65.00
(207)						DVE	Secondary	65.00
THE LORD IS MY SHEPHERD		Figurine						
PM-851	85	Girl Holding Lamb	MemOnly	$25.00	5.50"	DVE	Secondary	$75.00
(293)						OLB	Secondary	75.00
I LOVE TO TELL THE STORY		Figurine						
PM-852	85	Boy with Lamb	MemOnly	$27.50	3.50"	DVE	Secondary	$65.00
(294)		and Book				OLB	Secondary	65.00
GRANDMA'S PRAYER		Figurine						
PM-861	86	Praying Grandma	MemOnly	$25.00	4.50"	DVE	Secondary	$85.00
(305)						OLB	Secondary	80.00
						CED	Secondary	75.00
I'M FOLLOWING JESUS		Figurine						
PM-862	86	Boy in Car	MemOnly	$25.00	4.25"	OLB	Secondary	$85.00
(320)						CED	Secondary	85.00
FEED MY SHEEP		Figurine						
PM-871	87	Girl Feeding Lamb	MemOnly	$25.00	4.75"	CED	Secondary	$55.00
(366)						FLW	Secondary	50.00
IN HIS TIME		Figurine						
PM-872	87	Boy Waiting for	MemOnly	$25.00	4.10"	CED	Secondary	$50.00
(375)		Seed to Grow				FLW	Secondary	45.00
LOVING YOU DEAR VALENTINE		Figurine						
PM-873	87	Boy Painting	MemOnly	$25.00	5.50"	OLB	Secondary	$40.00
(321)		Valentine				FLW	Secondary	35.00
LOVING YOU DEAR VALENTINE		Figurine						
PM-874	87	Girl Drawing	MemOnly	$25.00	5.25"	OLB	Secondary	$45.00
(322)		Valentine				FLW	Secondary	38.00
GOD BLESS YOU FOR TOUCHING MY LIFE		Figurine						
PM-881	88	Girl Painting Butterfly	MemOnly	$27.50	4.75"	CED	Secondary	$65.00
(439)						FLW	Secondary	50.00
						B&A	Secondary	45.00

YOU JUST CANNOT CHUCK A GOOD FRIENDSHIP — Figurine
PM-882 88 Boy Rescuing Puppy — MemOnly — $27.50 — 5.00" — FLW — Secondary — $45.00
(442) — from Trash Can — B&A — Secondary — 40.00

BEAUTITUDE ORNAMENT SERIES — Ornaments — Set of 7*
PM-890 90 Chapel Stained Glass — MemOnly — $105.00 — 5.50" — UM — Secondary — $105.00
(542) — Window Replicas
*Set of 7 also individually numbered PM-190 through PM-790. For individual titles see the QUICK REFERENCE SECTION pg. 119.

YOU WILL ALWAYS BE MY CHOICE — Figurine
PM-891 89 Girl with Ballot Box — MemOnly — $27.50 — 4.75" — B&A — Secondary — $38.00
(485) — FLM — Secondary — 35.00

MOW POWER TO YA — Figurine
PM-892 89 Boy Pushing Lawn Mower — MemOnly — $27.50 — 4.75" — B&A — Secondary — $40.00
(486) — FLM — Secondary — 35.00

TEN YEARS AND STILL GOING STRONG — Figurine
PM-901 90 Girl in Race Car — MemOnly — $30.00 — 3.75" — FLM — Secondary — $35.00
(540) — VSL — Secondary — 32.00

YOU ARE A BLESSING TO ME — Figurine
PM-902 90 Girl Sewing Patch — MemOnly — $27.50 — 5.00" — FLM — Secondary — $35.00
(541) — on Teddy Bear — VSL — Secondary — 32.00

ONE STEP AT A TIME — Figurine
PM-911 91 Child Hold'g Mom's — MemOnly — $33.00 — 5.25" — VSL — Secondary — $33.00
(564) — Hands Tak'g First Steps — G/CL — Secondary — 33.00

LORD, KEEP ME IN TEEPEE TOP SHAPE — Figurine
PM-912 91 Indian Boy Holding Can — MemOnly — $27.50 — 4.50" — VSL — Secondary — $27.50
(565) — of Spinach — G/CL — Secondary — 27.50

ONLY LOVE CAN MAKE A HOME — Figurine
PM-921 92 Mr. Webb Building — MemOnly — $30.00 — 4.25" — G/CL — Primary — $30.00
(613) — Bird Home

COMMEMORATIVE MEMBERSHIP PIECES

GOD BLESS OUR YEARS TOGETHER — Figurine — 5th Anniversary Club Commemorative Piece
12440 85 Mom, Dad, Kids, and — MemOnly — $175.00 — 5.50" — DVE — Secondary — $275.00
(249) — Cake w/5 Candles

THIS LAND IS OUR LAND — Figurine
Commemorates 500th Anniversary Christopher Columbus' Voyage
527386 92 Explorer & Animal Crew — MemOnly — $350.00 — 9.50" — G/CL — Secondary — $375.00
(599) — Sailing The High Seas
in a Sail Boat

SHARING SEASON ORNAMENTS   (Gift to Club Members for signing up new members.)

BIRDS OF A FEATHER COLLECT TOGETHER   Ornament
PM-864   86   Girl with Embroidery   MemOnly $12.50   2.25"   OLB   Secondary $190.00
(295)   Hoop and Bird

SHARING SEASON ORNAMENT   Ornament
PM-009   87   Brass Filagree -   MemOnly $ 3.50   2.75"   UM   Secondary $45.00
(376)   Kids on Cloud

A GROWING LOVE   Ornament
520349   88   Girl with Flowerpot   MemOnly $15.00   2.80"   FLW   Secondary $90.00
(399)   and Sunflower

ALWAYS ROOM FOR ONE MORE   Ornament
522961   89   Girl with Puppies in Box   MemOnly $15.00   2.80"   B&A   Secondary $110.00
(444)

MY HAPPINESS   Ornament
PM-904   90   Girl at Table with Figurine   MemOnly $15.00   3.00"   FLM   Secondary $95.00
(489)

SHARING THE GOOD NEWS TOGETHER   Ornament
PM-037   91   Girl at Mailbox with Club   MemOnly   3.25"   VSL   Secondary $95.00
(562)   Newsletter

NOTES

THE ENESCO PRECIOUS MOMENTS BIRTHDAY CLUB

SYMBOLS OF CHARTER MEMBERSHIP

OUR CLUB CAN'T BE BEAT — Figurine

B-0001	86	Clown with Drum	MemOnly	$10.00	3.50"	DVE	Secondary	$80.00
(304)						OLB	Secondary	75.00
						CED	Secondary	70.00

A SMILE'S THE CYMBAL OF JOY — Figurine

B-0102	87	Clown with Cymbals	MemOnly	$15.00	4.50"	OLB	Secondary	$65.00
(364)						CED	Secondary	60.00

The first of these were shipped with a title error on the understamp decal - "A Smile's The Symbol Of Joy." The GREENBOOK Market Price for the "Symbol Error" is $85.00. Color photograph: 5th Ed., pg. 208.

THE SWEETEST CLUB AROUND — Figurine

B-0103	88	Pippin Popping out	MemOnly	$15.00	4.50"	FLW	Secondary	$40.00
(440)		of Cake				B&A	Secondary	35.00

HAVE A BEARY SPECIAL BIRTHDAY — Figurine

B-0104	89	Teddy Bear with Balloon	MemOnly	$20.00	4.50"	FLW	Secondary	$40.00
(487)						B&A	Secondary	35.00
						FLM	Secondary	30.00

OUR CLUB IS A TOUGH ACT TO FOLLOW — Figurine

B-0105	90	Clown with Puppy	MemOnly	$25.00	4.00"	FLM	Secondary	$35.00
(543)		Leaping thru Drum				VSL	Secondary	30.00

JEST TO LET YOU KNOW YOU'RE TOPS — Figurine

B-0106	91	Jester Clown Popping	MemOnly	$25.00	4.25"	VSL	Secondary	$25.00
(568)		out of Box				G/CL	Primary	25.00

ALL ABOARD FOR BIRTHDAY CLUB FUN — Figurine

B-0107	92	Engineer Riding	MemOnly	$25.00	4.50"	G/CL	Primary	$25.00
(612)		Locomotive						

SYMBOLS OF MEMBERSHIP

A SMILE'S THE CYMBAL OF JOY — Figurine

B-0002	87	Clown with Cymbals	MemOnly	$15.00	4.50"	OLB	Secondary	$60.00
(364)						CED	Secondary	55.00
						FLW	Secondary	55.00

THE SWEETEST CLUB AROUND — Figurine

B-0003	88	Pippin Popping out	MemOnly	$15.00	4.50"	FLW	Secondary	$35.00
(440)		of Cake				B&A	Secondary	30.00

HAVE A BEARY SPECIAL BIRTHDAY — Figurine

B-0004	89	Teddy Bear with Balloon	MemOnly	$20.00	4.50"	B&A	Secondary	$30.00
(487)						FLM	Secondary	25.00

OUR CLUB IS A TOUGH ACT TO FOLLOW — Figurine

B-0005	90	Clown with Puppy	MemOnly	$25.00	4.00"	FLM	Secondary	$25.00
(543)		Leaping thru Drum				VSL	Secondary	25.00

JEST TO LET YOU KNOW YOU'RE TOPS — Figurine

B-0006	91	Jester Clown Popping	MemOnly	$25.00	4.25"	VSL	Secondary	$25.00
(568)		out of Box				G/CL	Primary	25.00

ALL ABOARD FOR BIRTHDAY CLUB FUN — Figurine

B-0007	92	Engineer Riding	MemOnly	$25.00	4.50"	G/CL	Primary	$25.00
(612)		Locomotive						

MEMBERSHIP PIECES

FISHING FOR FRIENDS		Figurine						
BC-861	86	Raccoon Holding Fish	MemOnly	$10.00	2.50"	OLB	Secondary	$120.00
(335)						CED	Secondary	110.00
HI SUGAR!		Figurine						
BC-871	87	Mouse in Sugar	MemOnly	$11.00	2.60"	CED	Secondary	$85.00
(398)		Bowl				FLW	Secondary	80.00
						B&A	Secondary	75.00
SOMEBUNNY CARES		Figurine						
BC-881	88	Bunny with Carrot	MemOnly	$13.50	3.00"	FLW	Secondary	$55.00
(441)						B&A	Secondary	50.00
CAN'T BEE HIVE MYSELF WITHOUT YOU			Figurine					
BC-891	89	Teddy Bear with Bee	MemOnly	$13.50	2.50"	B&A	Secondary	$45.00
(488)		and Bee Hive				FLM	Secondary	40.00
						VSL	Secondary	35.00
COLLECTING MAKES GOOD SCENTS			Figurine					
BC-901	90	Skunk with Flowers	MemOnly	$15.00	2.50"	FLM	Secondary	$30.00
(544)						VSL	Secondary	28.00
I'M NUTS OVER MY COLLECTION			Figurine					
BC-902	90	Squirrel with Nuts/	MemOnly	$15.00	2.50"	FLM	Secondary	$30.00
(547)		Mesh Bag				VSL	Secondary	28.00
LOVE PACIFIES		Figurine						
BC-911	91	Baby Monkey in Bonnet	MemOnly	$15.00	3.00	VSL	Secondary	$15.00
(566)		with Pacifer				G/CL	Primary	15.00
TRUE BLUE FRIENDS		Figurine						
BC-912	91	Puppy & Kitten	MemOnly	$15.00	2.50"	VSL	Secondary	$15.00
(567)		Sharing Paint & Brush				G/CL	Primary	15.00

WE JUST WANTED YOU TO KNOW...

We'd never seen a photograph of all the Sharing Season Ornaments together. And interestingly enough, they are the only porcelain bisque collectibles not pictured each year in Enesco's Precious
Moments color catalog. From left to right they are:

1986	PM-864	Birds of a Feather Collect Together
1987	PM-009	Sharing Season Ornament
1989	522961	Always Room for One More
1991	PM-037	Sharing The Good News Together
1990	PM-904	My Happiness
1988	520349	A Growing Love

Then...

Now!

...the suspended E-1381 and the re-sculpted, re-introduced E-1381R.

WE JUST WANTED YOU TO KNOW... continued

Precious Moments Collectibles Temporarily Removed From Production, Second Half 1991:

E-2828	Precious Memories
E-2832	God Bless The Bride
E-2834	Sharing Our Joy Together
E-2852A-F	Baby Figurines
E-3116	Thee I Love
E-7182	Mother Sew Dear
E-7184	The Purr-Fect Grandma
E-9267A-F	Animal Collection
12009	Love Covers All
12238A-D	Clown Figurines
13293	Mother Sew Dear
13307	The Purr-fect Grandma
100056	Sending My Love
100064	Worship The Lord
100080	He's The Healer Of Broken Hearts
100110	Lord I'm Coming Home
100137	The Joy Of The Lord Is My Strength
100498	God Bless Our Family
100501	God Bless Our Family
101842	Smile Along The Way
101850	Lord Help Us Keep Our Act Together
102229	Worship The Lord
102369	Wedding Arch
103632	I Believe In The Old Rugged Cross
106194	God Bless You Graduate
106208	Congratulations, Princess
106798	Puppy Love Is From Above
106844	Sew In Love
109487	Believe The Impossible
109584	Happiness Divine
109886	Wishing You A Happy Easter
109924	Wishing You A Basket Full Of Blessings
109975	Mommy, I Love You
112143	Mommy, I Love You
114014	This Too Shall Pass
520624	My Heart Is Exposed With Love
520640	I'm So Glad You Fluttered Into My Life
520667	Eggspecially For You
520675	Your Love Is So Uplifting
520683	Sending You Showers Of Blessings
520721	Just A Line To Wish You A Happy Day
520756	Jesus Is The Only Way
520799	Someday My Love
521868	The Greatest Of These Is Love
521892	Easter's On It's Way
521957	High Hopes
523518	God Is Love Dear Valentine

Precious Moments Collectibles Temporarily Removed From Production, Second Half 1992:

E-2828	Precious Memories
E-3110B	Loving Is Sharing
E-3110G	Loving Is Sharing
E-3113	Thou Art Mine
E-7182	Mother Sew Dear
E-7184	The Purr-Fect Grandma
E-9265	Press On
12041	God's Precious Gift
12262	I Get A Bang Out Of You
12270	Lord Keep Me On The Ball
13293	Mother Sew Dear
13307	The Purr-Fect Grandma
100226	The Lord Giveth And The Lord Taketh Away
100498	God Bless Our Family
100501	God Bless Our Family
102369	Wedding Arch
103632	I Believe In The Old Rugged Cross
106844	Sew In Love
109886	Wishing You A Happy Easter
109924	Wishing You A Basket Full Of Blessings
114014	This Too Shall Pass
520667	Eggspecially For You
520799	Someday My Love
520829	You Are My Number One
521310	Yield Not To Temptation
521698	Thumb-body Loves You
521841	Love Is From Above
521892	Easter's On Its Way
521906	Hoppy Easter Friend
521957	High Hopes
521965	To A Special Mum
522201	Bon Voyage!
523518	God Is Love Dear Valentine

GIFT GIVER'S GUIDE

The GIFT GIVER'S GUIDE contains currently available pieces that are appropriate as gifts for special people and special occasions. Categories include Valentine's Day/Love, Easter, Graduation/School Days, Mother's Day, Communion/Christening, Father's Day, Friendship, Engagement/Wedding/Anniversary, Birthday, Miss You, Baby/Adoption, Thanksgiving, Inspirational, Get Well, and Christmas. Itemized for each piece are the Enesco Item Number, GREENBOOK ART CHART Number, Inspirational Title, Type of Product, and the current Suggested Retail Price.

VALENTINE'S DAY/LOVE

E-1375A	(6)	Love Lifted Me	FIG	$35.00
E-1376	(8)	Love One Another	FIG	35.00
522929			ORN	17.50
E-3110B	(34)	Loving Is Sharing	FIG	30.00
E-3110G	(35)	Loving Is Sharing	FIG	30.00
E-3113	(37)	Thou Art Mine	FIG	35.00
E-3115	(39)	But Love Goes On Forever	FIG	35.00
E-3116	(40)	Thee I Love	FIG	37.50
103497	(333)	My Love Will Never Let You Go	FIG	35.00
106844	(382)	Sew In Love	FIG	55.00
109967	(386)	Sending You My Love	FIG	45.00
520624	(458)	My Heart Is Exposed With Love	FIG	50.00
520675	(454)	Your Love Is So Uplifting	FIG	65.00
520764	(465)	Puppy Love	FIG	13.50
521418	(511)	I'll Never Stop Loving You	FIG	37.50
521698	(528)	Thumb-body Loves You	FIG	55.00
521841	(510)	Love Is From Above	FIG	45.00
522104	(575)	It's No Yoke When I Say I Love You	FIG	60.00
523518	(509)	God Is Love Dear Valentine	FIG	27.50
523542	(577)	You Are The Type I Love	FIG	40.00
524492	(538)	Can't Be Without You	FIG	16.00

EASTER

103632	(224)	I Believe In The Old Rugged Cross	FIG	$35.00
109886	(388)	Wishing You A Happy Easter	FIG	27.50
109924	(385)	Wishing You A Basket Full Of Blessings	FIG	27.50
520667	(455)	Eggspecially For You	FIG	50.00
521892	(508)	Easter's On Its Way	FIG	60.00
521906	(529)	Hoppy Easter Friend	FIG	40.00
525960	(140)	We Are God's Workmanship	EGG	27.50

GRADUATION/SCHOOL DAYS

E-4721	(47)	The Lord Bless You And Keep You	FIG	$30.00
12300	(238)	Love Never Fails	FIG	35.00
106194	(334)	God Bless You Graduate	FIG	30.00
106208	(318)	Congratulations, Princess	FIG	30.00
110086	(426)	September Calendar Girl	FIG	33.50

MOTHER'S DAY

Code	No.	Title	Type	Price
E-0514	(30)	Mother Sew Dear	ORN	$15.00
E-3106			FIG	27.50
E-7182			MUS	55.00
13293			THMBL	8.00
E-0516	(33)	The Purr-fect Grandma	ORN	15.00
E-3109			FIG	27.50
E-7184			MUS	55.00
13307			THMBL	8.00
E-2824	(164)	To A Very Special Mom	FIG	37.50
100137	(217)	The Joy Of The Lord Is My Strength	FIG	50.00
109975	(387)	Mommy, I Love You (Boy)	FIG	27.50
112143	(390)	Mommy, I Love You (Girl)	FIG	27.50
521434	(551)	To A Very Special Mom And Dad	FIG	35.00
521965	(530)	To A Special Mum	FIG	30.00
523453	(497)	The Good Lord Always Delivers	FIG	27.50

COMMUNION/CHRISTENING

Code	No.	Title	Type	Price
E-4724	(50)	Rejoicing With You	FIG	$45.00
100064	(213)	Worship The Lord (Girl)	FIG	35.00
100277	(220)	He Cleansed My Soul	FIG	35.00
102229	(223)	Worship The Lord (Boy)	FIG	35.00
523496	(506)	This Day Has Been Made In Heaven	FIG	30.00
523682			MUS	60.00

FATHER'S DAY

Code	No.	Title	Type	Price
E-5212	(59)	To A Special Dad	FIG	$35.00
521434	(551)	To A Very Special Mom And Dad	FIG	35.00

FRIENDSHIP ...

Code	No.	Title	Type	Price
12262	(236)	I Get A Bang Out Of You	FIG	$45.00
100048	(316)	To My Deer Friend	FIG	50.00
100072	(214)	To My Forever Friend	FIG	50.00
113956			ORN	17.50
100250	(219)	Friends Never Drift Apart	FIG	50.00
522937			ORN	17.50
104418	(420)	Friends To The End	FIG	18.50
109231	(355)	The Greatest Gift Is A Friend	FIG	37.50
520632	(449)	A Friend Is Someone Who Cares	FIG	32.50
520748	(453)	Friendship Hits The Spot	FIG	60.00

... FRIENDSHIP CONTINUED

521183	(520)	That's What Friends Are For	FIG	$45.00
521299	(526)	Hug One Another	FIG	45.00
521817	(492)	Good Friends Are Forever	FIG	50.00
522260	(484)	To Be With You Is Uplifting	FIG	22.50
524085	(578)	My Warmest Thoughts Are You	FIG	55.00
524123	(555)	Good Friends Are For Always	FIG	27.50
524271	(579)	Friendship Grows When You Plant A Seed	FIG	40.00
524905	(581)	It's So Uplifting To Have A Friend Like You	FIG	40.00
526142	(586)	I Would Be Lost Without You	FIG	27.50
526924	(558)	How Can I Ever Forget You	FIG	15.00
527270	(593)	Let's Be Friends	FIG	15.00

ENGAGEMENT/WEDDING/ANNIVERSARY ...

E-2828	(168)	Precious Memories	FIG	$60.00
E-2831	(170)	Bridesmaid	FIG	19.50
E-2832	(171)	God Bless The Bride	FIG	50.00
E-2833	(208)	Ringbearer	FIG	16.50
E-2835	(209)	Flower Girl	FIG	16.50
E-2836	(172)	Groomsman	FIG	19.50
E-2837	(269)	Groom	FIG	22.50
E-2845	(210)	Junior Bridesmaid	FIG	18.50
E-2846	(313)	Bride	FIG	25.00
E-2853	(179)	God Blessed Our Years Together With So Much Love & Happiness (Hpy)	FIG	50.00
E-2854	(180)	God Blessed Our Year Together With So Much Love & Happiness (1st)	FIG	50.00
E-2855	(181)	God Blessed Our Years Together With So Much Love & Happiness (5th)	FIG	50.00
E-2856	(182)	God Blessed Our Years Together With So Much Love & Happiness (10th)	FIG	50.00
E-2857	(183)	God Blessed Our Years Together With So Much Love & Happiness (25th)	FIG	50.00
E-2859	(184)	God Blessed Our Years Together With So Much Love & Happiness (40th)	FIG	50.00
E-2860	(185)	God Blessed Our Years Together With So Much Love & Happiness (50th)	FIG	50.00
E-3114	(38)	The Lord Bless You And Keep You	FIG	37.50
E-7166			FRM	32.50
E-7179			BELL	35.00
E-7180			MUS	80.00
E-3116	(40)	Thee I Love	FIG	37.50

... ENGAGEMENT/WEDDING/ANNIVERSARY CONTINUED

E-9255	(139)	Bless You Two	FIG	$32.50
100498	(325)	God Bless Our Family (Groom)	FIG	50.00
100501	(326)	God Bless Our Family (Bride)	FIG	50.00
102369	(332)	Wedding Arch	FIG	30.00
104019	(343)	With This Ring I ...	FIG	55.00
106755	(378)	Heaven Bless Your Togetherness	FIG	80.00
106763	(379)	Precious Memories	FIG	50.00
106798	(380)	Puppy Love Is From Above	FIG	55.00
110043	(372)	June Calendar Girl	FIG	50.00
520780	(460)	Wishing You Roads Of Happiness	FIG	65.00
520799	(446)	Someday My Love	FIG	45.00
520837	(466)	The Lord Is Your Light To Happiness	FIG	55.00
520845	(459)	Wishing You A Perfect Choice	FIG	60.00

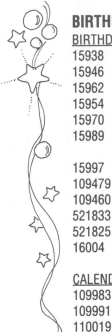

BIRTHDAY ...

BIRTHDAY CIRCUS TRAIN:

15938	(296)	May Your Birthday Be Warm (Baby)	FIG	$15.00
15946	(297)	Happy Birthday Little Lamb (1)	FIG	15.00
15962	(298)	God Bless You On Your Birthday (2)	FIG	16.50
15954	(299)	Heaven Bless Your Special Day (3)	FIG	16.50
15970	(300)	May Your Birthday Be Gigantic (4)	FIG	18.50
15989	(301)	This Day Is Something To Roar About (5)	FIG	20.00
15997	(302)	Keep Looking Up (6)	FIG	20.00
109479	(393)	Wishing You Grrr-eatness (7)	FIG	22.50
109460	(394)	Isn't Eight Just Great (8)	FIG	22.50
521833	(574)	Being Nine Is Just Divine (9)	FIG	25.00
521825	(573)	May Your Birthday Be Mammoth (10)	FIG	25.00
16004	(303)	Bless The Days Of Our Youth	FIG	22.50

CALENDAR GIRLS:

109983	(367)	January Calendar Girl	FIG	$45.00
109991	(368)	February Calendar Girl	FIG	33.50
110019	(369)	March Calendar Girl	FIG	33.50
110027	(370)	April Calendar Girl	FIG	35.00
110035	(371)	May Calendar Girl	FIG	30.00
110043	(372)	June Calendar Girl	FIG	50.00
110051	(424)	July Calendar Girl	FIG	45.00
110078	(425)	August Calendar Girl	FIG	50.00
110086	(426)	September Calendar Girl	FIG	33.50
110094	(427)	October Calendar Girl	FIG	45.00
110108	(428)	November Calendar Girl	FIG	37.50
110116	(429)	December Calendar Girl	FIG	33.50

... BIRTHDAY CONTINUED

106836	(381)	Happy Birthday Poppy	FIG	$33.50
524301	(536)	May Your Birthday Be A Blessing	FIG	30.00
527343	(597)	Happy Birdie	FIG	16.00

MISS YOU

102520	(287)	Let's Keep In Touch	MUS	$85.00
112364	(250)	Waddle I Do Without You	ORN	15.00
522201	(474)	Bon Voyage!	FIG	80.00
522287	(504)	Thinking Of You Is What I Really Like To Do	FIG	30.00
524492	(538)	Can't Be Without You	FIG	16.00
524913	(515)	We're Going To Miss You	FIG	50.00

BABY/ADOPTION

E-1372B	(1)	Jesus Loves Me (Boy)	FIG	$25.00
E-9278		⊥	FIG	15.00
E-1372G	(2)	Jesus Loves Me (Girl)	FIG	25.00
E-9279		⊥	FIG	15.00
E-2852A	(401)	Baby Figurine - Boy Standing	FIG	16.50
E-2852B	(402)	Baby Figurine - Girl w/Bow Standing	FIG	16.50
E-2852C	(403)	Baby Figurine - Boy Sitting	FIG	16.50
E-2852D	(404)	Baby Figurine - Girl Clapping	FIG	16.50
E-2852E	(405)	Baby Figurine - Boy Crawling	FIG	16.50
E-2852F	(406)	Baby Figurine - Girl Lying Down	FIG	16.50
12041	(311)	God's Precious Gift	FRM	27.50
100285	(221)	Heaven Bless You	MUS	60.00
520934		⊥	FIG	35.00
520705	(461)	Baby's First Pet	FIG	50.00
521175	(451)	Hello World!	FIG	15.00
521493	(552)	A Special Delivery	FIG	30.00
523178	(532)	Joy On Arrival	FIG	50.00
523453	(497)	The Good Lord Always Delivers	FIG	27.50
524077	(534)	Baby's First Meal	FIG	35.00
527238	(592)	Baby's First Word	FIG	25.00

THANKSGIVING

109762	(359)	We Gather Together To Ask The Lord's Blessing	FIGS	$150.00
110108	(428)	November Calendar Girl	FIG	37.50
522031	(472)	Thank You Lord For Everything	FIG	60.00

INSPIRATIONAL

E-0523	(128)	Onward Christian Soldiers	FIG	$35.00
E-3117	(41)	Walking By Faith	FIG	70.00
E-7158	(107)	Love Beareth All Things	FIG	37.50
E-9254	(138)	Praise The Lord Anyhow	FIG	50.00
E-9258	(140)	We Are God's Workmanship	FIG	27.50
E-9265	(146)	Press On	FIG	55.00
100137	(217)	The Joy Of The Lord Is My Strength	FIG	50.00
100226	(340)	The Lord Giveth And The Lord Taketh Away	FIG	40.00
100277	(220)	He Cleansed My Soul	FIG	35.00
112380		⊥	ORN	15.00
101826	(329)	No Tears Past The Gate	FIG	60.00
113964	(330)	Smile Along The Way	ORN	17.50
103632	(224)	I Believe In The Old Rugged Cross	FIG	35.00
522953		⊥	ORN	15.00
111155	(389)	Faith Takes The Plunge	FIG	33.50
114014	(391)	This Too Shall Pass	FIG	27.50
520535		The Lord Turned My Life Around	FIG	35.00
520551	(493)	Lord, Turn My Life Around	FIG	35.00
520691	(525)	Lord, Keep My Life In Balance	MUS	60.00
520756	(464)	Jesus Is The Only Way	FIG	45.00
521272	(550)	Take Heed When You Stand	FIG	55.00
521310	(505)	Yield Not To Temptation	FIG	27.50
521396	(496)	Faith Is A Victory	FIG	25.00
521450	(503)	Lord, Help Me Stick To My Job	FIG	30.00
521477	(476)	Tell It To Jesus	FIG	37.50
521485	(527)	There's A Light At The End Of The Tunnel	FIG	55.00
521779	(502)	Sweep All Your Worries Away	FIG	40.00
521957	(498)	High Hopes	FIG	30.00
522090	(500)	There Shall Be Showers Of Blessings	FIG	60.00

GET WELL

102407	(282)	Angel Of Mercy	ORN	$15.00
102482		⊥	FIG	30.00
521205	(494)	Hope You're Up And On The Trail Again	FIG	35.00
523739	(518)	Time Heals	FIG	37.50

CHRISTMAS NATIVITY

NATIVITY:

104000	(307)	Come Let Us Adore Him	FIGS	$110.00

NATIVITY ADDITIONS:

E-0511	(126)	Tubby's First Christmas	FIG	16.50
E-2360	(87)	I'll Play My Drum For Him	FIG	25.00
E-2363	(90)	Camel	FIG	32.50
E-5379	(189)	Isn't He Precious	FIG	30.00
E-5621	(63)	Donkey	FIG	13.50
E-5624	(65)	They Followed The Star	FIGS	200.00
E-5635	(66)	Wee Three Kings	FIGS	75.00
E-5636	(67)	Rejoice O Earth	FIG	30.00
E-5637	(68)	The Heavenly Light	FIG	27.50
E-5638	(69)	Cow	FIG	32.50
E-5644	(74)	Two Section Wall	FIGS	120.00
15490	(255)	Honk If You Love Jesus	FIGS	19.00
115274	(431)	Some Bunny's Sleeping	FIGS	18.50
523097	(468)	Jesus Is The Sweetest Name I Know	FIG	25.00
524875	(513)	Happy Birthday Dear Jesus	FIG	13.50
526959	(559)	We Have Come From Afar	FIG	17.50
527750	(607)	Wishing You A Comfy Christmas	FIG	27.50

MINI NATIVITY:

E-2395	(22)	Come Let Us Adore Him	FIGS	$120.00

MINI NATIVITY ADDITIONS:

E-2387	(101)	House Set And Palm Tree	FIGS	70.00
E-5384	(87)	I'll Play My Drum For Him	FIG	15.00
102261	(278)	Shepherd Of Love	FIG	15.00
102296	(279)	Animals	FIGS	19.00
108243	(65)	They Followed The Star	FIGS	100.00
520268	(67)	Rejoice O Earth	FIG	15.00
522988	(189)	Isn't He Precious	FIG	16.50
522996	(431)	Some Bunnies Sleeping	FIG	12.00
525278	(126)	Tubby's First Christmas	FIG	10.00
525286	(127)	It's A Perfect Boy	FIG	16.50

CHRISTMAS ...

E-0514	(30)	Mother Sew Dear	ORN	$15.00
E-0516	(33)	The Purr-Fect Grandma	ORN	15.00
E-0523	(128)	Onward Christian Soldiers	FIG	35.00
E-2374	(96)	Bundles Of Joy	FIG	45.00
E-2810	(22)	Come Let Us Adore Him	MUS	85.00
E-2829	(169)	I'm Sending You A White Christmas	FIG	50.00
112372			ORN	15.00
112402			MUS	70.00
12416	(246)	Have A Heavenly Christmas	ORN	16.00
15482	(254)	May Your Christmas Be Delightful	FIG	35.00
15849			ORN	15.00
15776	(260)	May You Have The Sweetest Christmas	FIG	25.00
15784	(261)	The Story Of God's Love	FIG	35.00
15792	(262)	Tell Me A Story	FIG	15.00
15806	(263)	God Gave His Best	FIG	19.00
15814	(264)	Silent Night	MUS	55.00
15857	(255)	Honk If You Love Jesus	ORN	15.00
101702	(277)	Our First Christmas Together	MUS	70.00
102288	(278)	Shepherd Of Love	ORN	15.00
102377	(237)	Trust And Obey	ORN	15.00
102385	(281)	Love Rescued Me	ORN	15.00
102407	(282)	Angel Of Mercy	ORN	15.00
109231	(355)	The Greatest Gift Is A Friend	FIG	37.50
109746	(341)	Peace On Earth	MUS	120.00
109754	(358)	Wishing You A Yummy Christmas	FIG	45.00
109800	(423)	Meowie Christmas	FIG	35.00
109819	(361)	Oh What Fun It Is To Ride	FIG	110.00
110116	(429)	December Calendar Girl	FIG	33.50
111163	(430)	'Tis The Season	FIG	33.50
112356	(161)	You Have Touched So Many Hearts	ORN	15.00
112364	(250)	Waddle I Do Without You	ORN	15.00
112380	(220)	He Cleansed My Soul	ORN	15.00
113956	(214)	To My Forever Friend	ORN	17.50
113964	(330)	Smile Along The Way	ORN	17.50
417777	(548)	May You Have An Old Fashioned Christmas	MJIB	200.00
417785			DOLL	150.00
520357	(437)	Jesus The Savior Is Born	FIG	32.50
520411	(570)	I'm Nuts About You	ORN	16.00
521302	(477)	May All Your Christmases Be White	ORN	15.00
521507	(475)	The Light Of The World Is Jesus	MUS	65.00
521566	(499)	Glide Through The Holidays	ORN	13.50
521574	(367)	Dashing Through The Snow	ORN	15.00
521949	(480)	Wishing You A Cozy Season	FIG	45.00

... CHRISTMAS CONTINUED

522112	(471)	Don't Let The Holidays Get You Down	FIG	45.00
521590			ORN	15.00
522082	(553)	May Your World Be Trimmed With Joy	FIG	55.00
522120	(478)	Wishing You A Very Successful Season	FIG	65.00
522244	(576)	Do Not Open Till Christmas	MUS	75.00
522252	(481)	He Is The Star Of The Morning	FIG	60.00
522317	(438)	Merry Christmas, Deer	FIG	55.00
522856	(469)	Have A Beary Merry Christmas	FIG	16.50
522910	(5)	Make A Joyful Noise	ORN	15.00
522929	(8)	Love One Another	ORN	17.50
522937	(219)	Friends Never Drift Apart	ORN	17.50
522953	(224)	I Believe In The Old Rugged Cross	ORN	15.00
523224	(494)	Happy Trails Is Trusting Jesus	ORN	15.00
524131	(555)	Good Friends Are For Always	ORN	15.00
524484	(514)	Not A Creature Was Stirring	FIG	17.00
524883	(512)	Christmas Fireplace	FIG	37.50
524913	(515)	We're Going To Miss You	FIG	50.00
524921	(557)	Angels We Have Heard On High	FIG	60.00
525332	(582)	Lord Keep Me On My Toes	ORN	15.00
525898	(583)	Ring Those Christmas Bells	FIG	95.00
527165	(497)	The Good Lord Always Delivers	ORN	15.00
527378	(598)	You Are My Favorite Star	FIG	60.00
527475	(600)	Baby's First Christmas (Girl)	ORN	15.00
527483	(601)	Baby's First Christmas (Boy)	ORN	15.00
527629	(605)	Wishing You A Ho Ho Ho	FIG	40.00
527688	(606)	But The Greatest Of These Is Love	FIG	27.50
527696			ORN	15.00
527718			THMBL	8.00
527726			BELL	25.00
527734			ORN	30.00
527742			PLATE	50.00
528870	(378)	Our First Christmas Together	ORN	17.50
617334	(545)	Rejoice, O Earth	T TOP	125.00

eralding it as "what may be the most important introduction in the history of the Enesco PRECIOUS MOMENTS Collection," Enesco unveiled SUGAR TOWN to collectors in April 1992. In SUGAR TOWN every building, figurine, and accessory will have, or be part of, a story related to the life of artist Sam Butcher. The name SUGAR TOWN honors Dr. Sam Sugar, the family doctor who assisted in the birth of Sam Butcher on New Year's Day 1939. All SUGAR TOWN buildings will be lighted and come with a Certificate of Residence for the collector. The figurines are on a slightly smaller scale than most in the Precious Moments Collection.

The GREENBOOK ART CHART & LISTINGS for SUGAR TOWN contain line drawings as well as factual information.

Factual information includes Title, Description, Year Of Introduction, Enesco Item Number, Material, is it part of a Set?, is it Lighted?, Market Status or edition limit, and the Suggested Retail Price. GREENBOOK Market Prices are included as well.

GREENBOOK divides SUGAR TOWN pieces into three categories: Buildings, Figurines, and Accessories.

Listings are by category and will be in chronological date of introduction order. Within each year they are in Enesco Item Number order.

Each piece has been assigned a GREENBOOK ART CHART Number comprised of a coded alphabetical prefix (STB = Sugar Town Buildings, STF = Sugar Town Figurines, STA = Sugar Town Accessories), followed by year of introduction, and then a sequential number.

Notes are in the shaded area of each listing. And in most cases there's room for your own notes as well.

ALPHABETICAL INDEX

CHAPEL NIGHT LIGHT

Country church with bow trimmed garlands. Belltower with heart shaped windows. Snow on roof. The Chapel represents Sam Butcher's faith and commitment.

ART CHART #	NAME	ITEM #	MATERIAL	SET?	✦ MARKET STATUS	ORIGINAL SRP	GREENBOOK MKT PRICE
STB92-1	CHAPEL NIGHT LIGHT	529621	Porcelain	NO	✓ OPEN	$ 85.00	$ 85.00

NOTES

1992 G Clef is first annual symbol. Send in response card to receive personalized "Honorary Citizenship Certificate" which identifies the official street name and number where collector resides. Size is 8".

SUGAR TOWN FIGURINES

STF92-1

AUNT RUTH & AUNT DOROTHY
Two little girls singing carols from songbook.

STF92-2

PHILIP
Little boy caroller snug in hat, earmuffs, and scarf
singing from upside-down songbook.

STF92-3

GRANDFATHER
Preacher kneels and prays.

STF92-4

SAM BUTCHER
Sam, as young man, painting Village Welcome Sign.

ART CHART #	NAME	ITEM #	MATERIAL	SET?	♉	MARKET STATUS	ORIGINAL SRP	GREENBOOK MKT PRICE
	NOTES							
STF92-1	AUNT RUTH & AUNT DOROTHY	529486	Porcelain	NO		OPEN	$ 20.00	$ 20.00
	1992 G Clef is first annual symbol. Size is 3.00".							
STF92-2	PHILIP	529494	Porcelain	NO		OPEN	17.00	17.00
	1992 G Clef is first annual symbol. Size is 3.00".							
STF92-3	GRANDFATHER	529516	Porcelain	NO		OPEN	15.00	15.00
	1992 G Clef is first annual symbol. Size is 2.50".							
STF92-4	SAM BUTCHER	529567	Porcelain	NO		ANNUAL	22.50	22.50
	1992 G Clef is first annual symbol. Size is 3.25". Sign reads, "Established 1992. Population 5 and Growing." Town population will change each year.							

SUGAR TOWN ACCESSORIES

1992

1992

STA92-1

STA92-2

EVERGREEN TREE

Evergreen tree decorated with garlands, ornaments, and large star as tree topper.

NATIVITY

Creche depicts Holy Family - Joseph, Mary, and Baby Jesus in manger. Size is 2.00".

ART CHART #	NAME	ITEM #	MATERIAL	SET?	☮	MARKET STATUS	ORIGINAL SRP	GREENBOOK MKT PRICE
STA92-1	EVERGREEN TREE	528684	Porcelain	NO		OPEN	$ 15.00	$ 15.00
	NOTES							
	1992 G Clef is first annual symbol. Size is 4.25".							
STA92-2	NATIVITY	529508	Porcelain	NO		OPEN	20.00	20.00
	1992 G Clef is first annual symbol. Size is 2.00".							

INSURANCE PREPARATION IS WORTH YOUR TIME -
What to do <u>before</u> you suffer a loss _____

THE BASICS

• Maintain a complete up-to-date inventory listing of your PRECIOUS MOMENTS collectibles including the title of each piece, the Enesco Item Number, a brief description, the annual symbol, what you paid, and the current value (GREENBOOK Market Price). If you have a one-of-a-kind piece and need a Market Price, write to us - being sure to include a photo of the piece. Keep the original bill of sale, or, if it was a gift, record the name of the person who gave it to you as well as the occasion or date.

• Take photos (video or still) of your collection in its normal setting to document ownership.

• Keep copies of the inventory listing and photos in a safe deposit box or another location outside the home.

WHAT NEXT?

For an answer to this question we turned to a specialist in the field. He writes:

"The following is an attempt to answer the question of insurance for the PRECIOUS MOMENTS collector. This is meant to be an overview of the coverage forms available. Collectors should consult their agent or brokers for more detail.

A Personal Article Floater or a Fine Art Floater can be attached to a Homeowner's Policy or separately written. These forms provide protection for those items you feel warrant specific coverage.

The forms are written on an All Risk basis and customarily are not subject to a deductible. The actual underwriting can be done three different ways: Blanket, Itemized, or a combination of the two.

The Blanket form is a one limit form that covers the entire collection. In the event of a loss, the limit would apply to either the entire collection or a portion of the collection. Normally this form has a sub-limit per item, i.e. if you have a $10,000 blanket limit the maximum paid for any one item might be $2,500. In other words, the company would only pay up to $2,500 per piece, if only one piece is damaged. With the

Blanket form, you should be certain the amount insured contemplates a total loss. Obviously, this form eliminated the need to list each piece specifically, but requires you to establish the value at the time of loss.

The Itemized form is more specific. A value per item is determined through appraisals, bill of sale, or for our purposes, the GREENBOOK Guide to The Enesco PRECIOUS MOMENTS Collection. Each item is then described and insured for the determined amount. Itemized lists should be updated periodically to make sure there is adequate coverage. In the event of a loss the itemized piece would be settled for the limit it is insured for. No other substantiation of value is required.

The combination of the Blanket form and the Itemized form separate out the high value pieces of the collection and losses are settled per an itemized list, with a Blanket up to $2,500 per piece for the balance.

With floaters your insurance company may consider the item to be insured as "fragile." If so, "Breakage" coverage should be included. Your insurance representative will be able to advise you - be sure to raise the question.

It is very important to insure your Fine Arts and/or Personal Articles to current value. This will ensure satisfaction at the time of loss as insurance companies pay up to the value insured and no more.

Without the above referred to coverage forms, your existing insurance policy may automatically provide protection for personal property. Generally it would be subject to a deductible with settlement on either an actual cash value basis or replacement cost basis and subject to a breakage exclusion. You should consult your agent or broker as to these details.

Please be advised that the above is an extremely broad explanation of coverage and it would be advisable to consult your agent or broker to define the coverage to your complete satisfaction."

Publisher's Note: The article that follows is reprinted from theJune/July issue of Precious Insights Magazine. Precious Insights is published bi-monthly by Sheryl J. Williams. Sheryl is a Precious Moments collector, has been a secondary market dealer, and is always more than willing to share her expertise. The magazine is an excellent source for timely information, show and convention news, club happenings around the country, Chapel events, classified ads, and educational articles.

Sheryl writes:

> "It's difficult to pick out a "favorite" figurine from the hundreds in the Precious Moments Collection, but this year's piece will probably have to be "Walking by Faith!" This is year five of publishing Precious Insights Magazine, and it may well go down as the most challenging year to date! Up until now, I've worked full-time in addition to publishing the magazine. However, this year I decided to give up my job and concentrate on the magazine full time.

> To do that, I've packed up myself and my collection, and moved out of the Twin Cities to a tiny little town in the middle or nowhere! Between writing and publishing the magazine, moving and reorganizing my life, hosting the Second Annual Precious Insights Family Reunion at the Precious Moments Chapel this summer, attending conventions and speaking around the country, it is proving to be a challenging year!

> However, I still enjoy hearing from collectors, and your letters would be most welcome! Hope to hear from you soon!"

Precious Insights Magazine
PO Box 151
Pillager, MN   56473-0151
(218) 746-3108

HOW TO BUY AND SELL ON THE SECONDARY MARKET
by Sheryl J. Williams

Over the past year, with all of the media attention which has been focused on the economy and "how tough it is out there," it has become increasingly apparent to me, as many collectors have called for assistance in selling their Precious Moments collections, that many collectors have a very limited understanding of "secondary market." How to purchase, how to sell, how to invest, what to invest in - these things are a great mystery to many Precious Moments collectors.

Of course, most of us collect Precious Moments figurines because we enjoy them and appreciate their inspirational messages and humorous depictions of our lives. None of us plan to part with our collections. And yet at the same time, most of us are a least somewhat aware of the fact that Precious Moments are an investment which could be sold at a profit, should we decide to part with our treasures at some future date. It is at this point that many Precious Moments collectors make their first contact with the secondary market. For many of us, searching retail stores for pieces no longer being produced, or with a particular understamp proved fruitless, so we turned to the secondary market to locate those items for our collections.

Collectors unfamiliar with the secondary market have come up with some amusing terminology to describe the market, including "selling used figurines," and "I understand there is a 'black market' for selling my Precious Moments figurines!"

What exactly is the "secondary market?" Perhaps we should begin by defining the "primary market" which is, of course, the retailer who has an account with Enesco and purchases Precious Moments collectibles for sale to their customers. My definition of "secondary market" is: any piece of the Enesco Precious Moment Collection which is **not readily available** at the retail stores in your area. This includes retired pieces, suspended pieces, dated - limited - annual editions from previous years, and many older understamps on pieces still currently in production. While collectors who enjoy the "hunt" for Precious Moments collectibles may travel far and wide to locate these pieces, and may enjoy limited success, the key to whether or not a piece is considered a secondary market item lies in the words "readily available." If you have to look high and low, traveling the country by car or by phone, the piece you are pursuing is a secondary market piece.

THE TOOLS OF THE TRADE

Whether buying or selling on the secondary market, it is very important that you become educated about the Precious Moments Collection, and there are "tools" which you as a collector will find useful in learning what you need to know to become successful in dealing on the Precious Moments secondary market.

Each year, Enesco produces a beautiful color catalog which includes photographs of the entire Precious Moments porcelain bisque collection. The catalog contains some annotation including suggested retail prices of the pieces and their current production status (retired, limited edition, dated, etc.) New collectors find this catalog very useful as they become acquainted with all of the pieces in the collection. Collectors who wish to sell pieces which they have had for some time, particularly pieces for the first years of the collection when no product numbers were placed on the bases of the figurines, will find the book useful in matching the pieces in their collection with the appropriate product code.

Whether buying, selling or insuring your Precious Moments Collection, a current edition of the GREENBOOK Guide To The Enesco Precious Moments Collection is a must. A new edition of the GREENBOOK for Precious Moments is introduced each year, and it is important to obtain each new edition because the values of your pieces change from year to year, some of them quite drastically. This is the publication where you will find, for less than the cost of a figurine, all pertinent information for each piece in the Collection, including original suggested retail prices and current secondary market values for each understamp. As the saying goes, "It's better to be safe than to be sorry." Keeping on top of the secondary market value of your collection can keep you from falling into that "sorry" category - sorry you didn't insure for the right value and your piece was broken -sorry that you paid too much for a piece - sorry that sold for too little! Many collectors wouldn't leave home without their Precious Moments GREENBOOK in tow, using it to keep track of pieces they own, what they're shopping for, and approximately what they should be paying.

When looking for pieces to purchase or looking to advertise your pieces for sale, there are several options available. Collectors meet with limited success in advertising or purchasing through collectibles columns in local papers. In this instance, what appears to happen is that the buyers expect to purchase your collection at "garage sale" prices. There are several publications on the market available on news stands and at bookstores which are general information collectible newspapers and magazines. These publications contain display advertising from retailers and classified advertising sections where you may find or place ads for selling Precious Moments collectibles. Many local chapters of the Enesco Precious Moments Collectors' Club allow some advertising in their club newsletters for club members. These newsletters, as well as Precious Insights - a Precious Moments Collector hobby magazine, provide a "pure" Precious Moments market - they are written by Precious Moments collectors for Precious Moments collectors - an exclusive audience - and probably the easiest, least expensive and most efficient way to get directly into the Precious Moments secondary market.

BUYING ON THE SECONDARY MARKET

Once you are familiar with the Enesco Precious Moments Collection and have found pieces which you would like to purchase for your collection from the secondary market, where do you begin your "shopping trip?"

Generally, there are three sources available to you when looking to purchase pieces on the secondary market. First of all, there are retailers who purchase collections from collectors and resell them in their stores. These retailers can be located through their ads in collectibles publications, and you will find that they are very knowledgeable about the Precious Moments collection and the secondary market.

The second source is secondary market dealers who deal exclusively in the secondary market on collectibles. They do not carry current merchandise, but concentrate their efforts on purchasing collections for resale. Once again, these people advertise in collectibles publications, and are also very knowledgeable about the collection.

The third source is the private collector who decides to sell his or her collection through the classified advertising section of the collectibles publications.

With your GREENBOOK in tow and advertising in hand, you have two options available to you - the post office or your telephone. While perusing the classified ads you will note that many advertisers have prepared lists of the Precious Moments collectibles which they have for sale. By sending a long, self-addressed, stamped envelope, you can obtain by return mail a list of the items, understamps and prices available from each seller. Most advertisers also list telephone numbers, so collectors who want to call rather than order listings may do so. It is important to note that retailers who also sell on the secondary market usually do not prepare lists to send to their customers. However, many provide toll-free 800 phone service to their retail stores for the convenience of their customers, and have members of their staff who specialize in the secondary market to assist collectors when they call.

A word of caution may be appropriate at this point. Some common sense must be applied to shopping for pieces for your Precious Moments collection. Everyone loves a bargain - and you, like everyone else, would like to save a few dollars on a figurine by shopping around for the best buy. Writing for lists is the least expensive way of doing that shopping. Sad to say, I've seen many collectors spend a fortune in long distance phone calls just to save a couple of dollars on the purchase of a figurine. If you find a piece you want at a price that you feel is appropriate (check your GREENBOOK), buy it when you find it - that bargain isn't a bargain if you spend too much money in postage and phone bills tracking it down!

Who are the people you'll be buying from? In most cases, advertisers are well-established retailers who also deal in secondary market, secondary market dealers, or private collectors selling extra pieces or their personal collections. Can you trust them? When buying through advertisements in collectibles publications, the answer is "Yes!" Over many years of collecting, I've heard of virtually no problems with secondary market sales of Precious Moments collectibles. Collectible publications will help investigate problems when reported, so in the event that a problem should arise which you are unable to resolve with the seller, contact the publication which ran the advertisement for their assistance.

What can you expect to happen during this secondary market transaction? Once you've located a piece which you'd like to purchase on someone's list, you should contact that person or business by phone to assure that they still have the piece in stock with the understamp and at the price listed. One quick phone call can save the hassle of returning checks if the piece has already been sold. You may also want to ask about the condition of the piece and whether or not it has a box (if the box is an important issue to you.) To date, repaired Precious Moments collectibles have had little if any secondary market value. Once assured that the piece is available, check with the seller about method of payment - are personal checks, money orders, credit cards acceptable for purchases? It has become standard practice to accept personal checks with the understanding that there will be a 2 week waiting period between receipt of the check and shipping of the merchandise to assure that the check clears the bank. Orders paid for with money orders are usually shipped immediately. You may also expect to pay some shipping and insurance charges - usually around $5.00 for the first item, and $1 for each additional item shipped.

Should it occur that you decide you cannot purchase the pieces you've had the seller hold for you, courtesy dictates that you notify the seller as soon as possible so that the pieces can be made available to other buyers.

COLLECTING FOR INVESTMENT

Although we enjoy collecting PRECIOUS Moments for many reasons, the fact that they increase in value is of importance to collectors. A careful study of the GREENBOOK will show many dramatic increases in value for individual pieces in the collection. If you are collecting not only for a love of the collection itself, but with an eye for the potential investment, studying the GREENBOOK carefully will give you a good insight into what to buy and what to avoid from an investment standpoint.

You will notice, for example, that the pieces suspended in 1984 have increased greatly in value, and if you've been trying to locate them for purchase on the secondary market, you will find that the law of supply and demand is most evident here - there is much demand for these pieces, but very little supply. Review of past editions of the GREENBOOK will show you a steady increase each year in the value of these pieces. Many are considered "hot" secondary market items. Most pieces were not in production for long, limiting the number of pieces available to an ever-growing group of collectors.

Take a look at the "Members Only" pieces. PM-811 "Hello Lord, It's Me Again," the first "Members Only" piece is nearly impossible to locate on the secondary market. This piece was available only to Charter Members of the Enesco Precious Moments Collectors' Club, one per club member. At the close of its Charter year, the Club had approximately 68,000 members. Today the Club has 10 times that number of members - ten collectors for each "Hello Lord" figurine produced!

What about markings? Once again, a quick glance through GREENBOOK will show you that the first understamps for figurines are more valuable than other understamps. The first versions of figurines that have been changed, such as "Faith Takes The Plunge (111155) which originally had a smiling mouth and was later changed to a pouting mouth are of more value than later versions. Collectors tend to like "originals" for their collections, demand is high and values increase. "Make A Joyful Noise" (E-1374G) has been in production since the collection began in 1979. Thousands and thousands of these figurines have been produced. The "original" of this piece is a "No Mark" understamp, and demands high prices on the secondary market. Values of other understamps are significantly lower for this piece, and this trend can also be noticed in many other pieces in the collection.

As with any investment, there are things to be cautious of when buying for your collection. First of all, there are pieces in the Collection which, in my opinion, will be there "forever" and therefore should not be looked at as having investment potential. These pieces fall more into the "gift" than "collectible" category, and include such things as wedding and anniversary figurines, mom, dad, grandma, and grandpa pieces and graduation pieces. On these pieces, the first understamps are the pieces which have secondary market potential, but history has proved them to be slow sellers on the secondary market.

Don't over buy! Buy what you want for your own collection and proceed with caution when purchasing extras of a piece. The greatest temptation to purchase everything in sight comes, of course, with the announcement of retired figurines, but as collectors become more and more aware that in many cases the suspended pieces are good investments, this is also beginning to occur when the suspended list is updated. Selling those extra pieces is expensive - trading them for something you want is next to impossible. In most cases, it takes several months after retirement or suspension announcements before the secondary market settles down and "real" prices as opposed to "panic" values on a piece can he determined. You may be spending a lot of money on pieces you'll have around for a long time before you're able to sell them.

I receive many letters each year requesting values on items with Precious Moments designs which are not documented in the GREENBOOK. And quite frankly, it's very difficult to answer these questions because nobody wants to play the "bad guy" and tell a collector that the items they have do not have any secondary market value. However, the truth must be told. The figurines, ornaments and other porcelain bisque pieces which make up the Enesco Precious Moments Collection are the only Precious Moments line which has a long established secondary market history and can be considered a serious investment. Accessory items produced by Enesco, which include such items as water domes, painted pewter, crystal, coffee mugs, etc. are from the giftware line, not the collectible line. Thousands of different giftware items have been produced over the years, but only some very rare pieces from the early years of the giftware line have seen any secondary activity, and this only within a small group of very avid collectors. Other Precious Moments items including vinyl dolls, soft dolls, jewelry, etc. also see extremely limited secondary market activity, and once again, has a very limited group of collectors.

WHEN IT'S TIME TO SELL YOUR COLLECTION

Eventually the time may come when you decide that you are going to sell your Precious Moments Collection. Once the decision is made to sell, you must decide how you will go about selling - do you want to sell your collection piece by piece, handling all transactions yourself, or do you want to avoid the hassle and sell the collection as a whole for one price?

No matter which option you chose, you need to prepare a list of the items you have for sale. Your list should include the Enesco Item Number, a description of the piece, the understamp (No Mark, Triangle, etc.), and the price you want for the piece. Potential buyers will also want to know if you have the correct boxes for the pieces, so if possible, this should be indicated, along with any shipping and insurance charges, your name, address, and phone number.

Selling Your Collection As A Whole

If you choose this option, chances are that you will be selling to a secondary market dealer. It is very rare, especially if your collection is sizeable, that a private collector purchases an entire collection from another individual collector.

In selling to a secondary market dealer, you must be aware of the fact that the dealer is a business person, and must purchase items which can be resold fairly quickly and at a profit. What this means to you as the seller is that you will not receive GREENBOOK prices for your collection. If the dealer purchases your collection as a whole, the price offered will depend greatly on what is in your collection. If you have a collection which includes "Members Only" pieces, first marks, suspended and retired collectibles, you have a collection which would be of great interest to a potential buyer.

However, if your collection has many newer pieces which are still in production and has few of the "prime" pieces in the collection, chances are that a secondary market dealer would not be interested in it. Once again, to determine the "saleability" of your collection, the GREENBOOK holds the answers - the more you have of the pieces with high secondary market value listed, the better chance you have of selling your collection to a secondary market dealer.

If a dealer is interested in purchasing your collection for resale, you can expect to realize about 50-60% of GREENBOOK value when selling your collection as a whole. (If you've recently purchased figurines on the secondary market, you will not receive what you paid for the piece if you sell your collection to a secondary market dealer).

Selling your collection to a secondary market dealer may be a good option for you if you don't want the hassle of advertising, phone calls, handling checks, packaging and shipping pieces and want to realize money from your collection quickly.

<u>Selling Your Collection by the Piece</u>

If you want to sell your collection at GREENBOOK prices, you will want to sell your collection by the piece to individual collectors. The first step in doing this is to prepare a list of the pieces you wish to sell. Once the list is completed, you must choose where you will advertise and prepare your ad copy. Personal preference will dictate how you compose your ad, but most advertisers list a few "prime" pieces such as "Free Puppies," and "Hello, Lord" and indicate that there are more pieces in the collection. Request that the collector send a self-addressed, stamped envelope for a free list, include your mailing address and phone number (optional). You may want to consider running your advertisements more than once in a publication, as readership is constantly changing.

As collectors call for pieces, it will be helpful if you ask for a name, address and contact phone number when you hold pieces for them, in the event that you need to contact them. You may wish to indicate to the buyer how long you will hold the pieces before you sell them to another collector (usually 10 working days). You must decide how you wish to handle payment for the pieces.

Selling your collection by the piece to private collectors is a good option if you are in no hurry, want GREENBOOK prices, don't mind handling the checks, shipping, etc. You may find that there are pieces which are difficult to sell, and you may have "leftovers" after most of your collection has been sold.

Becoming involved as a buyer or seller on the secondary market can be an enjoyable and interesting experience - IF you are willing to spend the time to educate yourself about the collection and the history and current activities of the secondary market for Precious Moments collectibles. The investment required each year for publications etc. to keep you informed about the Precious Moments Collection and the secondary market is minimal - less than $50.00 per year. That investment will pay for itself many times over if it helps prevent just one mistake as you become active on the secondary market. Don't panic, use your common sense, and keep "educated" on the Precious Moments Collection and the secondary market - the keys to success as a collector - the keys to success as a seller!

OTHER GUIDES FROM GREENBOOK...

The GREENBOOK Guide To Ornaments
·Including The Hallmark Keepsake,
Enesco Treasury Of Christmas,
and Carlton/Summit Heirloom
Collections
Second Edition
ISBN 0-923628-09-6

The GREENBOOK Guide To
The MEMORIES OF YESTERDAY
Collection by Enesco
Third Edition
ISBN 0-923628-11-8

Available Early Fall 1992:
The GREENBOOK Guide To
Department 56 Including
The Original Snow Village,
The Heritage Village Collection,
and Snowbabies
Second Edition
ISBN 0-923628-13-4